It's another Quality Book from CGP

This book is for anyone doing Edexcel IGCSE Mathematics (Specification A).

Whatever subject you're doing it's the same
old story — there are lots of facts and you've just got
to learn them. IGCSE Maths is no different.

Happily this CGP book gives you all that important
information as clearly and concisely as possible.

It's also got some daft bits in to try and make the whole
experience at least vaguely entertaining for you.

Higher

This book is suitable for both Foundation Tier and Higher Tier candidates.
The material which is required only for the Higher Tier is clearly indicated
in green boxes like this.

In addition, the Higher Tier questions in the book are printed in green.

Higher

What CGP is all about

Our sole aim here at CGP is to produce the highest quality
books — carefully written, immaculately presented and
dangerously close to being funny.

Then we work our socks off to get them out to you
— at the cheapest possible prices.

Contents

Contents

Published by CGP

Written by Richard Parsons

Updated by: Mary Falkner, Paul Jordin and Sharon Keeley-Holden

Contributors: Sally Gill, Helena Hayes, Kieran Wardell

With thanks to Rosie Gillham and Jane Appleton for the proofreading.

ISBN: 978 1 84762 554 0

Groovy website: www.cgpbooks.co.uk
Printed by Elanders Ltd, Newcastle upon Tyne.

Prime Numbers

You're in luck, my poor revising friend. There's no better place to start than <u>prime numbers</u>.

1) <u>Basically, PRIME Numbers don't divide by anything</u>

...and that's the best way to think of them. (Strictly, they divide by themselves and 1.)
So prime numbers are all the numbers that <u>don't</u> come up in times tables:

| 2 | 3 | 5 | 7 | 11 | 13 | 17 | 19 | 23 | 29 | 31 | 37 | ... |

As you can see, they're an awkward-looking bunch (that's because they don't divide by anything!).

For example:

> <u>The only numbers</u> that multiply to give 7 are 1 × 7
> <u>The only numbers</u> that multiply to give 31 are 1 × 31

In fact the <u>only way</u> to get <u>ANY PRIME NUMBER</u> is 1 × ITSELF

2) <u>They End in 1, 3, 7 or 9</u>

1) 1 is <u>NOT</u> a prime number.
2) The first four prime numbers are <u>2, 3, 5 and 7</u>.
3) <u>Prime numbers</u> end in <u>1, 3, 7 or 9</u> (2 and 5 are the only exceptions to this rule).
4) But <u>NOT ALL</u> numbers ending in <u>1, 3, 7 or 9</u> are primes, as shown here: (Only the <u>circled ones</u> are <u>primes</u>)

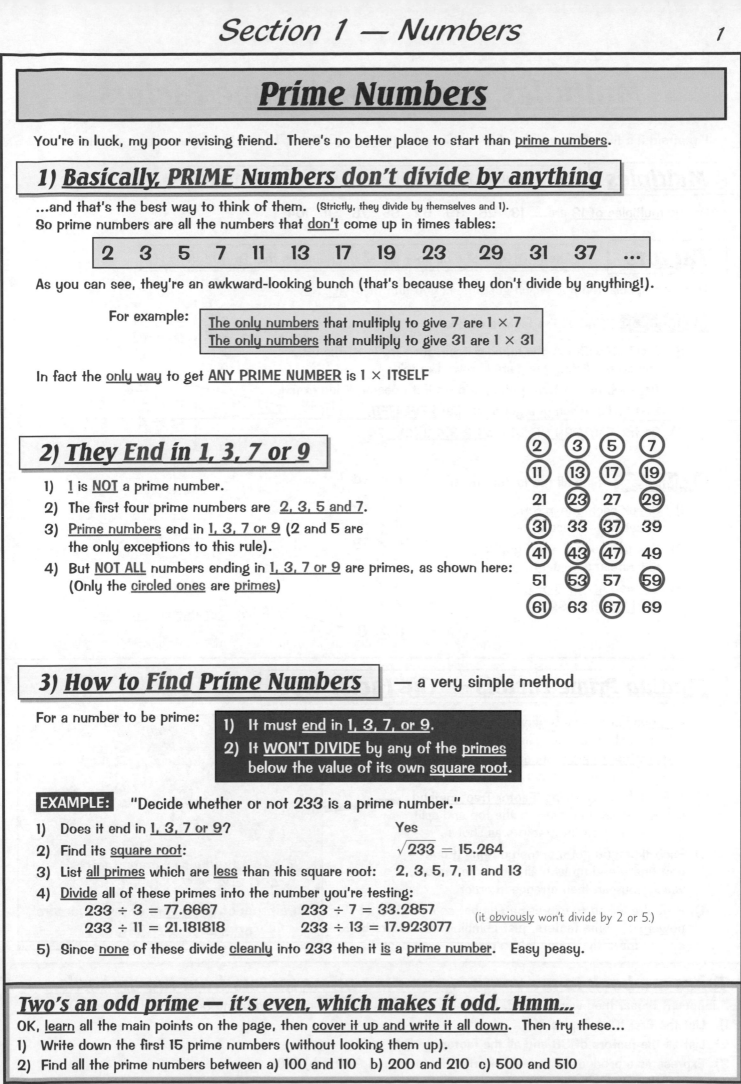

3) <u>How to Find Prime Numbers</u> — a very simple method

For a number to be prime:

> 1) It must <u>end</u> in <u>1, 3, 7, or 9</u>.
> 2) It <u>WON'T DIVIDE</u> by any of the <u>primes</u> below the value of its own <u>square root</u>.

EXAMPLE: "Decide whether or not 233 is a prime number."

1) Does it end in <u>1, 3, 7 or 9</u>? Yes
2) Find its <u>square root</u>: $\sqrt{233} = 15.264$
3) List <u>all primes</u> which are <u>less</u> than this square root: 2, 3, 5, 7, 11 and 13
4) <u>Divide</u> all of these primes into the number you're testing:
   $233 \div 3 = 77.6667$ $233 \div 7 = 33.2857$ (it <u>obviously</u> won't divide by 2 or 5.)
   $233 \div 11 = 21.181818$ $233 \div 13 = 17.923077$
5) Since <u>none</u> of these divide <u>cleanly</u> into 233 then it <u>is</u> a <u>prime number</u>. Easy peasy.

<u>Two's an odd prime — it's even, which makes it odd. Hmm...</u>

OK, <u>learn</u> all the main points on the page, then <u>cover it up and write it all down</u>. Then try these...
1) Write down the first 15 prime numbers (without looking them up).
2) Find all the prime numbers between a) 100 and 110 b) 200 and 210 c) 500 and 510

Multiples, Factors and Prime Factors

I'm afraid it's time for some good ol' fashioned <u>maths terms</u>. It was bound to happen sooner or later...

Multiples

The <u>MULTIPLES</u> of a number are simply its <u>TIMES TABLE</u>:

So the <u>multiples of 13</u> are... 13 26 39 52 65 78 91 104 ...

Factors

The <u>FACTORS</u> of a number are all the numbers that <u>DIVIDE INTO IT</u>.

There's a special method which guarantees you find them <u>ALL</u>...

EXAMPLE 1: "Find all the factors of 24."

1) Start off with 1 × the number itself, then try 2 ×, then 3 × and so on, listing the pairs in rows like this.
2) Try each one in turn, putting a dash if it doesn't divide exactly.
3) Eventually, when you get a number <u>REPEATED</u>, you <u>STOP</u>.
4) So the <u>FACTORS OF 24</u> are <u>1,2,3,4,6,8,12,24</u>

Increasing by 1 each time

1×24
2×12
3×8
4×6
$5 \times -$
6×4

EXAMPLE 2: "Find all the factors of 64."

1) <u>Check each one in turn</u>, to see if it divides or not.
2) Use your calculator if you're not totally confident.
3) So the <u>FACTORS of 64</u> are <u>1,2,4,8,16,32,64</u>

1×64
2×32
$3 \times -$
4×16
$5 \times -$
$6 \times -$
$7 \times -$
8×8

The 8 has <u>repeated</u> so <u>stop here</u>.

Finding Prime Factors — The Factor Tree

1) <u>Any number</u> can be broken down into a string of prime numbers all multiplied together — this is called '<u>Expressing it as a product of prime factors</u>'. To be honest it's pretty tedious — but it's in the Exam.

2) The mildly entertaining '<u>Factor Tree</u>' method is best, where you start at the top and split your number off into factors as shown.

3) Each time you get a prime you <u>ring it</u> and you finally end up with all the prime factors, which you can then arrange in order.

4) If you're asked to express a number as a product of <u>powers</u> of prime factors, just combine the factors that appear more than once into a power — see page 15.

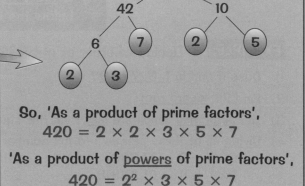

So, 'As a product of prime factors',
$420 = 2 \times 2 \times 3 \times 5 \times 7$

'As a product of <u>powers</u> of prime factors',
$420 = 2^2 \times 3 \times 5 \times 7$

Takes me back to my youth, scrumping prime factors from the orchards...

...innocent times, they were. Right, learn how to find <u>multiples, factors and prime factors</u> and do these Qs:

1) List the first 10 multiples of 7.
2) List all the factors of 36 and all the factors of 84.
3) Express as a product of powers of prime factors: a) 990 b) 160.

Common Factors and Common Multiples

There are a few more definitions to get to grips with on this page, but don't worry — they're nice easy ones.

A Common Factor is a Shared Factor of Two Numbers

If two or more numbers share a _factor_, then it's known as a __COMMON FACTOR__ of those numbers.
You can find the common factors of a group of numbers like _this_:

> 1) __LIST__ all the __FACTORS__ of __ALL__ the numbers.
> 2) Circle any numbers that are in __ALL the lists__.

EXAMPLE: Find the common factors of 36, 54 and 72

Factors of 36 are: (1) (2) (3) 4, (6) (9) 12, (18) 36
Factors of 54 are: (1) (2) (3) (6) (9) (18) 27, 54
Factors of 72 are: (1) (2) (3) 4, (6) 8, (9) 12, (18) 24, 36, 72

So the common factors of 36, 54, and 72 are: 1, 2, 3, 6, 9 and 18.

> The __HIGHEST COMMON FACTOR (HCF)__ is the __BIGGEST__
> number that will __DIVIDE INTO ALL__ the numbers in question.

If you use the method above to find the common factors, the _biggest number_ that you've circled is the highest common factor of the numbers. So, the highest common factor of 36, 54 and 72 is _18_.

A Common Multiple is a Multiple of two Different Numbers

If the _same number_ appears in the _times tables_ of two or more different numbers,
then it's known as a __COMMON MULTIPLE__ of those numbers.

Here's how you can find some common multiples for a group of numbers:

> 1) __LIST MULTIPLES__ of __ALL__ the numbers.
> 2) Circle any numbers that are in __ALL the lists__.

Don't try to list all the common multiples — you'll be there for ever (literally). Stop when you've found as many as you need.

EXAMPLE: Find four common multiples of 6 and 9.

Multiples of 6 are: 6, 12, (18) 24, 30, (36) 42, 48, (54) 60, 66, (72)...
Multiples of 9 are: 9, (18) 27, (36) 45, (54) 63, (72) 81, 90 ...

So 18, 36, 54 and 72 are all _common multiples_ of 6 and 9.

> The __LOWEST COMMON MULTIPLE (LCM)__ is the __SMALLEST__
> number that will __DIVIDE BY ALL__ the numbers in question.

In other words, it's just the _smallest number_ on your list of _common multiples_.
So, in the example above, the lowest common multiple of 6 and 9 is _18_.

I wanna live like common factors. I wanna do whatever common factors do...

I wanna sle... actually, best not go there. You need to learn what common multiples and common factors are, and _how to find them_. Then turn over and write it all down. And after that, some lovely questions — Bonus.

1) List _all_ the factors of 56 and _all_ the factors of 104. List all their common factors. What's their HCF?
2) What's the Highest Common Factor of 36 and 84?
3) List the first 10 multiples of 4, and the first 10 multiples of 5. Give 2 common multiples of 4 and 5.
4) What's the Lowest Common Multiple of 7 and 9? Give two other common multiples of 7 and 9.

Fractions, Decimals and Percentages

The one word that could describe all these three is __PROPORTION__. Fractions, decimals and percentages are simply __three different ways__ of expressing a __proportion__ of something — and it's pretty important you should see them as __closely related and completely interchangeable__ with each other. This table shows the really common conversions which you should know straight off without having to work them out:

Fraction	Decimal	Percentage
$\frac{1}{2}$	0.5	50%
$\frac{1}{4}$	0.25	25%
$\frac{3}{4}$	0.75	75%
$\frac{1}{3}$	0.333333... or $0.\dot{3}$	$33\frac{1}{3}\%$
$\frac{2}{3}$	0.666666... or $0.\dot{6}$	$66\frac{2}{3}\%$
$\frac{1}{10}$	0.1	10%
$\frac{2}{10}$	0.2	20%
$\frac{X}{10}$	0.X	X0%
$\frac{1}{5}$	0.2	20%
$\frac{2}{5}$	0.4	40%

Percentage means 'number of parts per 100'.

A number with a dot over it means that the number repeats forever — see the next page.

The more of those conversions you learn, the better — but for those that you __don't know__, you must __also learn__ how to __convert__ between the three types. These are the methods:

$$\text{Fraction} \xrightarrow[\text{e.g. } \frac{1}{2} \text{ is } 1\div 2]{\text{Divide}} \text{Decimal} \xrightarrow[\text{e.g. } 0.5 \times 100]{\times \text{ by } 100} \text{Percentage}$$

e.g. $\frac{1}{2}$ = 0.5   = 50%

$$\text{Fraction} \xleftarrow[\text{The awkward one}]{} \text{Decimal} \xleftarrow[\div \text{ by } 100]{\text{e.g. } 50 \div 100} \text{Percentage}$$

__Converting decimals to fractions__ is fairly easy to do when you have __exact__ (terminating) decimals. It's best illustrated by examples — you should be able to work out the rule...

$0.6 = \frac{6}{10}$ $0.3 = \frac{3}{10}$ $0.7 = \frac{7}{10}$ $0.x = \frac{x}{10}$ etc.

$0.12 = \frac{12}{100}$ $0.78 = \frac{78}{100}$ $0.45 = \frac{45}{100}$ $0.05 = \frac{5}{100}$ etc.

$0.345 = \frac{345}{1000}$ $0.908 = \frac{908}{1000}$ $0.024 = \frac{24}{1000}$ $0.xyz = \frac{xyz}{1000}$ etc.

These can then be __cancelled down__ — see p.6

Scary-looking __recurring__ decimals like $0.\dot{3}$ are actually just __exact fractions__ in disguise. There is a simple method for converting them into fractions — it's on the next page...

Not decimals again — they're like a recurring nightmare...

__Learn__ the whole of the top table and the 4 conversion processes. Then it's time to break into a mild sweat...

1) Turn the following decimals into fractions.

   a) 0.6   b) 0.02   c) 0.77   d) 0.555   e) 5.6

Turning Decimals into Fractions

You might think that a decimal is just a decimal. But oh no — things get a lot more juicy than that...

Recurring or Terminating...

1) Recurring decimals have a <u>pattern</u> of numbers which repeats forever, e.g. $\frac{1}{3}$ is the decimal 0.33333... Note, it doesn't have to be a single digit that repeats. You could have, for instance: 0.143143143....

2) <u>Terminating</u> decimals are <u>finite</u>, e.g. $\frac{1}{20}$ is the decimal 0.05.

> You can write 0.143143143... as $0.\overset{\bullet}{1}4\overset{\bullet}{3}$.
> You put a dot over the <u>first</u> and <u>last</u> digit in the repeating set.
> $0.1\overset{\bullet}{6}$ means just the 6 repeats, i.e. 0.1666...

The <u>denominator</u> (bottom number) of a fraction tells you if it'll be a <u>recurring</u> or <u>terminating</u> <u>decimal</u> when you convert it. Fractions where the denominator has <u>prime factors</u> of <u>only 2 or 5</u> will give <u>terminating decimals</u>. All <u>other fractions</u> will give <u>recurring decimals</u>.

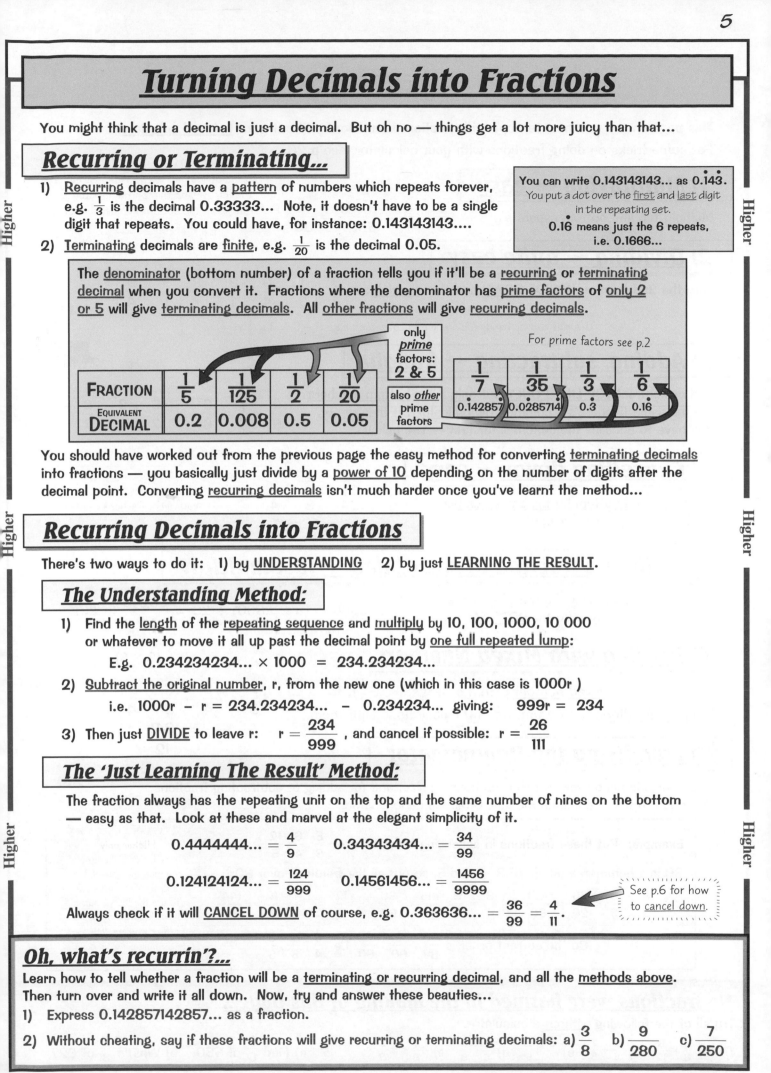

only *prime* factors: **2 & 5**

also *other* prime factors

For prime factors see p.2

FRACTION	$\frac{1}{5}$	$\frac{1}{125}$	$\frac{1}{2}$	$\frac{1}{20}$	$\frac{1}{7}$	$\frac{1}{35}$	$\frac{1}{3}$	$\frac{1}{6}$
EQUIVALENT DECIMAL	0.2	0.008	0.5	0.05	$0.\overset{\bullet}{1}4285\overset{\bullet}{7}$	$0.0\overset{\bullet}{2}8571\overset{\bullet}{4}$	$0.\overset{\bullet}{3}$	$0.1\overset{\bullet}{6}$

You should have worked out from the previous page the easy method for converting <u>terminating decimals</u> into fractions — you basically just divide by a <u>power of 10</u> depending on the number of digits after the decimal point. Converting <u>recurring decimals</u> isn't much harder once you've learnt the method...

Recurring Decimals into Fractions

There's two ways to do it: 1) by <u>UNDERSTANDING</u>   2) by just <u>LEARNING THE RESULT</u>.

The Understanding Method:

1) Find the <u>length</u> of the <u>repeating sequence</u> and <u>multiply</u> by 10, 100, 1000, 10 000 or whatever to move it all up past the decimal point by <u>one full repeated lump</u>:

   E.g. 0.234234234... × 1000 = 234.234234...

2) <u>Subtract the original number</u>, r, from the new one (which in this case is 1000r)

   i.e. 1000r − r = 234.234234... − 0.234234... giving: 999r = 234

3) Then just <u>DIVIDE</u> to leave r: $r = \frac{234}{999}$, and cancel if possible: $r = \frac{26}{111}$

The 'Just Learning The Result' Method:

The fraction always has the repeating unit on the top and the same number of nines on the bottom — easy as that. Look at these and marvel at the elegant simplicity of it.

$$0.4444444... = \frac{4}{9} \qquad 0.34343434... = \frac{34}{99}$$

$$0.124124124... = \frac{124}{999} \qquad 0.14561456... = \frac{1456}{9999}$$

Always check if it will <u>CANCEL DOWN</u> of course, e.g. $0.363636... = \frac{36}{99} = \frac{4}{11}$.

See p.6 for how to <u>cancel down</u>.

Oh, what's recurrin'?...

Learn how to tell whether a fraction will be a <u>terminating or recurring decimal</u>, and all the <u>methods above</u>. Then turn over and write it all down. Now, try and answer these beauties...

1) Express 0.142857142857... as a fraction.

2) Without cheating, say if these fractions will give recurring or terminating decimals: a) $\frac{3}{8}$ b) $\frac{9}{280}$ c) $\frac{7}{250}$

Fractions

This page shows you how to cope with fraction calculations without your <u>beloved calculator</u>. For some tricks on doing fractions with your calculator, see p.26.

1) Multiplying — easy

Multiply top and bottom separately:

$$\frac{3}{5} \times \frac{4}{7} = \frac{3 \times 4}{5 \times 7} = \frac{12}{35}$$

To multiply by an integer, you just multiply the integer and the top number together and keep the bottom number the same.

E.g. $4 \times \frac{2}{9} = \frac{4 \times 2}{9} = \frac{8}{9}$

2) Dividing — quite easy

Turn the 2nd fraction <u>UPSIDE DOWN</u> and then <u>multiply</u>:

$$\frac{3}{4} \div \frac{1}{3} = \frac{3}{4} \times \frac{3}{1} = \frac{3 \times 3}{4 \times 1} = \frac{9}{4}$$

This rule can be handy for dividing integers too. E.g. $3 \div 5 = 3 \times \frac{1}{5} = \frac{3}{5}$

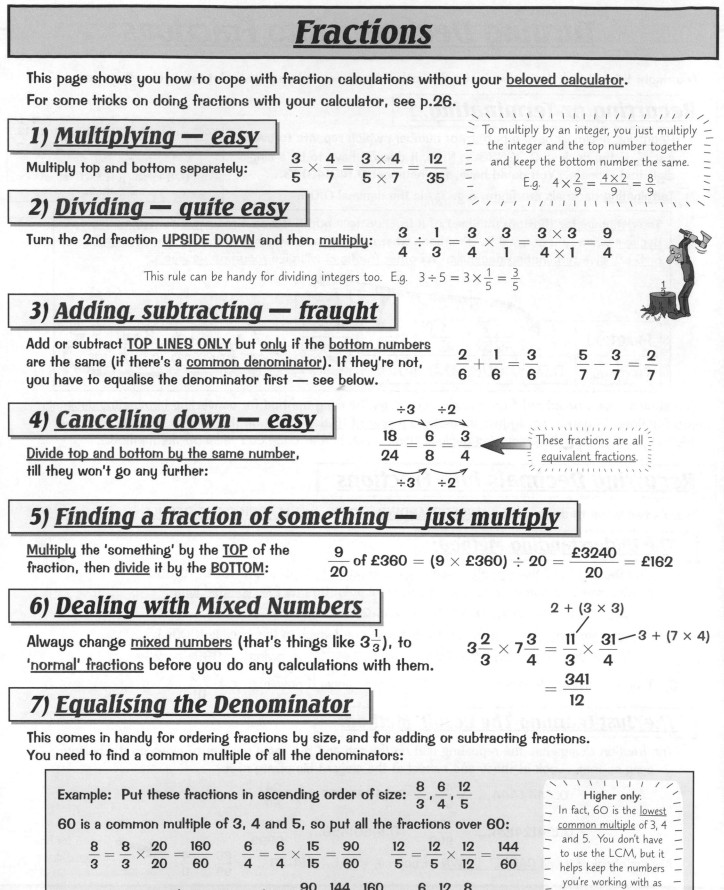

3) Adding, subtracting — fraught

Add or subtract <u>TOP LINES ONLY</u> but <u>only</u> if the <u>bottom numbers</u> are the same (if there's a <u>common denominator</u>). If they're not, you have to equalise the denominator first — see below.

$$\frac{2}{6} + \frac{1}{6} = \frac{3}{6} \qquad \frac{5}{7} - \frac{3}{7} = \frac{2}{7}$$

4) Cancelling down — easy

<u>Divide top and bottom by the same number</u>, till they won't go any further:

$$\overset{\div 3}{\overset{\frown}{\underset{\div 3}{\underbrace{\frac{18}{24}}}}} = \overset{\div 2}{\overset{\frown}{\underset{\div 2}{\underbrace{\frac{6}{8}}}}} = \frac{3}{4}$$

These fractions are all <u>equivalent fractions</u>.

5) Finding a fraction of something — just multiply

<u>Multiply</u> the 'something' by the <u>TOP</u> of the fraction, then <u>divide</u> it by the <u>BOTTOM</u>:

$$\frac{9}{20} \text{ of £360} = (9 \times £360) \div 20 = \frac{£3240}{20} = £162$$

6) Dealing with Mixed Numbers

Always change <u>mixed numbers</u> (that's things like $3\frac{1}{3}$), to <u>'normal' fractions</u> before you do any calculations with them.

$$3\frac{2}{3} \times 7\frac{3}{4} = \frac{11}{3} \times \frac{31}{4}$$

$2 + (3 \times 3)$ $3 + (7 \times 4)$

$$= \frac{341}{12}$$

7) Equalising the Denominator

This comes in handy for ordering fractions by size, and for adding or subtracting fractions. You need to find a common multiple of all the denominators:

Example: Put these fractions in ascending order of size: $\frac{8}{3}, \frac{6}{4}, \frac{12}{5}$

60 is a common multiple of 3, 4 and 5, so put all the fractions over 60:

$$\frac{8}{3} = \frac{8}{3} \times \frac{20}{20} = \frac{160}{60} \qquad \frac{6}{4} = \frac{6}{4} \times \frac{15}{15} = \frac{90}{60} \qquad \frac{12}{5} = \frac{12}{5} \times \frac{12}{12} = \frac{144}{60}$$

So the correct order is $\frac{90}{60}, \frac{144}{60}, \frac{160}{60}$ i.e. $\frac{6}{4}, \frac{12}{5}, \frac{8}{3}$

<u>Higher only</u>: In fact, 60 is the <u>lowest common multiple</u> of 3, 4 and 5. You don't have to use the LCM, but it helps keep the numbers you're working with as small as possible.

No fractions were harmed in the making of this page...

Try all of the following <u>without</u> a calculator.

1) a) $\frac{3}{8} \times \frac{5}{12}$ b) $\frac{4}{5} \div \frac{7}{8}$ c) $\frac{3}{4} + \frac{2}{5}$ d) $\frac{2}{5} - \frac{3}{8}$ e) $4\frac{1}{9} + 2\frac{2}{27}$ 2) a) Find $\frac{2}{5}$ of 550.   b) What's $\frac{7}{8}$ of £2?

Ratios

The whole grisly subject of <u>RATIOS</u> gets a whole lot easier when you do this:

Treat RATIOS like FRACTIONS

So for the <u>RATIO</u> 3:4, you'd treat it as the <u>FRACTION</u> $\frac{3}{4}$, which is 0.75 as a <u>DECIMAL</u>.

What the fraction form of the ratio actually means

1) Suppose in a class there's <u>girls and boys</u> in the ratio 3 : 4.
   This means there's $\frac{3}{4}$ as many girls as boys. ⟵

2) So if there were 20 boys, there would be $\frac{3}{4} \times 20 = 15$ girls.

Be really careful — it doesn't mean $\frac{3}{4}$ of the people in the class are girls.

Reducing Ratios to their simplest form

You reduce ratios just like you'd reduce fractions to their simplest form.
For the ratio 15:18, both numbers have a <u>factor</u> of 3, so <u>divide them by 3</u> — that gives 5:6. We can't reduce this any further. So the simplest form of 15:18 is <u>5 : 6</u>.

Treat them just like fractions — use your calculator if you can

Now this is really sneaky. If you stick in a fraction using the $a\frac{b}{c}$ button,
your calculator automatically cancels it down when you press $=$.

So for the ratio 8:12, just press 8 $a\frac{b}{c}$ 12 $=$, and you'll get the reduced fraction $\frac{2}{3}$.
Now you just change it back to ratio form ie. <u>2 : 3</u>. Ace.

The More Awkward Cases:

1) The $a\frac{b}{c}$ button will only accept whole numbers

So if the ratio is something like '2.4 : 3.6' or '1¼ : 3½' then you must...

MULTIPLY BOTH SIDES by the SAME NUMBER until they are both WHOLE NUMBERS

E.g. for '1¼ : 3½', multiplying both sides by 4 gives '<u>5 : 14</u>'   (Try $a\frac{b}{c}$, but it won't cancel further.)

2) If the ratio is MIXED UNITS

CONVERT BOTH SIDES into the SMALLER UNITS using the relevant CONVERSION FACTOR (see P.21)

E.g. '24 mm : 7.2 cm' ($\times$ 7.2 cm by 10) $\Rightarrow$ 24 mm : 72 mm = <u>1 : 3</u> (using $a\frac{b}{c}$)

3) To reduce a ratio to the form 1 : n or n : 1 (n can be any number)

Simply DIVIDE BOTH SIDES BY THE SMALLEST SIDE.

This form is often the <u>most useful</u>, since it shows the ratio very clearly.

E.g. take "<u>3 : 56</u>" — dividing both sides by 3 gives: <u>1 : 18.7</u> (56÷3) (i.e. 1 : n)

Ratios

There's just so much <u>great stuff</u> to say about ratios. I couldn't possibly fit it onto only one page...

Using The Formula Triangle in Ratio Questions

EXAMPLE: "Mortar is made from sand and cement in the ratio 7:2.
If 9 buckets of sand are used, how much cement is needed?"

This is a fairly common type of Exam question and it's pretty tricky for most people
— but once you start using the formula triangle method (see p.24), it's a bit of a breeze...

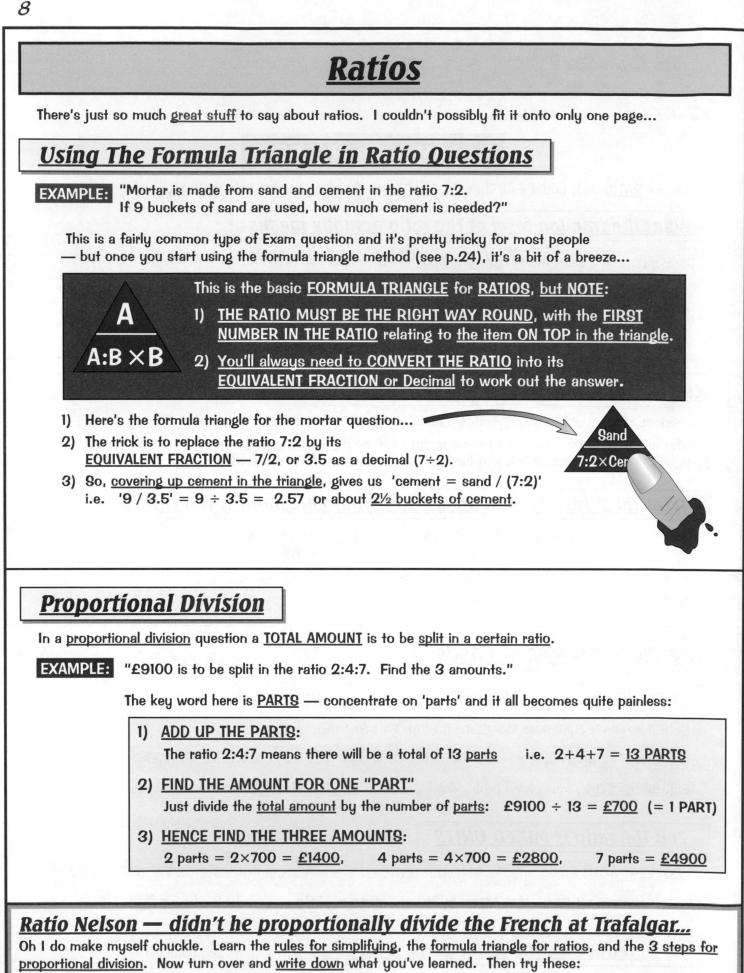

This is the basic <u>FORMULA TRIANGLE</u> for <u>RATIOS</u>, <u>but NOTE</u>:

1) <u>THE RATIO MUST BE THE RIGHT WAY ROUND</u>, with the <u>FIRST
NUMBER IN THE RATIO</u> relating to <u>the item ON TOP</u> in the triangle.

2) <u>You'll always need to CONVERT THE RATIO</u> into its
<u>EQUIVALENT FRACTION</u> or Decimal to work out the answer.

1) Here's the formula triangle for the mortar question...
2) The trick is to replace the ratio 7:2 by its
   <u>EQUIVALENT FRACTION</u> — 7/2, or 3.5 as a decimal (7÷2).
3) So, <u>covering up cement in the triangle</u>, gives us 'cement = sand / (7:2)'
   i.e. '9 / 3.5' = 9 ÷ 3.5 = 2.57 or about <u>2½ buckets of cement</u>.

Proportional Division

In a <u>proportional division</u> question a <u>TOTAL AMOUNT</u> is to be <u>split in a certain ratio</u>.

EXAMPLE: "£9100 is to be split in the ratio 2:4:7. Find the 3 amounts."

The key word here is <u>PARTS</u> — concentrate on 'parts' and it all becomes quite painless:

1) <u>ADD UP THE PARTS</u>:
   The ratio 2:4:7 means there will be a total of 13 <u>parts</u>   i.e. 2+4+7 = <u>13 PARTS</u>

2) <u>FIND THE AMOUNT FOR ONE "PART"</u>
   Just divide the <u>total amount</u> by the number of <u>parts</u>:   £9100 ÷ 13 = <u>£700</u>   (= 1 PART)

3) <u>HENCE FIND THE THREE AMOUNTS</u>:
   2 parts = 2×700 = <u>£1400</u>,   4 parts = 4×700 = <u>£2800</u>,   7 parts = <u>£4900</u>

Ratio Nelson — didn't he proportionally divide the French at Trafalgar...

Oh I do make myself chuckle. Learn the <u>rules for simplifying</u>, the <u>formula triangle for ratios</u>, and the <u>3 steps for
proportional division</u>. Now turn over and <u>write down</u> what you've learned. Then try these:

1) Simplify: a) 25:35   b) 3.4 : 5.1   c) 2¼ : 3¾
2) Porridge and ice-cream are mixed in the ratio 7:4.
   How much porridge should go with 10 bowls of ice-cream?
3) Divide £8400 in the ratio 5:3:4

Proportion

Sometimes you have two numbers that are <u>linked</u>. If one changes, the other changes too.

Directly Proportional Numbers Increase Together

1) Sometimes increasing one number means another number increases by the <u>same factor</u>.
   E.g. the <u>number of eggs</u> you need depends on <u>how many people</u> you're making omelettes for.
   This table shows how many eggs you need for different numbers of people.

2) If you <u>double</u> one value, you <u>double</u> the other, if you
   <u>times one of them by 5</u>, you <u>times the other by 5</u>, etc.

3) In cases like this, the pairs of numbers are in
   <u>DIRECT PROPORTION</u> to each other.

people	1	2	3	4	10	40
eggs	2	4	6	8	20	80

4) The <u>RATIO is the same for all pairs</u> of values, i.e.:

$$\frac{1}{2} = \frac{2}{4} = \frac{3}{6} = \frac{4}{8} = \frac{10}{20} = \frac{40}{80} = 0.5$$

This means direct proportion problems are just like <u>ratio</u> problems, so use the same method:

> **EXAMPLE:** "The height of a doo-dah tree is directly proportional to its number of leaves. If an 11 m tall doo-dah tree has 6 leaves, how tall will one with 14 leaves be?"
>
> 1) Make the formula triangle.
> 2) <u>Covering up 'Height'</u>, gives us 'height = (11:6) × leaves
>   i.e. '1.833 × 14 = <u>25.67 m tall</u>

Height / 11:6 × Leaves

Inverse Proportion — One Increases, One Decreases

1) Two numbers can also be <u>inversely proportional</u> to each other.
   Imagine you have £100 to share out equally. The <u>more people</u>
   it's shared between, the <u>less</u> each person gets.

people	1	2	4	5	10	100
£	100	50	25	20	10	1

2) If you <u>double</u> one value, you <u>halve</u> the other, if you
   <u>times one of them by 3</u>, you <u>divide the other by 3</u>, etc.

3) You need a bit of a different method to solve <u>inverse proportion problems</u>.
   The length of time a job takes with different numbers of people is an old favourite.

> **EXAMPLE:** "It takes 4 people 14 hours to paint a very big wall. How long would it have taken 7 people?"
>
> 1) Find the factor the number of people has <u>increased</u> by:
>
> × 1.75
>
> | people | 4 | 7 |
> |--------|---|---|
> | hours | 14 | |
>
> 2) So the time required must have <u>decreased</u> by the same factor.
>
> × 1.75
>
> | people | 4 | 7 |
> |--------|---|---|
> | hours | 14 | 8 |
>
> ÷ 1.75
>
> So, it'd have taken 7 people <u>8 hours</u>.

How long does it take to dig yourself into half a hole...

Well actually, you can't have half a hole. A hole is a hole. Anyway, enough philosophical debate. Try these:

1) A hairdresser charges an amount directly proportional to how long your hair is.
   Beth is charged £5.50 and her hair is 10 cm long. Sue's hair is 8 cm long. How much will Sue pay?

2) It takes 21 minutes to drive from A to B at 30 km/h. How long will it take to drive from A to B at 45 km/h?

Higher

Percentages

You shouldn't have any trouble with most percentage questions, especially <u>types 1 and 2</u>.
Watch out for <u>type 3</u> questions and make sure you know the <u>proper method</u> for solving them.

| **Type 1** | "Find x% of y" — e.g. Find 15% of £46 $\Rightarrow$ 0.15 × 46 = <u>£6.90</u> |

See page 4 for turning percents into decimals.

| **Type 2** | "Express x as a percentage of y"
 e.g. Give 40p as a percentage of £3.34 $\Rightarrow$ (40 ÷ 334) × 100 = <u>12%</u> |

| **Type 3** | — IDENTIFIED BY <u>NOT</u> GIVING THE "<u>ORIGINAL VALUE</u>" |

These are the type most people get wrong — but only because they don't
recognise them as a type 3 and don't apply this simple method:

EXAMPLE:

> A house increases in value by 20% to £72 000.
> Find what it was worth <u>before</u> the rise.

METHOD:

÷120 $\Big\lgroup$
    £72 000 = 120%

    £600 = 1%

×100 $\Big\lgroup$
    £60 000 = 100%

So the original price was <u>£60 000</u>

An <u>INCREASE</u> of 20% means that £72 000
represents <u>120% of the original</u> value.
(If it was a DROP of 20%, then we would
put '£72 000 = <u>80%</u>' instead, and then
divide by 80 on the LHS, instead of 120.)

Always set them out <u>exactly like this example</u>. The trickiest bit is deciding the top %
figure on the RHS — the 2nd and 3rd rows are <u>always</u> 1% and 100%.

Percentage Change

It is common to give a <u>change in value</u> as a <u>percentage</u>.
This is the formula for doing so — <u>LEARN IT, AND USE IT</u>:

$$\text{PERCENTAGE 'CHANGE'} = \frac{\text{'CHANGE'}}{\text{ORIGINAL}} \times 100$$

'Change' can mean all sorts of things, such as: 'profit', 'loss', 'appreciation', 'depreciation', 'increase', 'decrease', 'error', 'discount', etc.

E.g. "John buys a box of old toy cars for £20. He sells them for £32. What is his percentage profit?"

The profit (or 'change') is £32 – £20 = £12.   % 'profit' = $\dfrac{\text{'profit'}}{\text{original}} \times 100 = \dfrac{12}{20} \times 100 = \underline{60\%}$

You might be asked to find the <u>overall percentage change</u> when one percentage change is followed by another.

E.g. "A shop buys a coat from a factory for £y and increases its price by 30% to make a profit.
The coat doesn't sell, so it's reduced by 20% in the sale. Calculate the shop's overall profit."

Final cost of the coat = y × (1 + 0.3) × (1 – 0.2) = y × 1.3 × 0.8 = y × <u>1.04</u>

You multiply by this to get
cost after 30% increase...

...then by this to get cost
after 20% decrease...

...which is the same as
multiplying by this.

1.04 = 1 + 0.04, which is an overall increase of <u>4%</u>.

Fact — 70% of people understand percentages, the other 40% don't...

Learn the details for the different types of percentage question you might get, then <u>turn over</u> and <u>write it all down</u>.

1) A trader buys watches for £5 and sells them for £7. Find his profit as a percentage.
2) A car depreciates by 30% to £14 350. What was it worth before?
3) Find the percentage error in rounding 3.452 to 3.5. Give your answer to 2 d.p.

Compound Growth and Decay

Compound growth is dead useful for working out how much interest you'll get in your savings account. Compound decay is kind of the opposite of that — it's when an amount gets smaller by a certain proportion every year or month or whatever.

The Formula

This topic is simple if you LEARN THIS FORMULA. If you don't, it's pretty well impossible:

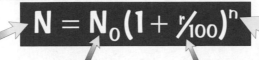

$$N = N_0\left(1 + \frac{r}{100}\right)^n$$

Existing amount at this time

Initial amount

Percentage change per day/hour/year

Number of days/hrs/yrs

Percentage Increase and Decrease

The $(1 + r/100)$ bit might look a bit confusing in the formula but in practice it's really easy:

E.g   5% increase will be 1.05   5% decrease will be 0.95 $(= 1 - 0.05)$
        26% increase will be 1.26   26% decrease will be 0.74 $(= 1 - 0.26)$

3 Examples to show you how EASY it is:

1) "A man invests £1000 in a savings account which pays 8% per year.
    How much will there be after 6 years?"
    ANSWER: Usual formula: Amount $= 1000(1.08)^6 = $ __£1586.87__

    Initial amount   8% increase   6 years

2) "A car depreciates by 7% per year. It was bought new for £12 000. How much is it worth after 4 years?"
    ANSWER: Same old formula:
    Value $=$ Initial value $\left(1 + \frac{-7}{100}\right)^n$

    Value $= 12\,000(1 - 0.07)^4 = 12\,000 \times (0.93)^4 = $ __£8976.62__

3) "£500 is invested in an account. It increases by 15% each year.
    Find the formula relating the amount in the account, n, and the number of years, y."
    ANSWER: Well stone me, it's the same old easy-peasy compound growth formula again:
    $n = n_0(1 + 0.15)^y$ or finished off: __$n = 500 \times (1.15)^y$__

Oh man, that last joke has still got me increases...

Bleurgh. What a horrible looking formula. 'Fraid you've still got to learn it though. And those three examples. Your reward is getting to do these questions. Hee hee. If you're struggling, go over the page again.

1) A business's value increases by 4% per week. Initially, it was worth £3000. What is it worth after 12 weeks?

2) The value of a bike decreases by 16% every year. If its initial value was £500, find the value after 20 years. How long will it take to become worthless?

12

Revision Summary

I know these questions might seem difficult, <u>but they are the very best revision you can do</u>.
The whole point of revision, remember, is <u>to find out what you don't know</u> and then learn it <u>until you do</u>.
These searching questions test how much you know <u>better than anything else ever can</u>.
They follow the order of the pages in Section 1, so you can easily look up anything you don't know.

KEEP LEARNING THESE BASIC FACTS UNTIL YOU KNOW THEM

1) List the first 5 prime numbers.

2) What are the steps of the method for determining if a number is prime?

3) Express these as a product of powers of prime factors: a) 270 b) 1050

4) Give two common multiples of 8 and 12.

5) Give all the common factors of 64 and 80.

6) Find the <u>HCF</u> of 42 and 28 and the <u>LCM</u> of 8 and 10.

7) Convert 3/8 into a decimal and then into a percentage.

8) What is 24% as a decimal and as a fraction?

9) Give three examples of recurring decimals and three examples of terminating decimals.

10) How can you tell if a fraction will become a recurring or terminating decimal when you convert it?

11) Demonstrate the 2 methods for converting recurring decimals to fractions.

12) Describe in words the method for cancelling a fraction down by hand.

13) Do these fraction calculations:

a) $\frac{3}{5} \times \frac{1}{4}$ b) $\frac{3}{5} \div \frac{1}{4}$ c) $1\frac{3}{5} + 4\frac{1}{4}$ d) $3\frac{7}{8} - 2\frac{1}{3}$

14) Find 5/7 of 42.

15) Put the fractions 5/7 and 1/6 over a common denominator.

16) Sarah is in charge of ordering new stock for a clothes shop. The shop usually sells red scarves and blue scarves in the ratio 5:8. Sarah orders 150 red scarves. How many blue scarves should she order?

17) What are the three steps of the method of proportional division?

18) Jill, Heather and Susie spent Saturday helping out in their mum's café. Jill worked for 3 hours, Heather worked the next 2.5 hours and Susie worked for the final 1.5 hours of the day. They were given £42 to split between them for the work they'd done. How much should each of them receive?

19) Write down 3 pairs of numbers that show direct proportion, and 3 pairs that show inverse proportion.

20) Do your own example to illustrate each different type of percentage question.

21) Do an example to illustrate a third type of percentage problem.

22) Martin is trying to sell his car. He paid £5300 for it two years ago and is advised to sell it for 30% less than this original value. What price should he sell the car for?

23) Sam buys some shares. In the first month they decrease in value by 12%. In the second month, their value increases by 8%. What is their overall percentage change in value?

24) Tim opens a savings account that pays 7% compound interest per year. He puts £100 into the account. How much will he have after 5 years?

$100(1\cdot07)^5$

Section 1 — Numbers

Square Roots and Cube Roots

Take a deep breath, and get ready to tackle this page. Good luck with it, I'll be rootin' for ya...

Square Numbers

Squaring a number means 'multiplying it by itself': $P \times P = P^2$
The square of any integer is called a 'square number':

(1x1) (2x2) (3x3) (4x4) (5x5) (6x6) (7x7) (8x8) (9x9) (10x10) (11x11) (12x12) (13x13) (14x14) (15x15)

| 1 | 4 | 9 | 16 | 25 | 36 | 49 | 64 | 81 | 100 | 121 | 144 | 169 | 196 | 225... |

Square Roots

Finding the square root is the reverse of squaring.

The best way to think of it is this: **'Square Root' means 'What Number Times by Itself gives...'**

Example: 'Find the square root of 49' (i.e. 'Find $\sqrt{49}$')
To do this you should say "what number times by itself gives 49?"
And the answer, of course, is 7.

Square Roots can be Positive or Negative

When you take the square root of a number, the answer can actually be positive or negative...
You always get a positive and negative version of the same number.

E.g. $x^2 = 4$ gives $x = \pm\sqrt{4} = +2$ or -2

To understand why, look at what happens when you work backwards by squaring the answers:
$2^2 = 2 \times 2 = 4$ but also $(-2)^2 = (-2) \times (-2) = 4$

On your calculator, it's easy to find the positive square root
using the SQUARE ROOT BUTTON: Press $\sqrt{}$ 49 = 7

Cube Numbers

Cubing a number means 'multiplying it by itself 3 times': $J \times J \times J = J^3$
The cube of any integer is called a 'cube number':

(1×1×1) (2×2×2) (3×3×3) (4×4×4) (5×5×5) (6×6×6) (7×7×7) (8×8×8) (9×9×9) (10×10×10)

| 1 | 8 | 27 | 64 | 125 | 216 | 343 | 512 | 729 | 1000... |

Well, strictly there are only two × signs, but you know what I mean

Cube Roots

Finding the cube root is the reverse of cubing.

Think of this as: **'Cube Root' means 'What Number Times by Itself THREE TIMES gives...'**

Example: "Find the cube root of 64" (i.e 'Find $\sqrt[3]{64}$')
You should say "What number times by itself three times gives 64?"
And after a few guesses, the answer is 4.

Or on your calculator just use the cube root button:
Press $\sqrt[3]{}$ 64 = 4

Unlike square roots, there's only one answer. A positive number cubed is always positive, and a negative number cubed is always negative.

"Cue brute", that's what I call Charley when I play him at snooker...

LEARN the definitions and the methods for finding roots. Then turn the page and write it all down.
1) Use your calculator to find to 2 d.p. a) $\sqrt{200}$ b) $\sqrt[3]{8000}$
   For a) what is the other value that your calculator didn't give?
2) a) If $g^2 = 36$, find g. b) If $b^3 = 64$, find b. c) $r = 3$, find r^3.

Manipulating Surds

What a page. First a few types of number — then a bit of surd manipulation.

Numbers are Either Rational or Irrational

RATIONAL NUMBERS Most numbers you deal with are rational. They can always be written as <u>fractions</u>.
You'll come across them in **3** different forms:

1) A <u>whole number</u> (either positive or negative), e.g. $4 \left(= \frac{4}{1}\right)$, $-5 \left(= \frac{-5}{1}\right)$, $-12 \left(= \frac{-12}{1}\right)$

2) A <u>fraction</u> p/q, where p and q are whole numbers (and q is not zero), e.g. $\frac{1}{4}$, $-\frac{1}{2}$, $\frac{3}{4}$

3) A <u>terminating or recurring decimal</u>, e.g. 0.125 $\left(= \frac{1}{8}\right)$, 0.3333333333... $\left(= \frac{1}{3}\right)$, 0.143143143... $\left(= \frac{143}{999}\right)$

IRRATIONAL NUMBERS are messy! They <u>can't</u> be written as fractions

1) They are always <u>never-ending non-repeating decimals</u>. π is irrational.

2) <u>Square roots</u> of non-square numbers are irrational. As are <u>cube roots</u> of non-cube numbers.

Manipulating Surds — 7 Rules to Learn

Surds are expressions with irrational square roots in them, e.g. $\sqrt{2}$ or $3\sqrt{7}$.
You **MUST USE THEM** if you're asked for an **EXACT** answer. There are 7 rules you need to learn...

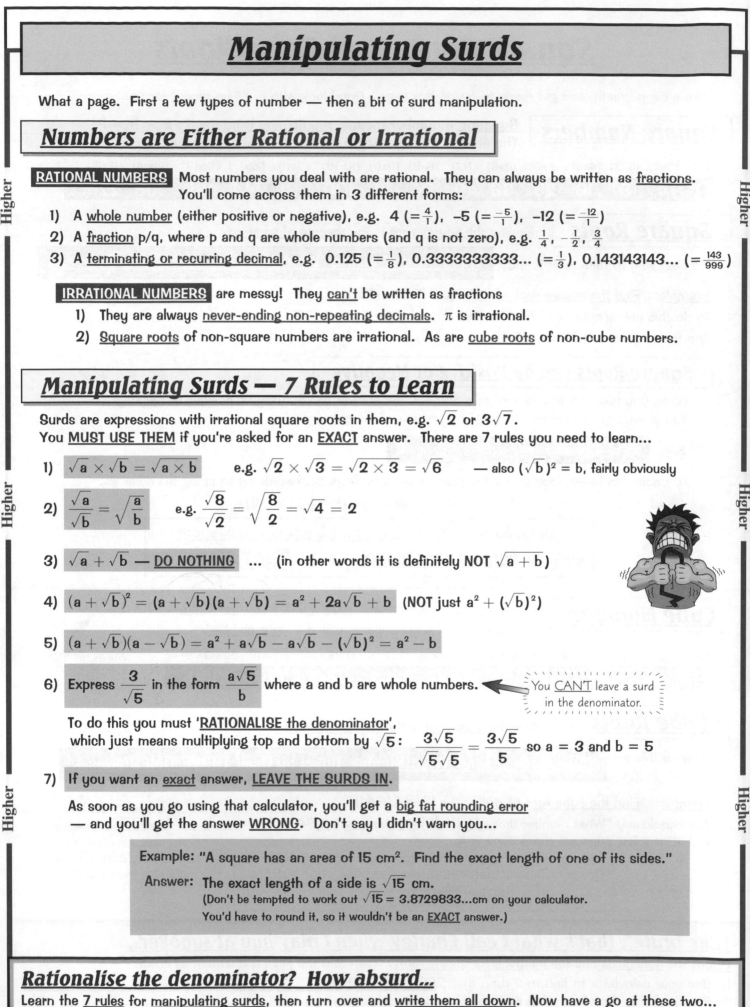

1) $\boxed{\sqrt{a} \times \sqrt{b} = \sqrt{a \times b}}$ e.g. $\sqrt{2} \times \sqrt{3} = \sqrt{2 \times 3} = \sqrt{6}$ — also $(\sqrt{b})^2 = b$, fairly obviously

2) $\boxed{\dfrac{\sqrt{a}}{\sqrt{b}} = \sqrt{\dfrac{a}{b}}}$ e.g. $\dfrac{\sqrt{8}}{\sqrt{2}} = \sqrt{\dfrac{8}{2}} = \sqrt{4} = 2$

3) $\boxed{\sqrt{a} + \sqrt{b} - \textbf{DO NOTHING}}$ ... (in other words it is definitely NOT $\sqrt{a+b}$)

4) $\boxed{(a + \sqrt{b})^2 = (a + \sqrt{b})(a + \sqrt{b}) = a^2 + 2a\sqrt{b} + b}$ (NOT just $a^2 + (\sqrt{b})^2$)

5) $\boxed{(a + \sqrt{b})(a - \sqrt{b}) = a^2 + a\sqrt{b} - a\sqrt{b} - (\sqrt{b})^2 = a^2 - b}$

6) Express $\dfrac{3}{\sqrt{5}}$ in the form $\dfrac{a\sqrt{5}}{b}$ where a and b are whole numbers. ← You **CAN'T** leave a surd in the denominator.

To do this you must '<u>RATIONALISE the denominator</u>',
which just means multiplying top and bottom by $\sqrt{5}$: $\dfrac{3\sqrt{5}}{\sqrt{5}\sqrt{5}} = \dfrac{3\sqrt{5}}{5}$ so a = 3 and b = 5

7) If you want an <u>exact</u> answer, <u>**LEAVE THE SURDS IN**</u>.

As soon as you go using that calculator, you'll get a <u>big fat rounding error</u>
— and you'll get the answer <u>WRONG</u>. Don't say I didn't warn you...

> Example: "A square has an area of 15 cm². Find the exact length of one of its sides."
>
> Answer: The exact length of a side is $\sqrt{15}$ cm.
> (Don't be tempted to work out $\sqrt{15} = 3.8729833...$cm on your calculator.
> You'd have to round it, so it wouldn't be an <u>EXACT</u> answer.)

Rationalise the denominator? How absurd...

Learn the <u>7 rules</u> for <u>manipulating surds</u>, then turn over and <u>write them all down</u>. Now have a go at these two...
Simplify: 1) $(1 + \sqrt{2})^2 - (1 - \sqrt{2})^2$ 2) $(1 + \sqrt{2})^2 - (2\sqrt{2} - \sqrt{2})^2$

Powers and Roots

Powers are a very useful shorthand: $2 \times 2 \times 2 \times 2 \times 2 \times 2 \times 2 = 2^7$ ('two to the power 7')

That bit is easy to remember. Unfortunately, there are some <u>special rules</u> for powers that are not tremendously exciting — but you do need to know them for the Exam:

The Seven Easy Rules:

The first two only work for powers of the same number.

1) When <u>MULTIPLYING</u>, you <u>ADD THE POWERS</u>.   e.g. $3^4 \times 3^6 = 3^{6+4} = 3^{10}$

2) When <u>DIVIDING</u>, you <u>SUBTRACT THE POWERS</u>.   e.g. $5^4 \div 5^2 = 5^{4-2} = 5^2$

3) $X^1 = X$, <u>ANYTHING</u> to the <u>POWER 1</u> is just <u>ITSELF</u>.   e.g. $3^1 = 3$, $6 \times 6^3 = 6^4$

4) $1^x = 1$, <u>1 TO ANY POWER</u> is <u>STILL JUST 1</u>.   e.g. $1^{23} = 1$ $1^{89} = 1$ $1^2 = 1$

5) $X^0 = 1$, <u>ANYTHING</u> to the <u>POWER 0</u> is just <u>ONE</u>.   e.g. $5^0 = 1$ $67^0 = 1$

6) When <u>RAISING</u> one power to another, you <u>MULTIPLY THEM</u>.   e.g. $(3^2)^4 = 3^{2 \times 4} = 3^8$

7) <u>FRACTIONS</u> — Apply power to <u>both TOP and BOTTOM</u>.   e.g. $\left(\frac{3}{4}\right)^2 = \frac{3^2}{4^2} = \frac{9}{16}$

$$\left(1\frac{3}{5}\right)^3 = \left(\frac{8}{5}\right)^3 = \frac{8^3}{5^3} = \frac{512}{125}$$

The Three Tricky Rules:

8) <u>NEGATIVE POWERS</u> — Turn it Upside-Down

People do have quite a bit of difficulty remembering this.

Whenever you see a negative power you're supposed to immediately think:
"Aha, that means turn it the other way up and make the power positive"

Like this: e.g. $7^{-2} = \frac{1}{7^2} = \frac{1}{49}$ $\left(\frac{3}{5}\right)^{-2} = \left(\frac{5}{3}\right)^{+2} = \frac{5^2}{3^2} = \frac{25}{9}$

9) <u>FRACTIONAL POWERS</u>

> The power $\frac{1}{2}$ means <u>Square Root</u>,
> The power $\frac{1}{3}$ means <u>Cube Root</u>,
> The power $\frac{1}{4}$ means <u>Fourth Root</u> etc.

e.g. $25^{1/2} = \sqrt{25} = 5$
$64^{1/3} = \sqrt[3]{64} = 4$
$81^{1/4} = \sqrt[4]{81} = 3$ etc.

Don't forget — square roots can be positive or negative. See page 13.

The one to really watch is when you get a <u>negative fraction</u> like $49^{-1/2}$ — people get mixed up and think that the minus is the square root, and forget to turn it upside down as well. $49^{-1/2} = \frac{1}{49^{1/2}} = \frac{1}{\sqrt{49}} = \frac{1}{7}$

10) <u>TWO-STAGE FRACTIONAL POWERS</u>

They really like putting these in Exam questions so learn the method:
With fractional powers like $64^{5/6}$ always <u>split the fraction</u> into a <u>root</u> and a <u>power</u>, and do them in that order: <u>root</u> first, then <u>power</u>: $(64)^{1/6 \times 5} = (64^{1/6})^5 = (2)^5 = 32$

Square Roots? Must be a geomer-tree...*

Learn the <u>exciting rules</u> on this page. Then turn over and write them all down with <u>examples</u>. <u>Keep trying till you can</u>.

1) Simplify: a) $3^2 \times 3^6$ b) $4^3 \div 4^2$ c) $(8^3)^4$ d) $(3^2 \times 3^3 \times 1^6) \div 3^5$ e) $7^3 \times 7 \times 7^2$

2) Evaluate   a) $(1/4)^{-3}$ b) 25^{-2} c) $25^{-1/2}$ d) $(27/216)^{-1/3}$ e) $625^{3/4}$ f) $125^{-2/3}$

3) Use your calculator to find: a) 5.2^{24} b) $40^{3/4}$ c) $\sqrt[5]{200}$

*winner of Best Maths Gag in a Supporting Role, International Algebra Awards 2010   *Section 2 — More Numbers*

Standard Form

Standard form is only really useful for writing <u>VERY BIG</u> or <u>VERY SMALL</u> numbers in a more convenient way, e.g.

56 000 000 000 would be 5.6×10^{10} in standard form.

0.000 000 003 45 would be 3.45×10^{-9} in standard form.

But <u>ANY NUMBER</u> can be written in standard form and you need to know how to do it:

What it Actually is:

A number written in standard form must <u>ALWAYS</u> be in <u>EXACTLY</u> this form:

$$A \times 10^n$$

This <u>number</u> must <u>always</u> be <u>BETWEEN 1 AND 10</u>.

(The fancy way of saying this is: $1 \leq A < 10$ — they sometimes write that in Exam questions — don't let it put you off, just remember what it means).

This number is just the <u>NUMBER OF PLACES</u> the <u>Decimal Point</u> moves.

Learn The Three Rules:

1) The <u>front number</u> must always be <u>BETWEEN 1 AND 10</u>.

2) The power of 10, n, is purely: <u>HOW FAR THE D.P. MOVES</u>.

3) n is <u>+ve</u> for BIG numbers, n is <u>–ve</u> for SMALL numbers.

(This is much better than rules based on which way the D.P. moves.)

Two Very Simple Examples:

1) "Express 35 600 in standard form."

<u>METHOD</u>:
1) Move the D.P. until 35 600 becomes 3.56 ('$1 \leq A < 10$')
2) The D.P. has moved 4 places so n=4, giving: 10^4
3) 35 600 is a BIG number so n is +4, not –4

<u>ANSWER</u>:
3.5600
$= 3.56 \times 10^4$

2) "Express 0.0000623 in standard form."

<u>METHOD</u>:
1) The D.P. must move <u>5 places to give 6.23</u> ('$1 \leq A < 10$'),
2) So the power of 10 is 5
3) Since 0.0000623 is a <u>SMALL NUMBER</u> it must be 10^{-5} not 10^{+5}.

<u>ANSWER</u>:
0.0000623
$= 6.23 \times 10^{-5}$

Standard Form

Four Very Important Examples

This stands for 'significant figures' and it's one way of rounding numbers — there's more about this on page 19.

1) The Calculator's Scientific Mode

This mode <u>gives all numbers in standard form</u> to a specified number of sig fig. A little SCI will be displayed somewhere when you're in this mode. To get into this mode, press MODE and select SCI from one of the menus you get. (On other calculators look for a button with 'SCI' written above it as the 2nd or 3rd function.)

It'll ask you for the number of sig figs to display, something like this: `SCI 0-9?`
So if you choose 4, all numbers and answers will be displayed to 4 sig fig.

<u>EXAMPLE</u>: $565 \div 3$ would give `188.3333333` in normal mode,

...or `1.883 02` in 4 sig fig mode.

(Or maybe `1.883E02`)

Different calculators show answers in standard form in different ways. You should ALWAYS write your answers in the form 1.883×10^2 (1.883^{02} means something <u>completely different</u>). So you need to <u>understand</u> what the display on <u>your own calculator</u> means.

2) What is 146.3 million in standard form?

The two favourite wrong answers for this are:

1) 146.3×10^6 — which is kind of right but it's not in <u>STANDARD FORM</u> because 146.3 is not between 1 and 10 (i.e. $1 \leq A < 10$ has not been done)

2) 1.463×10^6 — this one <u>is</u> in standard form but it's not big enough.

This is a very typical Exam question, which <u>too many people get wrong</u>.

Just <u>take your time</u> and <u>do it IN TWO STAGES</u> like this:

<u>ANSWER</u>: 146.3 million = 146 300 000 = <u>1.463×10^8</u>

The EXP button means '$\times 10^x$'. (Some calculators have a button saying this instead.)

3) Remember, 10^5 means 1×10^5

So to enter 10^5 into the calculator you must remember it's actually 1×10^5 and press [1] [EXP] [5]

<u>EXAMPLE</u>: "A nanometre is 10^{-9} m. How many nanometres are there in 0.35 m? "

<u>ANSWER</u>: $0.35 \div (1 \times 10^{-9})$, so press [0.35] [÷] [1] [EXP] [(-)] [9] [=] $= 3.5 \times 10^8$.

4) The 'Googol' is 10^{100} and is a pest

It's a pest because it goes off the scale of your calculator, so you have to do it 'by hand' — which means they like it for Exam questions. So make sure you LEARN this example: "<u>Express 56 googols in standard form.</u>"

ANS: 56 googols is $56 \times 10^{100} = 5.6 \times 10 \times 10^{100} = 5.6 \times 10^{101}$.

Note: you split the 56 into 5.6×10 and then <u>COMBINE THE POWERS OF 10</u>

How come I can get Google ™ on my phone, but not on my calculator..?

Learn the <u>three rules</u> and <u>the four important examples</u>, then turn over and <u>write them down</u>. Then lookie here...

1) Express 0.854 million and 0.00018 in standard form.

2) Express 4.56×10^{-3} and 2.7×10^5 as ordinary numbers.

3) a) Work out $(3.2 \times 10^7) \div (1.6 \times 10^{-4})$.   b) How many nanometres are there in 10^{-1} m?

4) Write down 650 googols in standard form.

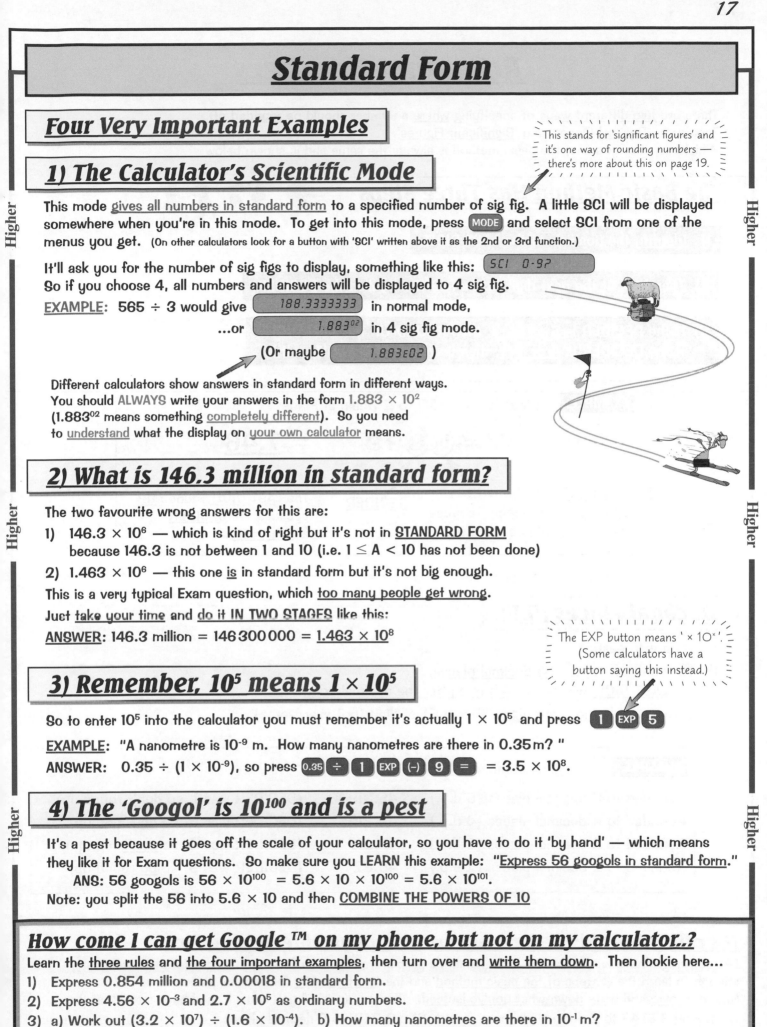

Rounding Numbers

There are two different ways of specifying where a number should be rounded off.
They are: 'Decimal Places' and 'Significant Figures'.
Whichever way you use, the basic method is always the same and is shown below:

The Basic Method Has Three Steps

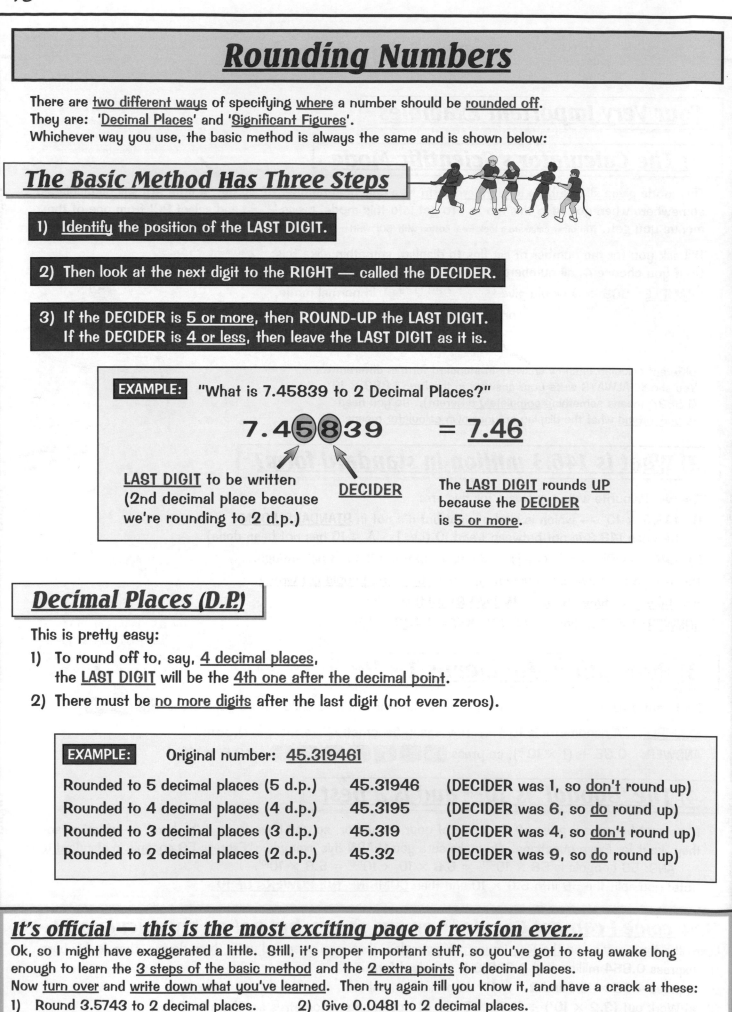

1) Identify the position of the LAST DIGIT.

2) Then look at the next digit to the RIGHT — called the DECIDER.

3) If the DECIDER is 5 or more, then ROUND-UP the LAST DIGIT.
   If the DECIDER is 4 or less, then leave the LAST DIGIT as it is.

EXAMPLE: "What is 7.45839 to 2 Decimal Places?"

$$7.45839 = \underline{7.46}$$

LAST DIGIT to be written
(2nd decimal place because
we're rounding to 2 d.p.)

DECIDER

The LAST DIGIT rounds UP
because the DECIDER
is 5 or more.

Decimal Places (D.P)

This is pretty easy:

1) To round off to, say, 4 decimal places,
   the LAST DIGIT will be the 4th one after the decimal point.

2) There must be no more digits after the last digit (not even zeros).

EXAMPLE: Original number: 45.319461

Rounded to 5 decimal places (5 d.p.)   45.31946   (DECIDER was 1, so don't round up)
Rounded to 4 decimal places (4 d.p.)   45.3195   (DECIDER was 6, so do round up)
Rounded to 3 decimal places (3 d.p.)   45.319   (DECIDER was 4, so don't round up)
Rounded to 2 decimal places (2 d.p.)   45.32   (DECIDER was 9, so do round up)

It's official — this is the most exciting page of revision ever...

Ok, so I might have exaggerated a little. Still, it's proper important stuff, so you've got to stay awake long
enough to learn the 3 steps of the basic method and the 2 extra points for decimal places.
Now turn over and write down what you've learned. Then try again till you know it, and have a crack at these:

1) Round 3.5743 to 2 decimal places.
2) Give 0.0481 to 2 decimal places.
3) Express 12.9096 to 3 d.p.
4) Express 3546.054 to 1 d.p.

Rounding Numbers

Obviously all numbers are significant, but when it comes to <u>rounding</u>, some are more significant than others...

Significant Figures (S.F. or sig. fig.)

The method for significant figures is <u>identical</u> to that for decimal places except that finding the <u>position</u> of the <u>LAST DIGIT</u> is more difficult — <u>it wouldn't be so bad, but for the ZEROS</u>...

1) The <u>1st significant figure</u> of any number is simply **THE FIRST DIGIT WHICH ISN'T A ZERO.**

2) The <u>2nd, 3rd, 4th,</u> etc. <u>significant figures</u> follow on immediately after the 1st, **REGARDLESS OF BEING ZEROS OR NOT ZEROS.**

E.g. **0.002309**   **2.03070**

<u>SIG FIGS</u>:   1st 2nd 3rd 4th   1st 2nd 3rd 4th

(If we're rounding to say, 3 s.f., then the LAST DIGIT is simply the 3rd sig. fig.)

3) After <u>Rounding Off</u> the LAST DIGIT, <u>end ZEROS</u> must be filled in <u>up to, BUT NOT BEYOND,</u> the decimal point.

E.g. 8 756 to 2 S.F. = 8 800.

<u>LAST DIGIT</u>   Zeros filled in up to decimal point

No <u>extra zeros</u> must ever be put in <u>after</u> the decimal point.

Examples	to 4 s.f.	to 3 s.f.	to 2 s.f.	to 1 s.f.
1) 54.7651	54.77	54.8	55	50
2) 17.0067	17.01	17.0	17	20
3) 0.0045902	0.004590	0.00459	0.0046	0.005
4) 30 895.4	30 900	30 900	31 000	30 000

I asked Stacey for her significant figures. Data? Nah, we're just friends.

Appropriate Accuracy

To decide what is appropriate accuracy, you need only remember these three rules:

1) For fairly **CASUAL MEASUREMENTS**, **2 SIGNIFICANT FIGURES** is most appropriate.
   E.g. Cooking — 250 g (2 s.f.) of sugar, not 253 g (3 s.f.), or 300 g (1 s.f.)
   Distance of a journey — 450 km or 25 km or 3500 km (all 2 s.f.)
   Area of a garden or floor — 330 m² or 15 m²

2) For more **IMPORTANT OR TECHNICAL THINGS**, **3 SIGNIFICANT FIGURES** is essential.
   E.g. <u>A technical figure</u> like <u>34.2</u> metres per second, rather than 34 metres per second
   A length that is <u>cut to fit</u>, e.g. measure a shelf <u>25.6 cm</u> long not just 26 cm
   Any <u>accurate</u> measurement with a ruler: <u>67.5 cm</u> not 70 cm or 67.54 cm

3) Only for **REALLY SCIENTIFIC WORK** would you have <u>more than 3 SIG FIG</u>.

A bit of inappropriate humour — 5 significant figures walk into a bar...

LEARN the <u>rules for significant figures</u> and the <u>rules for appropriate accuracy</u>. Then <u>turn over and write them down</u>.
1) Round these to 3 s.f. :   a) 567.78 b) 23 445 c) 0.04563 d) 0.90876
2) Decide which category of accuracy these should belong in and round them off accordingly:
   a) A jar of jam weighs 345.56g b) A car's max speed is 134.25 km/h c) A cake needs 852.3g of flour

Bounds and Estimating

At first, it might seem like these two topics are pretty unrelated. That's because they are. Don't let that bother you though, they've both still got to be learned.

1) Upper and Lower bounds of a Measurement

The simple rule is this: **The real value can be as much as HALF THE ROUNDED UNIT above and below the rounded-off value.**

1) A room is given as being '9 m long to the nearest METRE' — its actual length could be anything from 8.5 m to 9.5 m — i.e. HALF A METRE either side of 9 m. So 8.5 m and 9.5 m are the lower and upper bounds.

2) If a length is given as 2.4 m to the nearest 0.1 m, the rounded unit is 0.1 m. So the real value could be anything up to 2.4 m ± 0.05 m, giving answers of 2.45 m and 2.35 m for the upper and lower bounds.

Higher

2) Maximum and Minimum Values for Calculations

When a calculation is done using rounded-off values there will be a DISCREPANCY between the CALCULATED VALUE and the ACTUAL VALUE:

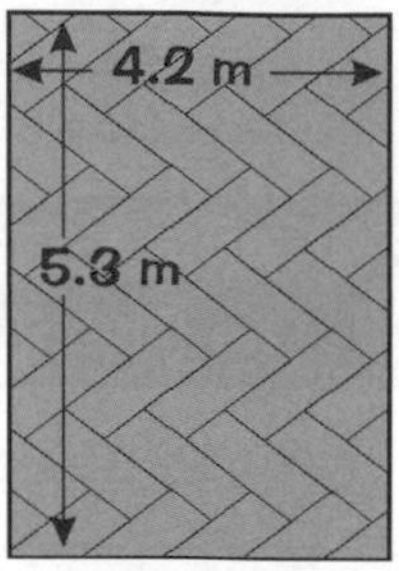

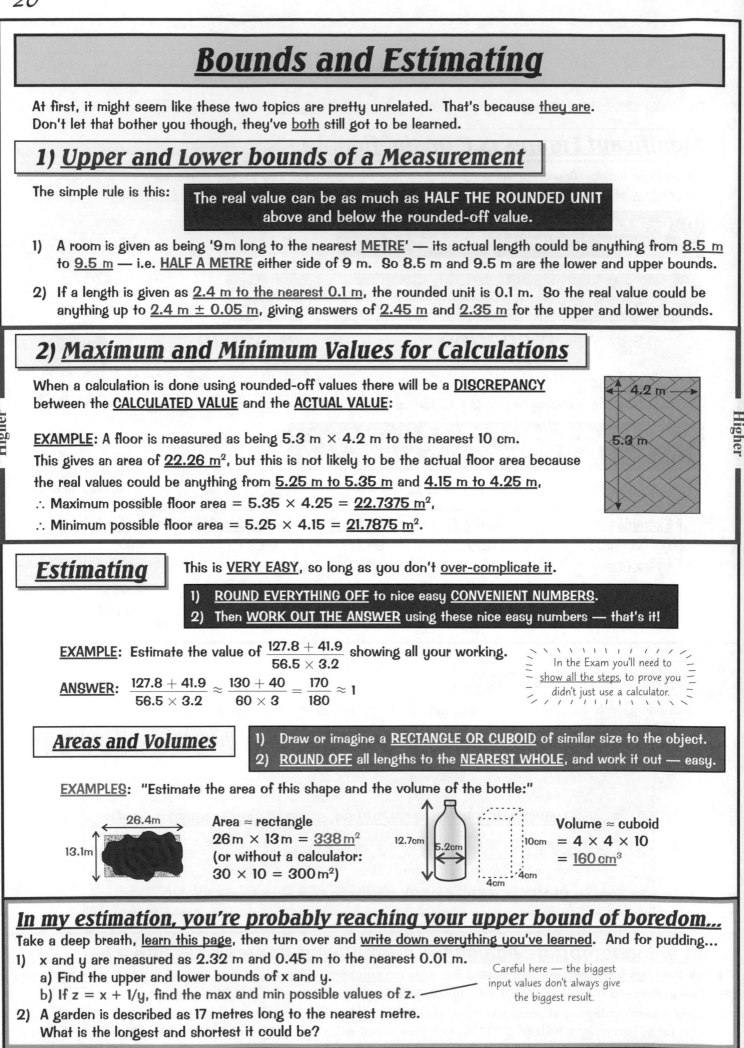

EXAMPLE: A floor is measured as being 5.3 m × 4.2 m to the nearest 10 cm.
This gives an area of $22.26\ m^2$, but this is not likely to be the actual floor area because the real values could be anything from 5.25 m to 5.35 m and 4.15 m to 4.25 m,

$\therefore$ Maximum possible floor area = $5.35 \times 4.25 = 22.7375\ m^2$,

$\therefore$ Minimum possible floor area = $5.25 \times 4.15 = 21.7875\ m^2$.

Higher

Estimating

This is VERY EASY, so long as you don't over-complicate it.

1) **ROUND EVERYTHING OFF to nice easy CONVENIENT NUMBERS.**
2) **Then WORK OUT THE ANSWER using these nice easy numbers — that's it!**

EXAMPLE: Estimate the value of $\frac{127.8 + 41.9}{56.5 \times 3.2}$ showing all your working.

ANSWER: $\frac{127.8 + 41.9}{56.5 \times 3.2} \approx \frac{130 + 40}{60 \times 3} = \frac{170}{180} \approx 1$

In the Exam you'll need to show all the steps, to prove you didn't just use a calculator.

Areas and Volumes

1) **Draw or imagine a RECTANGLE OR CUBOID of similar size to the object.**
2) **ROUND OFF all lengths to the NEAREST WHOLE, and work it out — easy.**

EXAMPLES: "Estimate the area of this shape and the volume of the bottle:"

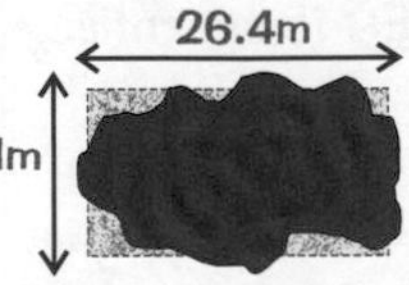

Area ≈ rectangle
$26\text{m} \times 13\text{m} = 338\text{m}^2$
(or without a calculator:
$30 \times 10 = 300\text{m}^2$)

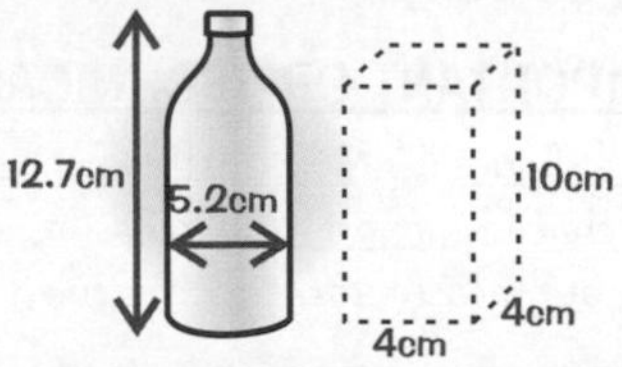

Volume ≈ cuboid
$= 4 \times 4 \times 10$
$= 160\ \text{cm}^3$

In my estimation, you're probably reaching your upper bound of boredom...

Take a deep breath, learn this page, then turn over and write down everything you've learned. And for pudding...

1) x and y are measured as 2.32 m and 0.45 m to the nearest 0.01 m.
   a) Find the upper and lower bounds of x and y.
   b) If $z = x + 1/y$, find the max and min possible values of z.

   Careful here — the biggest input values don't always give the biggest result.

2) A garden is described as 17 metres long to the nearest metre. What is the longest and shortest it could be?

Conversion Factors

Conversion factors are a mighty powerful tool for dealing with a wide variety of questions.
And what's more the method is <u>really easy</u>. Learn it now. It's ace.

> 1) Find the <u>Conversion Factor (C.F.)</u> (always easy)
>
> 2) <u>Multiply</u> by it AND <u>divide</u> by it
>
> 3) Choose the <u>common sense</u> answer

Three Important Examples

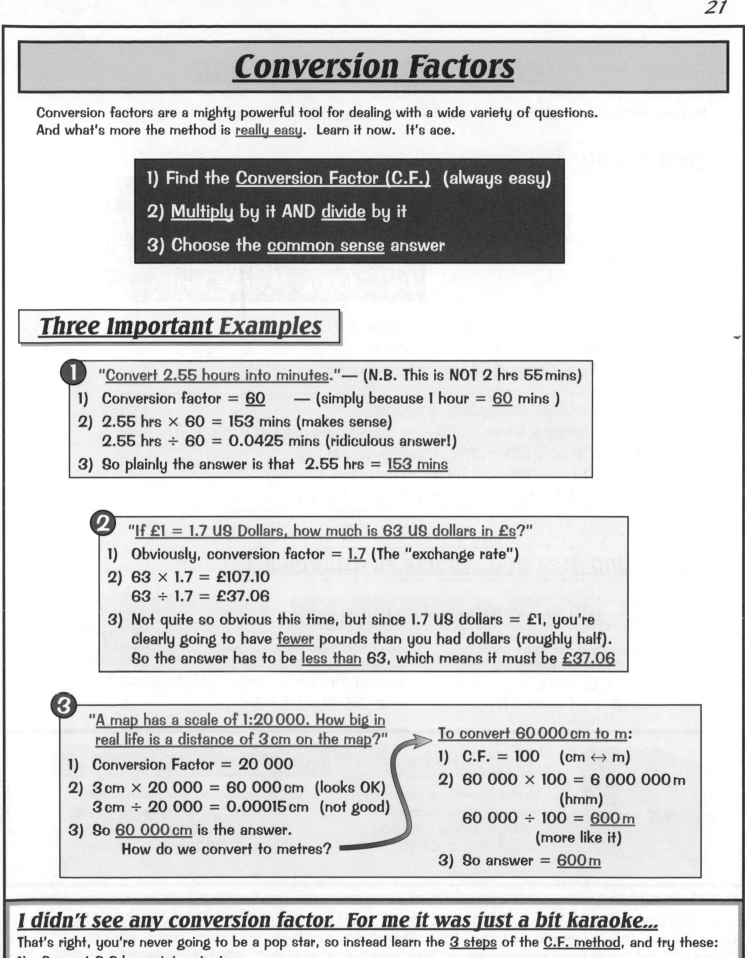

1 "<u>Convert 2.55 hours into minutes.</u>"— (N.B. This is NOT 2 hrs 55 mins)

1) Conversion factor = <u>60</u> — (simply because 1 hour = <u>60</u> mins)

2) 2.55 hrs × 60 = 153 mins (makes sense)
   2.55 hrs ÷ 60 = 0.0425 mins (ridiculous answer!)

3) So plainly the answer is that 2.55 hrs = <u>153 mins</u>

2 "If £1 = 1.7 US Dollars, how much is 63 US dollars in £s?"

1) Obviously, conversion factor = <u>1.7</u> (The "exchange rate")

2) 63 × 1.7 = £107.10
   63 ÷ 1.7 = £37.06

3) Not quite so obvious this time, but since 1.7 US dollars = £1, you're clearly going to have <u>fewer</u> pounds than you had dollars (roughly half). So the answer has to be <u>less than</u> 63, which means it must be <u>£37.06</u>

3 "A map has a scale of 1:20 000. How big in real life is a distance of 3 cm on the map?"

1) Conversion Factor = 20 000

2) 3 cm × 20 000 = 60 000 cm (looks OK)
   3 cm ÷ 20 000 = 0.00015 cm (not good)

3) So <u>60 000 cm</u> is the answer.
   How do we convert to metres?

To convert 60 000 cm to m:

1) C.F. = 100 (cm ↔ m)

2) 60 000 × 100 = 6 000 000 m
                  (hmm)
   60 000 ÷ 100 = <u>600 m</u>
                  (more like it)

3) So answer = <u>600 m</u>

I didn't see any conversion factor. For me it was just a bit karaoke...

That's right, you're never going to be a pop star, so instead learn the <u>3 steps</u> of the <u>C.F. method</u>, and try these:

1) Convert 3.3 hours into minutes.
2) Convert 390 minutes into hours.
3) Which is more, £34 or €45 ? (Exchange rate: £1 = €1.4)
4) A map is drawn to a scale of 2 cm = 5 km. A road is 8 km long. How many cm will this be on the map?
   (Hint, C.F. = 5÷2, i.e. 1 cm = 2.5 km)

Length, Area and Volume

And now for a nice straightforward page with some <u>measurement</u> facts to learn. Hooray!

Metric Units

1) <u>Length</u>   mm, cm, m, km
2) <u>Area</u>   mm², cm², m², km²,
3) <u>Volume</u>   mm³, cm³, m³, ml, litres
4) <u>Weight</u>   g, kg, tonnes
5) <u>Speed</u>   km/h, m/s

> ### MEMORISE THESE KEY FACTS:
> 1 cm = 10 mm   1 tonne = 1000 kg
> 1 m = 100 cm   1 litre = 1000 ml
> 1 km = 1000 m   1 litre = 1000 cm³
> 1 kg = 1000 g   1 cm³ = 1 ml

Converting from one unit of measure to another isn't too hard — as long as you know the conversion factor.

Just use the <u>three-step method</u> from the previous page.

E.g.   "<u>Convert 3.78 metres into centimetres</u>."
1) Conversion factor = <u>100</u>   — (simply because 1 m = <u>100</u> cm)
2) 3.78 m × 100 = 378 cm (makes sense)
   3.78 m ÷ 100 = 0.0378 cm (ridiculous answer!)
3) So plainly the answer is that 3.78 m = <u>378 cm</u>

Converting Area and Volume Measurements

> 1 m² = 100 cm × 100 cm = 10 000 cm²

1) To change area measurements from m² to cm² multiply the area in m² by 10 000 (e.g. 3 m² = 30 000 cm²).

2) To change area measurements from cm² to m² divide the area in cm² by 10 000 (e.g. 45 000 cm² = 4.5 m²).

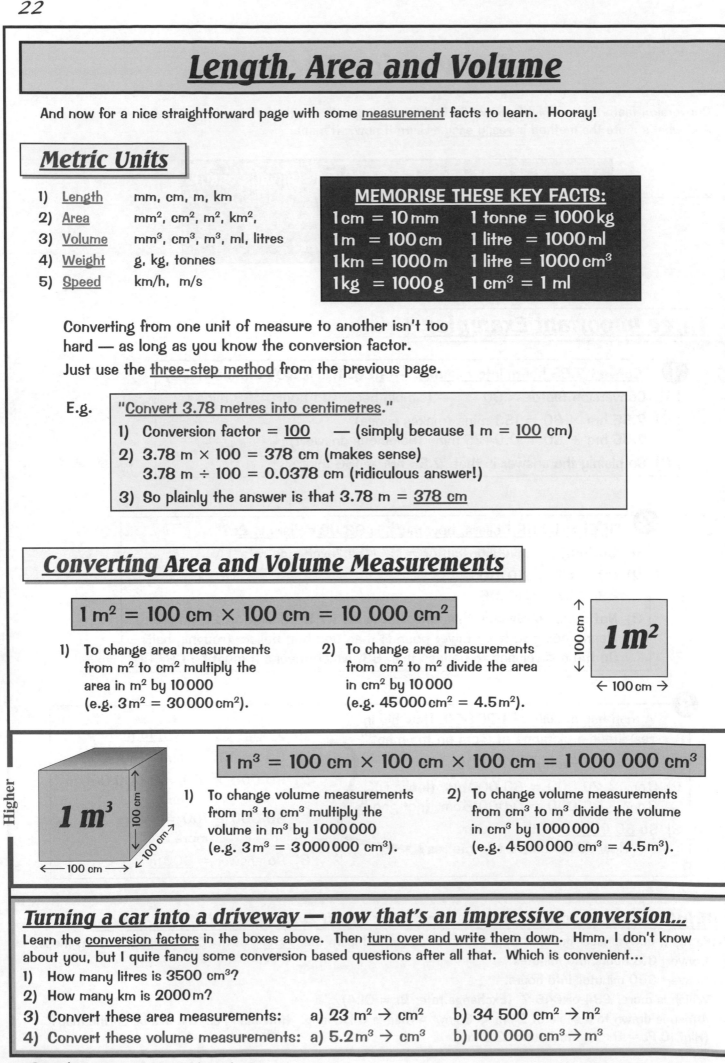

1 m² (↑ 100 cm ↓, ← 100 cm →)

> 1 m³ = 100 cm × 100 cm × 100 cm = 1 000 000 cm³

1 m³ (100 cm, 100 cm, 100 cm)

1) To change volume measurements from m³ to cm³ multiply the volume in m³ by 1 000 000 (e.g. 3 m³ = 3 000 000 cm³).

2) To change volume measurements from cm³ to m³ divide the volume in cm³ by 1 000 000 (e.g. 4 500 000 cm³ = 4.5 m³).

Higher

Turning a car into a driveway — now that's an impressive conversion...

Learn the <u>conversion factors</u> in the boxes above. Then <u>turn over and write them down</u>. Hmm, I don't know about you, but I quite fancy some conversion based questions after all that. Which is convenient...
1) How many litres is 3500 cm³?
2) How many km is 2000 m?
3) Convert these area measurements: a) 23 m² → cm²   b) 34 500 cm² → m²
4) Convert these volume measurements: a) 5.2 m³ → cm³   b) 100 000 cm³ → m³

Time Questions

You see 24 hour clocks in lots of places so hopefully you're an expert in how to read them. The only thing you might need reminding about is 'a.m.' and 'p.m.' in the 12 hour clock:

1) a.m. and p.m.

'a.m.' means 'morning'. It runs from 12 midnight to 12 noon.
'p.m.' means 'afternoon and evening'. It runs from 12 noon to 12 midnight.

(though I guess you know that already)

2) Conversions

You'll definitely need to know these very important facts:

1 day = 24 hours
1 hour = 60 minutes
1 minute = 60 seconds

3) Exam questions involving 'Time'

There are lots of different questions they can ask involving time but the same GOOD OLD RELIABLE DEPENDABLE METHOD will work wonders on all of them.

"And what is this good old reliable dependable method?", I hear you cry. Well, it's this:

Take your time, write it down, and split it up into SHORT EASY STAGES

EXAMPLE: Find the time taken by a train which sets off at 1325 and arrives at 1910.

WHAT YOU DON'T DO is try to work it all out in your head in one go — this method fails nearly every time. Instead, split it into short easy stages like this:

1325 → 1400 → 1900 → 1910
35 mins   5 hours   10 mins

This is a nice safe way of finding the total time from 1325 to 1910:
5 hours + 35 mins + 10 mins = 5 hours 45 mins.

4) If you use your Calculator, beware...

Try to avoid using the calculator with time measurements — it's a pain in the neck. You'll get answers in decimals, and you have to convert them into hours and minutes. So learn this example:

2.5 hours = 2 ½ hours = 2 hours and 30 minutes

That sound right? Of course it does.

SO DON'T GO WRITING ANYTHING STUPID, like: 2.5 hours = 2 hours and 50 minutes ← WRONG WRONG WRONG WRONG!!

BREAKING NEWS: Public panic after warning over calculator use...
You probably know lots of this stuff already. The tips are useful though — so don't just ignore them.
1) What is 1715 in the 12 hour clock? (don't forget a.m./p.m.)
2) A plane sets off at 10.15 a.m. The flight lasts 5 hrs 50 mins. What is the arrival time?
3) How many minutes are there in a day? And how many seconds are there in a day?
4) What is 3.5 hours in hours and minutes? What is 5¾ hours in hours and minutes?

Speed, Distance and Time

Speed-distance-time questions are <u>very common</u>, and they never give you the formula.
Either you learn it beforehand or you wave goodbye to several easy marks.

1) <u>The Formula Triangle</u>

The formula triangle method is by far the best way to tackle speed-distance-time questions.

You have to <u>remember the order of the letters</u> in the triangle (SDT) — the word <u>SoDiT</u> might help.
So if it's a question on speed, distance and time just say: <u>SOD IT</u>.

Once you've got the formula triangle sorted out, the rest is easy:

1) <u>COVER UP the thing you want to find</u> and just <u>WRITE DOWN what's left showing</u>.

<u>TIME</u>
= DISTANCE/SPEED

<u>SPEED</u>
= DISTANCE/TIME

<u>DISTANCE</u>
= SPEED × TIME

2) <u>PUT IN THE VALUES</u> for the other two things and <u>WORK IT OUT</u>.

Note: This is <u>AVERAGE</u> speed over the distance travelled — the car or whatever mightn't have gone at this speed for the whole time.

<u>EXAMPLE</u>: "A car travels 90 miles at 36 miles per hour. How long does it take?"

<u>ANS</u>: We want to find the <u>time</u>, so <u>cover up T</u> in the triangle which leaves D/S, so T = D/S = Distance ÷ speed = 90 ÷ 36 = <u>2.5 hours</u>

You can use formula triangles for any formula of the type A = B × C or B = A ÷ C:

2) <u>Units — Getting them right</u>

By <u>units</u> we mean things like <u>cm, m, m/s, km²</u>, etc. and quite honestly they should always be in your mind when you <u>write an answer down</u>. When you're using a FORMULA, there is one special thing you need to know.
It's simple enough but you must know it:

The <u>UNITS you get out</u> of a Formula <u>DEPEND ENTIRELY</u> upon <u>the UNITS you put into it</u>.

For example, if you put a <u>distance in cm</u> and a <u>time in seconds</u> into the formula triangle to work out SPEED, the answer will come out in <u>cm per second</u> (cm/s).

If the <u>time is in hours</u> and the speed in <u>kilometres per hour</u> (km/h) then the distance you calculate will come out in <u>kilometres</u>. It's pretty simple when you think about it.

But Don't Mix Units

E.g. <u>Don't</u> mix <u>KILOMETRES Per HOUR</u> in a formula with a <u>time in MINUTES</u> (convert it to <u>hours</u>).

Example: "A boy walks 800 m in 10 minutes. Find his speed in km/h."

If you use 800 m and 10 minutes your answer will be a speed in <u>metres per minute</u> (m/min).
Instead you must <u>convert</u>: 800 m = <u>0.8 km</u>, 10 mins = <u>0.1667 hours</u> (mins ÷ 60).
Then you can divide 0.8 <u>km</u> by 0.1667 <u>hours</u> to get <u>4.8 km/h</u>.

<u>Together we shall rule the universe as finger and formula triangle...</u>

Oh yes, it is your <u>destiny</u>. One step at a time though. First of all you need to learn this page, so turn over and briefly summarise both topics, with examples. Keep trying until you can <u>remember it all</u>. Then as your big finale:
1) Find the time taken, in hours, mins and secs, for a purple-nosed buffalo walking at 3.2 km/h to cover 5.2 km.
2) Also find how far it would go in 35 mins and 25 seconds. Give your answer in both km and m.

Order of Operations

When you're faced with a <u>multi-step calculation</u>, you need to know what <u>order</u> to do the different parts in. That's where the <u>order of operations</u> comes in...

The Order of Operations

If you're doing a calculation that's got lots of <u>steps</u> in it, you have to do them in the <u>right order</u>. There's a <u>set of rules</u> that tells you what the right order is — it's called the <u>order of operations</u>.

The way to remember the order of operation is using BODMAS. This stands for:

<u>B</u>rackets, <u>O</u>ther, <u>D</u>ivision, <u>M</u>ultiplication, <u>A</u>ddition, <u>S</u>ubtraction

BODMAS tells you to:
1) Sort out any bits in <u>Brackets</u> first.
2) Then deal with <u>Other</u> things, like <u>powers</u> and <u>square roots</u>.
3) Next do any <u>Division</u> or <u>Multiplication</u> steps (going from <u>left to right</u>).
4) Finally do any <u>Additions</u> and <u>Subtractions</u> (going from <u>left to right</u>).

EXAMPLE: $T = (P - 7)^2 + -2 \times 3$
Find the value of T when P = 4.

1) Put the value of P into the equation: $T = (4 - 7)^2 - 2 \times 3$
2) Then work it out <u>in stages</u>:
$$= (-3)^2 - 2 \times 3$$
$$= 9 - 6$$
$$= \underline{3}$$

BODMAS in action:
<u>Brackets</u> worked out...
...then <u>squared</u>,...
...the <u>multiplication</u> is done first...
...then the <u>subtraction</u>.

Brackets are Really Important in BODMAS

Brackets have <u>top priority</u> in BODMAS — <u>anything</u> in brackets is worked out <u>before</u> anything else happens to it. By adding brackets, you can <u>change the order</u> that the steps are done in.

Imagine that you want to ask somebody to <u>add 19 to 26</u>, and <u>divide the result by 3</u>.

- You could write $19 + 26 \div 3$. But BODMAS says to do <u>division first</u>, and <u>then addition</u>. They'll look at the expression and say $19 + 26 \div 3 = 19 + 8.7 = 27.7$

- If you want them to do the <u>addition first</u>, and <u>then the division</u>, you need to put <u>brackets</u> in, like this: $(19 + 26) \div 3$. BODMAS tells you to do the bits in <u>brackets first</u>. So that's $(19 + 26) \div 3 = 45 \div 3 = 15$.

This is <u>really important</u> to remember when you're using a <u>calculator</u>. They <u>always</u> follow the BODMAS rules — so you <u>must</u> use brackets to tell your calculator which bits of the calculation to do <u>first</u>.

Remember — order the that you things do in really important is...

Remember to <u>practise</u> everything you've just learnt on this page. Start with this question.

1) Calculate the following to 2 d.p.   a) $4 + 3^2 \times (8 \div 4) - 10$ b) $\dfrac{74^2 - 10^3}{\sqrt{49} \times 2^4}$

Using Calculators

This page is full of <u>lovely calculator tricks</u> to save you a lot of button-bashing.

The Fraction Button: $\boxed{a\frac{b}{c}}$

Use this <u>as much as possible</u> in the Exams — it'll really save you time.
It's very easy, so make sure you know how to use it properly — you'll lose a lot of marks if you don't:

1) To enter $\frac{1}{4}$ press [1] [$a\frac{b}{c}$] [4]

2) To enter $1\frac{3}{5}$ press [1] [$a\frac{b}{c}$] [3] [$a\frac{b}{c}$] [5]

3) To work out $\frac{1}{5} \times \frac{3}{4}$ press [1] [$a\frac{b}{c}$] [5] [×] [3] [$a\frac{b}{c}$] [4] [=]

4) To <u>reduce a fraction to its lowest terms</u> enter it and then press [=] .
   E.g. $\frac{9}{12}$ — [9] [$a\frac{b}{c}$] [12] [=] $\boxed{3 \rfloor 4}$ $= \frac{3}{4}$

5) To convert between <u>mixed</u> and <u>top-heavy</u> fractions press [SHIFT] [$a\frac{b}{c}$].
   E.g. $2\frac{3}{8}$ — [2] [$a\frac{b}{c}$] [3] [$a\frac{b}{c}$] [8] [=] [SHIFT] [$a\frac{b}{c}$] which gives $\frac{19}{8}$

The MEMORY BUTTONS ([STO] Store, [RCL] Recall)

These are really useful for keeping a number you've just calculated,
so you can use it again shortly afterwards.

E.g. Find $\dfrac{840}{15 + 12\sin 40}$ — just work out the <u>bottom line</u> first and <u>stick it in the memory</u>.

So press [15] [+] [12] [SIN] [40] [=] and then [STO] [M] to keep the result of the bottom line in the memory.
Then you simply press [840] [÷] [RCL] [M] [=], and the answer is 36.98.

The memory buttons might work a bit differently on your calculator.
Note: if your calculator has an 'Ans' button, you can do the same thing as above using that
instead — the Ans button gives you the result you got when you <u>last pressed</u> the '=' button.

Check Your Answers using Estimation

When you use a <u>calculator</u> to find the answer to a question, you should check that answer using
<u>estimation</u>. This is to get an idea of whether your answer's <u>roughly right</u> — if the estimate's
miles different from your answer, you know something's <u>gone wrong</u>. This is all you need to do:

> 1) ROUND EVERYTHING OFF to nice easy CONVENIENT NUMBERS.
> 2) Then WORK OUT THE ANSWER using those nice easy numbers
>   — and see if it roughly matches your calculator answer.

Example: Find 3119 × 1.97   Calculator shows: $\boxed{6144.43}$
Do 3000 × 2 in your head as a check. 3000 × 2 = 6000.
That's pretty close — so you can be pretty sure that your answer's right.

Learn these two pages, store, then recall...

Learn your calculator buttons. <u>Practise</u> until you can answer all of these without having to refer back:
1) Convert these into top-heavy fractions: a) 2¾ b) 16½ c) 8¼
2) Explain what [STO] and [RCL] do and give an example of using them.

Sets

If you like collections of things, you'll love <u>sets</u> — because...well...they're collections of things.

A Set is a Group of Objects

1) A <u>SET</u> is just a maths word for a <u>collection of objects</u>, or <u>numbers</u>. All of the things in a set have some kind of connection. These are all examples of sets:

| Prime numbers | Negative numbers | Odd numbers between 2 and 16 | Things that are red |

2) Each individual object in set is called an <u>ELEMENT</u>. So 7 is <u>an element</u> of the set of prime numbers, and a strawberry is <u>an element</u> of the set of things that are red.

3) You can use a <u>capital letter</u> to stand for <u>a set</u>, e.g. A = the set of numbers that are multiples of four. This just makes it quicker and easier to write about the set later.

4) A <u>lower case letter</u> stands for <u>an element</u> in the set, e.g. "x is in set A, so x must be an even number".

You can Describe a set by Describing Its Elements

If you want to tell somebody what <u>elements</u> are in a <u>set</u>, then there are two ways to do it.

1) You can write out a <u>complete list</u> of all the elements, like this:
   {1, 3, 5, 7, 9, 11, 13, 15, 17, 19, 21, 23, 25, 27, 29} ⬅ The curly brackets are there to tell you that this is a set.

2) Or you can write out the <u>rule</u> that connects the elements: {odd numbers between 0 and 30}

You can write Rules in Numbers and Symbols too

It's fine to write out the description of the elements of a set in <u>words</u>, like the example in point 2. But you'll often see <u>numbers and symbols</u> used to write the description too.

{x: x is a negative number} ⬅ This means that if x stands for any negative number, then the elements of the set are all the possible values of x.

{x: x < 0} ⬅ This is a different way of writing the same thing — saying that x < 0 means that x must be a negative number.

{(x,y): y = 2x + 2} ⬅ This one is a set of all the points that lie on the line y = 2x + 2. Each element is a pair of coordinates — that's what the (x, y) bit means.

Learn how to write about sets using Set Notation

Here are four handy little bits of <u>set notation</u> — learn what these symbols mean, and how to use them.

∈ **...IS AN ELEMENT OF...** Rather than writing "5 is an element of Set A", you can just write "5 ∈ A"

∉ **...IS NOT AN ELEMENT OF...** This is the opposite — so "2 ∉ A" means "2 is not an element of Set A".

{} or ∅ **THE EMPTY SET** If a set has <u>no elements</u> in it at all, it's called <u>the empty set</u>.
   E.g. if set B = {negative numbers between 1 and 10} then set B = ∅.

n(A) **NUMBER OF ELEMENTS IN SET A** Instead of writing "There are 12 elements in set A" you can write n(A) = 12.

Collect similar things to make sets — this reminds me of Monopoly...

...except that it doesn't end with your brother trying to shove hotels up his nose. It ends with practice questions.

1) Come up with your own example of a set, and write a description of it using one of the methods shown above.

2) B = {x: x is a square number and x < 110}. List all the elements that are in set B.
   Use set notation to say that 22 is not an element of set B.

Sets

This page is all about how you can <u>describe</u> the ways that sets <u>relate to each other</u>.
There are a couple more symbols to learn, but don't worry — it's not as scary as it might look.

Venn Diagrams use Circles to Represent Sets

A Venn diagram is just a <u>visual way</u> of showing the <u>relationships between sets</u>. Here are the basics:

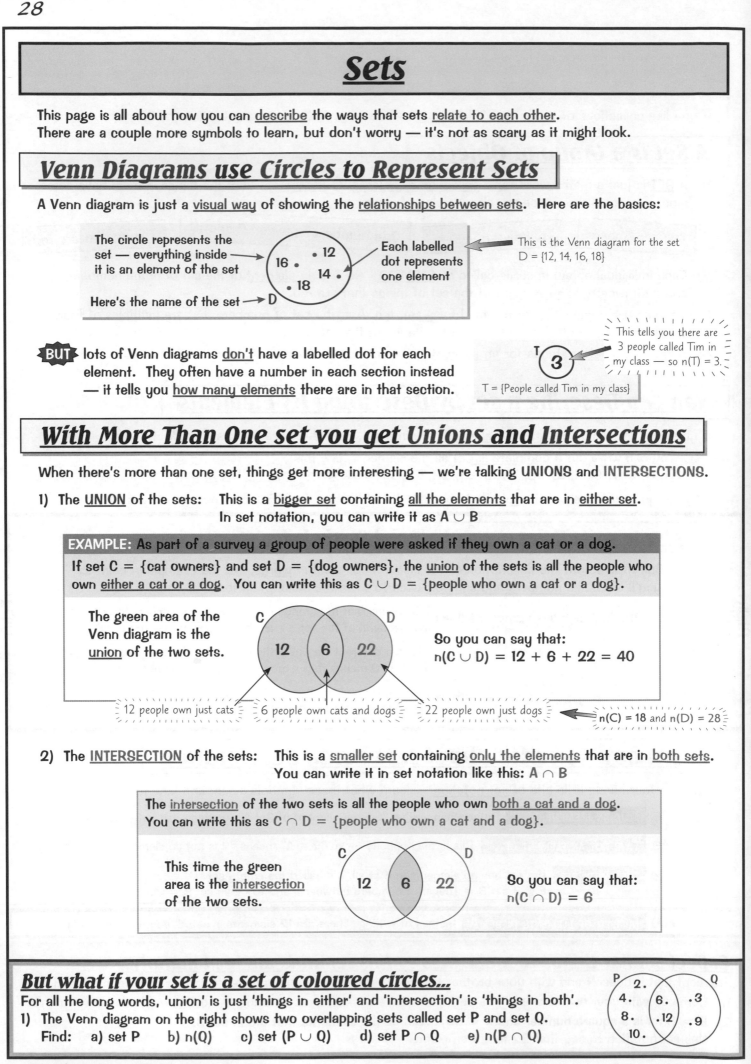

The circle represents the set — everything inside it is an element of the set

16 • • 12
14 •
• 18
D

Each labelled dot represents one element

This is the Venn diagram for the set D = {12, 14, 16, 18}

Here's the name of the set → D

BUT lots of Venn diagrams <u>don't</u> have a labelled dot for each element. They often have a number in each section instead — it tells you <u>how many elements</u> there are in that section.

T 3

This tells you there are 3 people called Tim in my class — so n(T) = 3.

T = {People called Tim in my class}

With More Than One set you get Unions and Intersections

When there's more than one set, things get more interesting — we're talking UNIONS and INTERSECTIONS.

1) The <u>UNION</u> of the sets: This is a <u>bigger set</u> containing <u>all the elements</u> that are in <u>either set</u>.
   In set notation, you can write it as A ∪ B

EXAMPLE: As part of a survey a group of people were asked if they own a cat or a dog.

If set C = {cat owners} and set D = {dog owners}, the <u>union</u> of the sets is all the people who own <u>either a cat or a dog</u>. You can write this as C ∪ D = {people who own a cat or a dog}.

The green area of the Venn diagram is the <u>union</u> of the two sets.

C 12 6 22 D

So you can say that:
n(C ∪ D) = 12 + 6 + 22 = 40

12 people own just cats   6 people own cats and dogs   22 people own just dogs   ← n(C) = 18 and n(D) = 28

2) The <u>INTERSECTION</u> of the sets: This is a <u>smaller set</u> containing <u>only the elements</u> that are in <u>both sets</u>.
   You can write it in set notation like this: A ∩ B

The <u>intersection</u> of the two sets is all the people who own <u>both a cat and a dog</u>.
You can write this as C ∩ D = {people who own a cat and a dog}.

This time the green area is the <u>intersection</u> of the two sets.

C 12 6 22 D

So you can say that:
n(C ∩ D) = 6

But what if your set is a set of coloured circles...

For all the long words, 'union' is just 'things in either' and 'intersection' is 'things in both'.

1) The Venn diagram on the right shows two overlapping sets called set P and set Q.
   Find: a) set P   b) n(Q)   c) set (P ∪ Q)   d) set P ∩ Q   e) n(P ∩ Q)

P 2. Q
4. 6. •3
8. •12 •9
10.

Sets

We're on the home stretch now — it's the last page about <u>sets</u>, and the last page of the section.

The Universal Set contains every Possible Value

1) The UNIVERSAL SET is the group of things that you <u>select the elements</u> of your <u>set</u> from. It's represented by ξ.

> E.g. all the elements in a set of '<u>people in my class with blue hair</u>' belong to the universal set of '<u>people in my class</u>'.

2) On a Venn diagram, the universal set is shown as a <u>rectangle</u> that goes <u>around all of the circles</u>, like this:

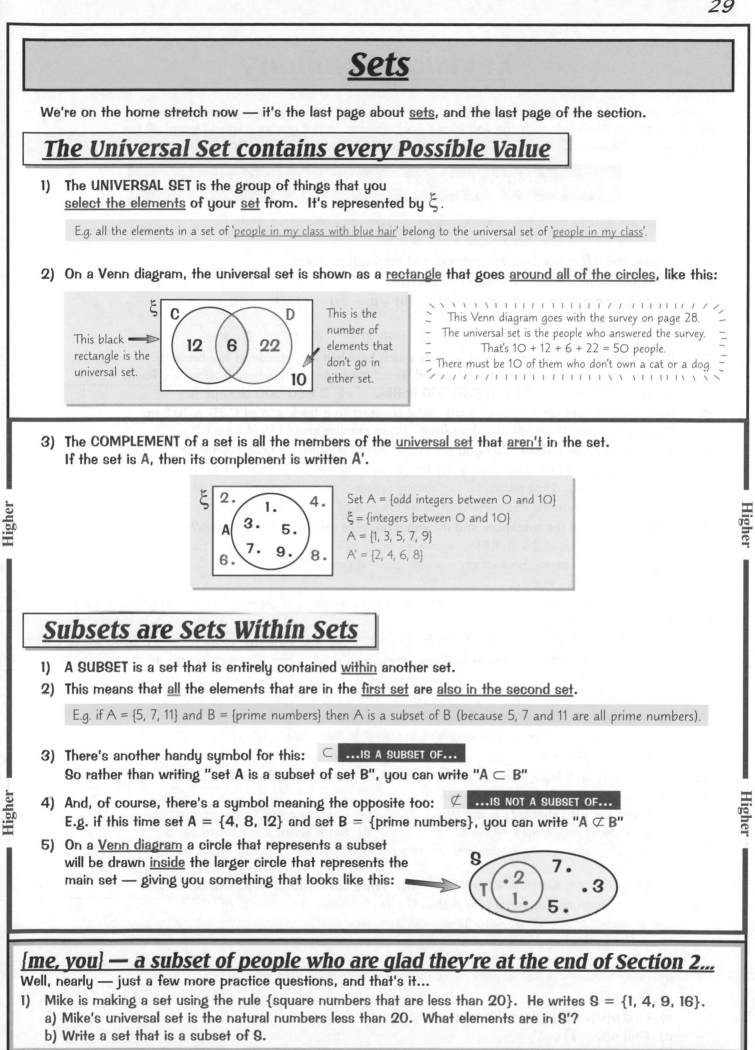

This black → rectangle is the universal set.

This is the number of elements that don't go in either set.

This Venn diagram goes with the survey on page 28. The universal set is the people who answered the survey. That's 10 + 12 + 6 + 22 = 50 people. There must be 10 of them who don't own a cat or a dog.

3) The COMPLEMENT of a set is all the members of the <u>universal set</u> that <u>aren't</u> in the set. If the set is A, then its complement is written A'.

Set A = {odd integers between 0 and 10}
ξ = {integers between 0 and 10}
A = {1, 3, 5, 7, 9}
A' = {2, 4, 6, 8}

Subsets are Sets Within Sets

1) A SUBSET is a set that is entirely contained <u>within</u> another set.

2) This means that <u>all</u> the elements that are in the <u>first set</u> are <u>also in the second set</u>.

> E.g. if A = {5, 7, 11} and B = {prime numbers} then A is a subset of B (because 5, 7 and 11 are all prime numbers).

3) There's another handy symbol for this: $\subset$ ...IS A SUBSET OF...
So rather than writing "set A is a subset of set B", you can write "A $\subset$ B"

4) And, of course, there's a symbol meaning the opposite too: $\not\subset$ ...IS NOT A SUBSET OF...
E.g. if this time set A = {4, 8, 12} and set B = {prime numbers}, you can write "A $\not\subset$ B"

5) On a <u>Venn diagram</u> a circle that represents a subset will be drawn <u>inside</u> the larger circle that represents the main set — giving you something that looks like this: →

[me, you] — a subset of people who are glad they're at the end of Section 2...

Well, nearly — just a few more practice questions, and that's it...

1) Mike is making a set using the rule {square numbers that are less than 20}. He writes S = {1, 4, 9, 16}.
   a) Mike's universal set is the natural numbers less than 20. What elements are in S'?
   b) Write a set that is a subset of S.

Revision Summary

More questions, but just keep reminding yourself that they're the very best revision you can do. These questions don't ask anything too tricky, just whether or not you've actually learnt all the basic facts in Section 2. It's really important to keep practising these as often as you can.

KEEP LEARNING THESE BASIC FACTS UNTIL YOU KNOW THEM

1) What are square numbers, cube numbers, square roots and cube roots?

2) What are the two possible square roots of 9?

3) Explain the difference between rational and irrational numbers.

4) Write down the 7 rules for manipulating surds.

5) Simplify where possible: a) $(p + \sqrt{q})^2$ b) $\sqrt{p} + \sqrt{q}$ c) $\sqrt{p} \times \sqrt{q}$

6) Simplify the following.
   a) $5^2 \times 5^6$ b) $3^9 \div 3^6$ c) $(5^2)^6$ d) 3^{-2} e) $4^{1/2}$ f) $4^{-1/2}$

7) Anja is filling in some forms to show how much beer has been made at her brewery. The numbers must be entered in standard form. Write Anja's numbers in standard form:
   a) 970 000 cans b) 6 830 000 bottles c) 3 560 000 000 pints

8) Paul needs to set his machine to cut metal sheeting to a thickness of 2.75×10^{-6} m. The machine won't accept standard form. What number should Paul type in?

9) What is scientific mode? Can you get in and out of it easily on your calculator?

10) Jenny and two of her friends went out for dinner. The bill came to £51.98 and they decided to split it equally. How much, to two decimal places, should each of them pay?

11) How do you determine the upper and lower bounds of a rounded measurement?

12) How do you find the maximum and minimum possible values of a calculation?

13) Kylie is on holiday in South Africa, where £1 = 12.12 rand. She pays 250 rand to go to a safari park. How much has she spent in pounds?

14) Give 8 metric conversions.

15) Kevin needs to weigh out 1.2 kg of flour. His scales measure in grams. How many grams does he need?

16) Convert the following:
    a) 30 000 cm² to m² b) 3.56 m² to cm² c) 30 000 cm³ to m³ d) 3.56 m³ to cm³

17) John's train leaves the station at 1.15 pm. He knows it takes him 25 mins to walk to the station. What is the latest time he should leave the house?

18) A film is 190 minutes long. It starts at 18.15. When will it finish?

19) What is the formula triangle for speed, distance and time?

20) What two main rules apply to the units involved with formula triangles?

21) Explain what BODMAS is. Does your calculator know about it?

22) Q = {x: x is an integer and $3 \leq x \leq 11$}. List all of the elements that are in set Q.

23) Write the following using set notation:
    a) There are fifty elements in set W. b) Set H is equal to the empty set.
    c) Cheddar is an element of set Z. d) Set F is not a subset of set G.

24) Draw a Venn diagram to illustrate these two overlapping sets: set A = {1, 3, 5, 7, 9}
    set B = {5, 6, 7, 8, 9}

    Find set (A ∪ B), set (A ∩ B) and n(A ∪ B). Write out a subset of A, and call it C.

25) Kate asks everyone at her school if they like tea, coffee and limeade. She ends up with three sets: T = {like tea}, C = {like coffee} and L = {like limeade}. The Venn diagram on the right shows her results.
    a) What is Kate's universal set? How many elements does it have?
    b) Find n(T).
    c) Find n(L'). What does this number represent?
    d) Find n(C ∩ L) ∪ T')

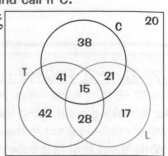

Basic Algebra

Normally I don't like to be too negative, but sometimes being negative is important.
As are the other basic algebra rules...

Watch out for Negative Numbers

Negative numbers crop up everywhere so you need to learn this rule for dealing with them:

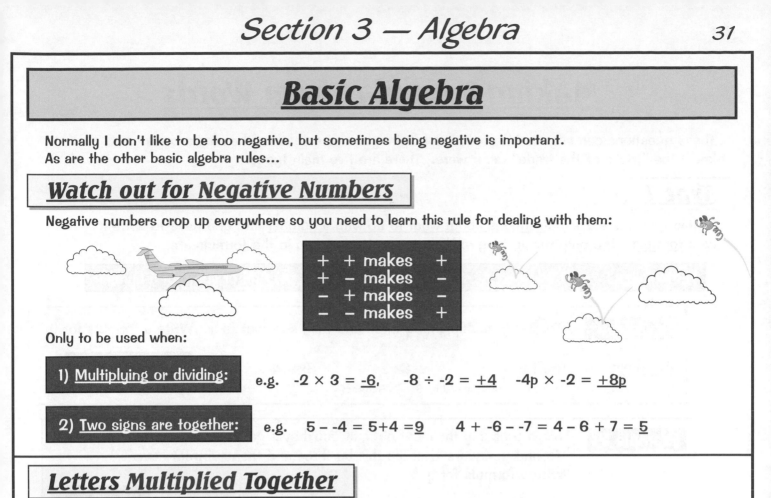

+	+	makes	+
+	−	makes	−
−	+	makes	−
−	−	makes	+

Only to be used when:

1) Multiplying or dividing: e.g. $-2 \times 3 = \underline{-6}$, $-8 \div -2 = \underline{+4}$ $-4p \times -2 = \underline{+8p}$

2) Two signs are together: e.g. $5 - -4 = 5+4 = \underline{9}$ $4 + -6 - -7 = 4 - 6 + 7 = \underline{5}$

Letters Multiplied Together

Watch out for these <u>combinations of letters</u> in algebra that regularly catch people out:

1) abc means $a \times b \times c$. The ×'s are often <u>left out</u> to make it clearer.
2) gn^2 means $g \times n \times n$. Note that <u>only</u> the n is squared, <u>not</u> the g as well, e.g. $\pi r^2 = \pi \times r \times r$.
3) $(gn)^2$ means $g \times g \times n \times n$. The brackets mean that <u>BOTH</u> letters are squared.
4) $p(q-r)^3$ means $p \times (q-r) \times (q-r) \times (q-r)$. <u>Only</u> the brackets get cubed.
5) $-a^2$ is a bit <u>ambiguous</u>. It should either be written $(-a)^2$ or $-(a^2)$, e.g. $(-3)^2 = 9$, or $-(3^2) = -9$

Algebra Follows the BODMAS Rule

<u>BODMAS</u> tells you in which <u>ORDER</u> to do the operations in a multi-step calculation.
You work out <u>Brackets</u> first, then <u>Other</u> things like powers and roots, then
<u>Divide</u> / <u>Multiply</u> groups of numbers before <u>Adding</u> or <u>Subtracting</u> them.
BODMAS applies to algebraic expressions too:

See page 25 for more on BODMAS.

EXAMPLE: "A mysterious quantity, X, is given by: $X = \sqrt{P+Z} - Y \div Z^2$
Find the value of X when P = 6, Y = 4 and Z = –2."

1) Write down the formula: $X = \sqrt{P+Z} - Y \div Z^2$
2) Put the numbers in: $X = \sqrt{6+(-2)} - 4 \div (-2)^2$
3) Then work it out <u>in stages</u> : $= \sqrt{4} - 4 \div (-2)^2$
                                           $= 2 - 4 \div 4$
                                           $= 2 - 1$
                                           $= \underline{1}$

Note BODMAS in operation:
<u>Brackets</u> worked out first (the long square root symbol is acting like a pair of brackets here),
then <u>powers and roots</u>.
<u>Multiplications</u> and <u>divisions</u> done
<u>before</u> finally <u>adding</u> and <u>subtracting</u>.

Ahhh algebra, it's as easy as abc, or 2(ab) + c, or something like that...

Learn everything on this page. Now <u>turn over and write it all down</u>. Then do these without a calculator:
1) a) -4×-3 b) $-4 + -5 + 3$ c) $(3x + -2x - 4x) \div (2+-5)$ d) $120 \div -40$
2) If m=2 and n=-3 work out: a) mn^2 b) $(mn)^3$ c) $m(4+n)^2$ d) n^3 e) $3m^2n^3 + 2mn$

Making Formulas from Words

These questions can seem a bit confusing but they're not as bad as they look, once you know the "tricks of the trade", as it were. There are two main types.

Type 1

In this type there are <u>instructions about what to do with a number</u> and you have to write it as a <u>formula</u>. The only things they're likely to want you to do in the formula are:

1) Multiply x	2) Divide x	3) Square x (x^2)	4) Add or subtract a number

---

Example 1: "To find y, multiply x by three and then subtract four. Write a formula for y."

Answer: Start with x $\rightarrow$ 3x $\rightarrow$ 3x – 4   so $\underline{y = 3x - 4}$

Times it by 3   Subtract 4   (not too gruelling, is it?)

Example 2: This is probably the most difficult you'd ever get:
"To find y, square x, divide this by three and then subtract seven. Write a formula for y."

Answer: Start with x $\rightarrow$ x^2 $\rightarrow$ $\dfrac{x^2}{3}$ $\rightarrow$ $\dfrac{x^2}{3} - 7$ $y = \dfrac{x^2}{3} - 7$

Square it   Divide it by 3   Subtract 7

Type 2

This is a bit harder. <u>You have to make up a formula</u> by putting in letters like 'C' for '<u>cost</u>' or 'n' for '<u>number of something-or-others</u>'. Although it may look confusing the formulas usually turn out to be <u>**PRETTY SIMPLE**</u>, so make sure you give it a go.

Example: Dean is designing a rectangular sign. The length of the sign must be 1.5 m greater than its width. The plastic the sign is to be made from costs £9 per m². Write a formula that Dean could use to work out the cost, C, of the plastic needed to make a sign of width w m.

Answer: The width of the sign is w m, so the length is (w + 1.5) m.

The area of the sign $= l \times w = (w + 1.5) \times w = w^2 + 1.5w$

So the cost of the plastic is $C = 9(w^2 + 1.5w)$
                     or $C = 9w^2 + 13.5w$

I'm so impressed with this page that words fail me...

Nope. I got nothin'. Best just do these questions:

1) The value of y is found by taking x, multiplying it by five and then subtracting three. Write down a formula for y in terms of x.

2) Lauren has a part-time job as a waitress. She earns £6 per hour, plus tips. She saves half of the money she earns, and pays £5 per week in bus fares to get to work. If she works h hours per week, and receives a total £t in tips that week, write down a formula for the total amount, A, that Lauren has left to spend.

More Basic Algebra

The next two pages have some really important algebra rules. You'll find yourself using these at least once a day for the rest of your lives*, so it's a good idea to learn them now rather than struggling later on...

1) Terms

Before you can do anything else, you must understand what a term is:

1) **A TERM IS A COLLECTION OF NUMBERS, LETTERS AND BRACKETS, ALL MULTIPLIED/DIVIDED TOGETHER.**

2) Terms are separated by $\underline{+ \text{ and } - \text{ signs}}$. E.g. $4x^2 - 3py - 5 + 3p$

3) Terms always have a $+$ or $-$ attached to the <u>front of them</u>.

E.g.   (+4xy) (+ 5x²) (– 2y) (+ 6y²) (+ 4)

Invisible + sign   'xy' term   'x²' term   'y' term   'y²' term   'number' term

2) Simplifying or 'Collecting Like Terms'

1) Put <u>bubbles</u> round each term — be sure you capture the $\underline{+/- \text{ sign}}$ in front of each.

2) "<u>Like terms</u>" have exactly the same combination of letters, e.g. x-terms or xy-terms.

3) Move the bubbles into the <u>best order</u> so that <u>like terms</u> are together, and combine them.

<u>EXAMPLE</u>: Simplify $2x - 4 + 5x + 6$

                                        number terms

Invisible + sign   (2x)(–4)(+5x)(+6)   =   (+2x)(+5x)(–4)(+6)
                                                            x-terms   = $7x$ $+2$ $= \underline{7x + 2}$

3) Multiplying out Brackets

> Remember, $R \times R = R^2$, and TY^2 means $T \times Y \times Y$, whilst $(TY)^2$ means $T \times T \times Y \times Y$.

1) The thing <u>outside</u> the brackets multiplies <u>each separate term</u> inside the brackets.

2) When letters are multiplied together, they are just written next to each other, like this: pq.

3) Remember a minus outside the bracket <u>REVERSES ALL THE SIGNS</u> when you multiply.

1) $3(2x + 5) = \underline{6x + 15}$ 2) $4p(3r - 2t) = \underline{12pr - 8pt}$

3) $-4(3p^2 - 7q^3) = -12p^2 + 28q^3$ (note both signs have been reversed — Rule 3)

4) <u>DOUBLE BRACKETS</u> — you get <u>4 terms</u>, and usually 2 of them combine to leave <u>3 terms</u>.

$(y - 2)(y - 3)$ $= (y \times y) + (y \times -3) + (-2 \times y) + (-2 \times -3)$
                    $= y^2 + -3y + -2y + 6 = \underline{y^2 - 5y + 6}$

— these 2 combine together

$(2P - 4)(3P + 1)$ $= (2P \times 3P) + (2P \times 1) + (-4 \times 3P) + (-4 \times 1)$
                    $= 6P^2 + 2P + -12P + -4 = \underline{6P^2 - 10P - 4}$

5) <u>SQUARED BRACKETS</u> — Always write these out as <u>TWO BRACKETS</u>:

E.g. $(3d + 5)^2$ should be written out as $(3d + 5)(3d + 5)$ and then worked out as above.
YOU SHOULD ALWAYS GET <u>FOUR</u> TERMS from a pair of brackets.
The usual <u>WRONG ANSWER</u> is $(3d + 5)^2 = 9d^2 + 25$ (eeek)
It should be: $(3d + 5)^2 = (3d + 5)(3d + 5) = 9d^2 + 15d + 15d + 25 = \underline{9d^2 + 30d + 25}$

*Possibly a slight exaggeration. They are pretty useful though.

More Basic Algebra

4) Factorising — putting brackets in

This is the <u>exact reverse</u> of multiplying-out brackets. Here's the method to follow:

1) Take out the <u>biggest number</u> that goes into all the terms.
2) <u>Take each letter in turn</u> and take out the <u>highest power</u> (e.g. x, x^2 etc) that will go into EVERY term.
3) Open the brackets and fill in all the bits needed to <u>reproduce each term</u>.

<u>EXAMPLE:</u>   Factorise $15x^4y + 20x^2y^3z - 35x^3yz^2$
<u>Answer:</u> $5x^2y(3x^2 + 4y^2z - 7xz^2)$

Biggest number
that'll divide into
15, 20 and 35.

Highest powers of
x and y that will go
into all three terms.

z was not in ALL terms so it can't
come out as a <u>common factor</u>.

<u>REMEMBER:</u>   The bits <u>taken out</u> and put at the front are the <u>common factors</u>.
The bits <u>inside the brackets</u> are what's needed to get back to the
<u>original terms</u> if you multiply the brackets out again.

5) Algebraic Fractions

The basic rules are exactly the same as for ordinary fractions.

I love algebraic fractions.

1) Multiplying (easy)

Multiply top and bottom separately and cancel if possible:

$$\text{e.g.} \quad \frac{st}{10w^3} \times \frac{35s^2tw}{6} = \frac{35s^3t^2w}{60w^3} = \frac{7s^3t^2}{12w^2}$$

2) Dividing (easy)

Turn the second one upside down, then multiply and cancel if possible:

$$\text{e.g.} \quad \frac{12}{p+4} \div \frac{4(p-3)}{3(p+4)} = \frac{\cancel{12}^3}{\cancel{p+4}} \times \frac{3\cancel{(p+4)}}{\cancel{4}(p-3)} = \frac{9}{p-3}$$

3) Adding/subtracting (not so easy)

Get a common denominator, i.e. same bottom line (by cross-multiplying) and then <u>ADD TOP LINES ONLY</u>:

$$\frac{t-2p}{3t-p} - \frac{1}{3} = \frac{3(t-2p)}{3(3t-p)} - \frac{1(3t-p)}{3(3t-p)} = \frac{3t-6p-3t+p}{3(3t-p)} = \frac{-5p}{3(3t-p)}$$

Go forth and multiply out brackets...

Learn the <u>details</u> of the different <u>sections</u> on the last two pages. Then get your nimble maths brains around these:

1) Simplify: $5x + 3y - 4 - 2y - x$
2) Expand $2pq(3p - 4q^2)$
3) Expand $(2g + 5)(4g - 2)$
4) Factorise $14x^2y^3 + 21xy^2 - 35x^3y^4$
5) Simplify $\frac{5abc^3}{18de} \div \frac{15abd^2}{9ce}$
6) Simplify $\frac{3}{5} + \frac{5g}{3g-4}$

Solving Equations

Solving equations means finding the value of x from something like: $3x + 5 = 4 - 5x$.
(Now, not a lot of people know this, but <u>exactly the same method applies</u> to both <u>solving equations</u> and <u>rearranging formulas</u>, as illustrated over the next two pages.)

The Six Steps Applied to Equations

To illustrate the sequence of steps we'll use this equation: $\sqrt{2 - \dfrac{x+4}{2x+5}} = 3$

1) Get rid of any square root signs by <u>squaring both sides</u>: $\quad 2 - \dfrac{x+4}{2x+5} = 9$

2) Get everything off the bottom by <u>cross-multiplying</u> up to **EVERY OTHER TERM**:

$$② - \dfrac{x+4}{2x+5} = ⑨ \quad \Rightarrow \quad 2(2x+5) - (x+4) = 9(2x+5)$$

3) <u>Multiply out</u> any brackets: $\quad 4x + 10 - x - 4 = 18x + 45$

4) Collect all <u>subject terms</u> (x is the subject) on one side of the '=' and all <u>non-subject terms</u> on the other. Remember to reverse the +/– sign of any term that crosses the '='

   +18x moves across the '=' and becomes –18x
   +10 moves across the '=' and becomes –10
   –4 moves across the '=' and becomes +4

   $4x + 10 - x - 4 = 18x + 45$

   $4x - x - 18x = 45 - 10 + 4$

5) <u>Combine like terms</u> on each side of the equation, and reduce it to the form '<u>Ax = B</u>', where A and B are just numbers (or bunches of letters, in the case of formulas):

   $-15x = 39$

   'Ax = B':   A = -15, B = 39, x is the subject

6) Finally <u>slide the A underneath the B</u> to give '$x = \dfrac{B}{A}$', divide, and that's your answer.

   $x = \dfrac{39}{-15} = -2.6$

   So $\underline{x = -2.6}$

The Seventh Step (if You Need It)

If the term you're trying to find is squared, don't panic.

Follow steps 1) to 6) like normal, but solve it for x^2 instead of x:

   $x^2 = 9$

   $x = \pm 3$

7) <u>Take the square root</u> of both sides and stick a ± sign in front of the expression on the right:

   Don't forget the ± sign...
   (Page 13 if you don't know what I mean).

Solving equations — more fun than greasing a seal...

Definitely. I never ever exaggerate. Learn the <u>7 steps</u> for <u>solving equations</u>. Then have a go at answering these:

1) Solve these equations: a) $5(x + 2) = 8 + 4(5 - x)$ b) $\dfrac{4}{x+3} = \dfrac{6}{4-x}$ c) $x^2 - 21 = 3(5 - x^2)$

Rearranging Formulas

Rearranging formulas means making one letter the subject, e.g. getting 'y = ' from '2x + z = 3(y + 2p).'
Generally speaking 'solving equations' is easier, but don't forget:

1) EXACTLY THE SAME METHOD APPLIES TO BOTH FORMULAS AND EQUATIONS
2) THE SAME SEQUENCE OF STEPS APPLIES EVERY TIME.

The Six Steps Applied to Formulas

We'll illustrate this by making 'y' the subject of this formula: $M = \sqrt{2K - \dfrac{K^2}{2y + 1}}$

1) Get rid of any square root signs by squaring both sides: $M^2 = 2K - \dfrac{K^2}{2y + 1}$

2) Get everything off the bottom by cross-multiplying up to EVERY OTHER TERM:

$$M^2 = 2K - \frac{K^2}{2y + 1} \Rightarrow M^2(2y + 1) = 2K(2y + 1) - K^2$$

3) Multiply out any brackets: $2yM^2 + M^2 = 4Ky + 2K - K^2$

4) Collect all subject terms on one side of the '=' and all non-subject terms on the other. Remember to reverse the +/− sign of any term that crosses the '='.

+4Ky moves across the '=' and becomes −4Ky
+M² moves across the '=' and becomes −M²

$2yM^2 + M^2 = 4Ky + 2K - K^2$
$2yM^2 - 4Ky = -M^2 + 2K - K^2$

5) Combine together like terms on each side of the equation, and reduce it to the form 'Ax = B', where A and B are just bunches of letters which DON'T include the subject (y). Note that the LHS has to be FACTORISED:

$$(2M^2 - 4K)y = 2K - K^2 - M^2$$

('Ax = B' i.e. A = (2M² − 4K),   B = 2K − K² − M²,   y is the subject)

6) Finally slide the A underneath the B to give 'x = B/A', (cancel if possible) and that's your answer.   So $y = \dfrac{2K - K^2 - M^2}{(2M^2 - 4K)}$

The Seventh Step (if You Need It)

If the term you're trying to make the subject of the equation is squared, this is what you do:

$M = \sqrt{2K - \dfrac{K^2}{2y^2 + 1}}$

Follow steps 1) to 6), $y^2 = \dfrac{2K - K^2 - M^2}{(2M^2 - 4K)}$ (I've skipped steps 1) - 6) because they're exactly the same as the first example — but with y² instead of y.)
and then...

7) Take the square root of both sides and stick a ± sign in front of the expression on the right: $y = \pm\sqrt{\dfrac{2K - K^2 - M^2}{(2M^2 - 4K)}}$ Remember — square roots can be +ve or −ve. See p.13.

If I could rearrange my subjects, I'd have maths all day every day...

But that's probably just me. Learn the 7 steps for rearranging formulas. Then get rearrangin' with these:
1) Rearrange 'F = 9/5 C + 32' from 'F= ', to 'C= ' and then back the other way.
2) Make p the subject of these: a) $\dfrac{p}{p + y} = 4$ b) $\dfrac{1}{p} = \dfrac{1}{q} + \dfrac{1}{r}$ c) $\dfrac{1}{p^2} = \dfrac{1}{q} + \dfrac{1}{r}$

Inequalities

Inequalities aren't <u>half as difficult as they look</u>. Once you've learned the tricks involved, most of the algebra for them is <u>identical to ordinary equations</u>.

The Inequality Symbols:

> means '<u>Greater than</u>'   ≥ means '<u>Greater than or equal to</u>'
< means '<u>Less than</u>'   ≤ means '<u>Less than or equal to</u>'

<u>REMEMBER</u>, the one at the <u>BIG</u> end is <u>BIGGEST</u>

so   x > 4   and   4 < x   both say: '<u>x is greater than 4</u>'

I > All of you.

Algebra With Inequalities

The thing to remember here is that <u>inequalities are just like regular equations</u> in the sense that all the normal rules of algebra apply <u>WITH ONE BIG EXCEPTION</u>:

$5x < x + 2$
$5x = x + 2$

Whenever you MULTIPLY OR DIVIDE BY A <u>NEGATIVE NUMBER</u>, you must <u>FLIP THE INEQUALITY SIGN</u>.

Three Important Examples

1) Solve $5x < 6x + 2$

The equivalent equation is $5x = 6x + 2$, which is easy — and so is the inequality:

First subtract 6x from both sides: $5x - 6x < 2$ which gives $-x < 2$
Then divide both sides by -1: $\underline{x > -2}$ (i.e. x is greater than -2)

The < has flipped around into a >, because we divided by a negative number.

You can show the solution x > –2 on a number line:

The open circle means −2 is <u>NOT</u> included in the solution.

This arrowhead shows that the red line carries on forever.

2) Find all integer values of x where $-4 \le x < 1$

This type of expression is <u>very common</u>.
<u>Learn them in this way</u>: 'x is between -4 and +1, possibly equal to -4, but never equal to +1'.
(So the answers are <u>-4, -3, -2, -1, 0</u> (but <u>not</u> 1))

Here's $-4 \le x < 1$ plotted on the number line:

This closed circle means −4 <u>IS</u> included in the solution.

1 is <u>NOT</u> included in the solution.

3) Find the range of values of x where $x^2 \le 25$ The trick here is: <u>Don't forget the negative values</u>.

When you square-root both sides, the obvious solution is $x \le 5$. However, this is <u>only half the story</u>, because $x \ge -5$ is also true (if $x^2 = 25$, then $x = \pm 5$). There's little alternative but to simply learn this:

$x^2 \le 25$ gives the solution $-5 \le x \le 5$, (x is between -5 and 5, possibly equal to either).
$x^2 \ge 36$ gives the solution $x \le -6$ or $x \ge 6$
(x is 'less than or equal to -6' or 'greater than or equal to +6').

I saw you flip the inequality sign — how rude...

Learn all of this page including the <u>important examples</u>, then turn over and write it all down. Now try these:
1) Solve this inequality: $4x + 3 \le 6x + 7$. Display the solution on a number line.
2) Find all integer values of p, such that   a) $p^2 < 49$ b) $-20 < 4p \le 17$

<u>Graphical Inequalities</u>

These questions always involve <u>shading a region on a graph</u>. The method sounds very complicated, but once you've seen it in action with an example, you'll see that it's OK...

| <u>Method</u> |

1) <u>CONVERT each INEQUALITY to an EQUATION</u>
   by simply putting an '=' in place of the '<' or '>'

2) <u>DRAW THE GRAPH FOR EACH EQUATION</u>

3) <u>Work out WHICH SIDE</u> of each line you want
   Put x=0 and y=0 into the inequality to see if the <u>ORIGIN</u> is on the correct side.

4) <u>SHADE THE REGION</u> this gives you

| <u>Example</u> | "Shade the region represented by: x + y < 5, y ≥ x + 2 and y > 1"

1) <u>CONVERT EACH INEQUALITY TO AN EQUATION:</u>
   The inequalities become x + y = 5, y = x + 2 and y = 1

2) <u>DRAW THE GRAPH FOR EACH EQUATION</u> (see p.56)

3) <u>WORK OUT WHICH SIDE OF EACH LINE YOU WANT</u>
   This is the fiddly bit. Substitute x = 0 and y = 0 (the origin) into each inequality and see if this makes the inequality <u>true</u> or <u>false</u>.

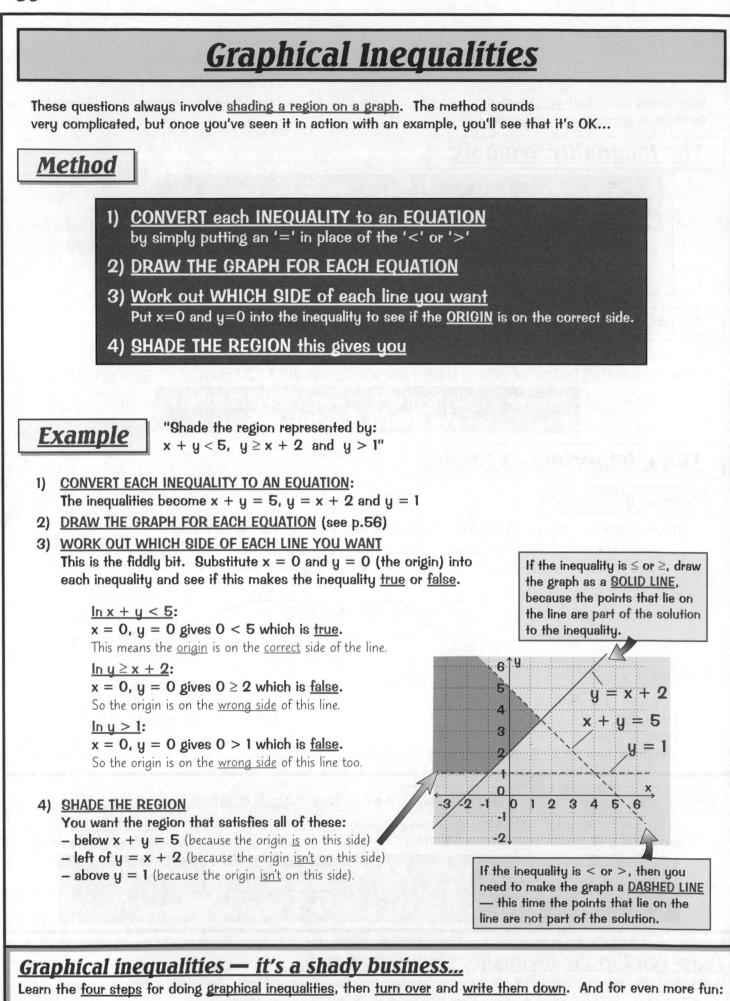

> If the inequality is ≤ or ≥, draw the graph as a <u>SOLID LINE</u>, because the points that lie on the line are part of the solution to the inequality.

<u>In x + y < 5:</u>
x = 0, y = 0 gives 0 < 5 which is <u>true</u>.
This means the <u>origin</u> is on the <u>correct</u> side of the line.

<u>In y ≥ x + 2:</u>
x = 0, y = 0 gives 0 ≥ 2 which is <u>false</u>.
So the origin is on the <u>wrong side</u> of this line.

<u>In y > 1:</u>
x = 0, y = 0 gives 0 > 1 which is <u>false</u>.
So the origin is on the <u>wrong side</u> of this line too.

4) <u>SHADE THE REGION</u>
   You want the region that satisfies all of these:
   – below x + y = 5 (because the origin <u>is</u> on this side)
   – left of y = x + 2 (because the origin <u>isn't</u> on this side)
   – above y = 1 (because the origin <u>isn't</u> on this side).

> If the inequality is < or >, then you need to make the graph a <u>DASHED LINE</u> — this time the points that lie on the line are not part of the solution.

<u>Graphical inequalities — it's a shady business...</u>

Learn the <u>four steps</u> for doing <u>graphical inequalities</u>, then <u>turn over</u> and <u>write them down</u>. And for even more fun:

1) Show on a graph the region described by the following three conditions:
   x + y ≤ 6, y ≥ 0.5, y ≤ 2x − 2

Factorising Quadratics

There are several ways of <u>solving a quadratic equation</u> as detailed on the following pages. You need to know all the methods.

Factorising a Quadratic

'<u>Factorising a quadratic</u>' means '<u>putting it into 2 brackets</u>'.

(There are several different methods for doing this, so stick with the one you're happiest with. If you have no preference then learn the one below.)

The standard format for quadratic equations is: $ax^2 + bx + c = 0$

Most Exam questions have <u>a = 1</u>, making them <u>much easier</u>.

   E.g. $x^2 + 3x + 2 = 0$ (See next page for when a is not 1)

Factorising Method When a = 1

1) <u>ALWAYS</u> rearrange into the <u>STANDARD FORMAT</u>: $ax^2 + bx + c = 0$

2) Write down the <u>TWO BRACKETS</u> with the x's in: (x   )(x   )=0

3) Then <u>find 2 numbers</u> that <u>MULTIPLY</u> to give 'c' (the end number) but also <u>ADD/SUBTRACT to give 'b'</u> (the coefficient of x)

4) Put them in and check that the +/– signs work out properly.

An Example   "Solve $x^2 - x = 12$ by factorising."

<u>ANSWER</u>:   1) <u>First rearrange it</u> (into the standard format): $x^2 - x - 12 = 0$

   2) a = 1, so the initial brackets are (as ever): $(x \quad)(x \quad) = 0$

   3) We now want to look at <u>all pairs of numbers</u> that <u>multiply to give c</u> (=12), and find the pair which <u>add or subtract to give the value of b</u>:

      1 × 12 Add/subtract to give: 13 or 11
      2 × 6 Add/subtract to give: 8 or 4   this is what
      3 × 4 Add/subtract to give: 7 or ① ← we're after (=±b)

   4) 3 and 4 will give b = ±1, so put them in: (x   3)(x   4)=0

   5) <u>Now fill in the +/– signs</u> so that the 3 and 4 add/subtract to give -1 (=b), Clearly it must be +3 and –4 so we have: (x + 3)(x – 4)=0

   6) <u>As an ESSENTIAL check, EXPAND the brackets</u> out again to make sure they give the original equation:
      $(x + 3)(x - 4) = x^2 + 3x - 4x - 12 = \underline{x^2 - x - 12}$

   We're not finished yet mind, because <u>(x + 3)(x – 4) = 0</u> is only the <u>factorised form of the equation</u> — we have yet to give the actual <u>SOLUTIONS</u>. This is very easy:

   7) <u>THE SOLUTIONS</u> are simply <u>the two numbers in the brackets</u>, but with <u>OPPOSITE +/– SIGNS</u>: i.e. x = -3 or +4

   Make sure you remember that last step. <u>It's the difference</u> between <u>SOLVING THE EQUATION</u> and merely <u>factorising it</u>.

Factorising Quadratics

When 'a' is not 1   E.g. $3x^2 + 5x + 2 = 0$

The basic method is still the same but it's <u>a lot messier</u>. Chances are, the Exam question will be one with a=1, so <u>make sure you can do that type easily</u>. Only then should you try to get to grips with these harder ones.

An Example   "Solve $3x^2 + 7x = 6$ by factorising."

1) <u>First rearrange it</u> (into the standard format): $3x^2 + 7x - 6 = 0$

2) Now because a = 3, the two x-terms in the brackets will have to multiply to give $3x^2$ so the initial brackets will have to be: $(3x \quad)(x \quad)=0$

   (i.e. <u>you put in the x-terms first</u>, with coefficients that will multiply to give 'a')

3) We now want to look at <u>all pairs of numbers</u> that <u>multiply with each other to give 'c'</u> (=6, ignoring the minus sign for now):   i.e. 1×6 and 2×3

4) <u>Now the difficult bit</u>: to find the combination which does this:

> <u>multiply with the 3x and x terms in the brackets and then</u>
> <u>add or subtract to give the value of b (=7):</u>

The best way to do this is by trying out all the possibilities in the brackets until you find the combination that works. Don't forget that <u>EACH PAIR</u> of numbers can be tried in <u>TWO</u> different positions:

> $(3x \quad 1)(x \quad 6)$ <u>multiplies</u> to give <u>18x and 1x</u> which <u>add/subtract</u> to give <u>19x or 17x</u>
> $(3x \quad 6)(x \quad 1)$ <u>multiplies</u> to give <u>3x and 6x</u> which <u>add/subtract</u> to give <u>9x or 3x</u>
> $(3x \quad 3)(x \quad 2)$ <u>multiplies</u> to give <u>6x and 3x</u> which <u>add/subtract</u> to give <u>9x or 3x</u>
> $(3x \quad 2)(x \quad 3)$ <u>multiplies</u> to give <u>9x and 2x</u> which <u>add/subtract</u> to give <u>11x or ⑦x</u>

So $(3x \quad 2)(x \quad 3)$ is the combination that gives b = 7, (give or take a +/–)

5) <u>Now fill in the +/– signs</u> so that the combination will add/subtract to give +7 (=b). Clearly it must be +3 and –2 which gives rise to +9x and -2x. So the final brackets are: $(3x - 2)(x + 3)$

6) <u>As an ESSENTIAL check, EXPAND the brackets</u> out again to make sure they give the original equation: $(3x - 2)(x + 3) = 3x^2 + 9x - 2x - 6 = \underline{3x^2 + 7x - 6}$

> 7) The last step is to get <u>THE SOLUTIONS TO THE EQUATION</u>: $(3x - 2)(x + 3)=0$ which you do <u>by separately putting each bracket = 0</u> :
> i.e. $(3x - 2) = 0 \Rightarrow \underline{x = 2/3}$ $(x + 3) = 0 \Rightarrow \underline{x = -3}$
> Don't forget that last step. <u>Again, it's the difference</u> between <u>SOLVING THE EQUATION</u> and merely <u>factorising it</u>.

It's not scary — just think of it as brackets giving algebra a hug...

Actually, don't 'cause that won't really help you in the Exam. What will help is learning the 7 steps for solving quadratics by factorising — both for 'a = 1' and 'a ≠ 1'. And then answering these questions:
1) Solve these by the factorising method:
a) $x^2 + 5x - 24 = 0$ b) $x^2 - 6x + 9 = 16$ c) $(x + 3)^2 - 3 = 13$ d) $5x^2 - 17x - 12 = 0$

The Quadratic Formula

The solutions to any quadratic equation $ax^2 + bx + c = 0$ are given by this formula:

$$x = \frac{-b \pm \sqrt{b^2 - 4ac}}{2a}$$

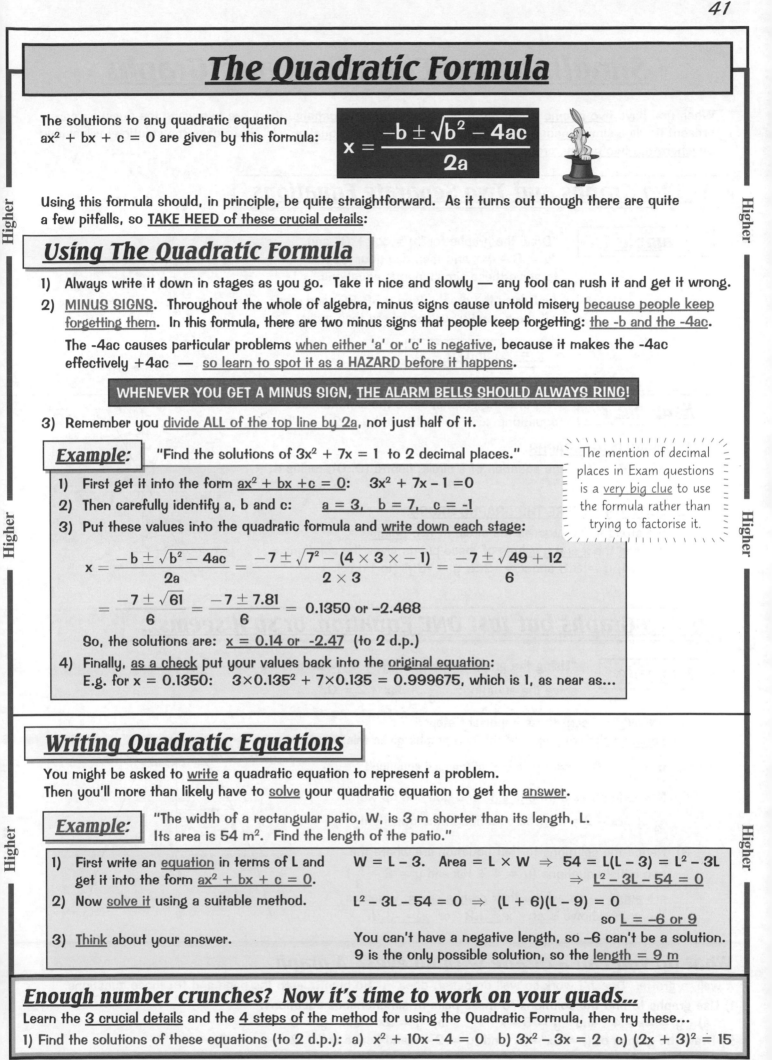

Using this formula should, in principle, be quite straightforward. As it turns out though there are quite a few pitfalls, so <u>TAKE HEED of these crucial details</u>:

Using The Quadratic Formula

1) Always write it down in stages as you go. Take it nice and slowly — any fool can rush it and get it wrong.

2) <u>MINUS SIGNS</u>. Throughout the whole of algebra, minus signs cause untold misery <u>because people keep forgetting them</u>. In this formula, there are two minus signs that people keep forgetting: <u>the -b and the -4ac</u>.

   The -4ac causes particular problems <u>when either 'a' or 'c' is negative</u>, because it makes the -4ac effectively +4ac — <u>so learn to spot it as a HAZARD before it happens</u>.

   WHENEVER YOU GET A MINUS SIGN, <u>THE ALARM BELLS SHOULD ALWAYS RING!</u>

3) Remember you <u>divide ALL of the top line by 2a</u>, not just half of it.

Example: "Find the solutions of $3x^2 + 7x = 1$ to 2 decimal places."

> *The mention of decimal places in Exam questions is a <u>very big clue</u> to use the formula rather than trying to factorise it.*

1) First get it into the form <u>$ax^2 + bx + c = 0$</u>: $3x^2 + 7x - 1 = 0$

2) Then carefully identify a, b and c: <u>$a = 3$, $b = 7$, $c = -1$</u>

3) Put these values into the quadratic formula and <u>write down each stage</u>:

$$x = \frac{-b \pm \sqrt{b^2 - 4ac}}{2a} = \frac{-7 \pm \sqrt{7^2 - (4 \times 3 \times -1)}}{2 \times 3} = \frac{-7 \pm \sqrt{49 + 12}}{6}$$

$$= \frac{-7 \pm \sqrt{61}}{6} = \frac{-7 \pm 7.81}{6} = 0.1350 \text{ or } -2.468$$

So, the solutions are: <u>$x = 0.14$ or -2.47</u>   (to 2 d.p.)

4) Finally, <u>as a check</u> put your values back into the <u>original equation</u>:
   E.g. for x = 0.1350: $3 \times 0.135^2 + 7 \times 0.135 = 0.999675$, which is 1, as near as...

Writing Quadratic Equations

You might be asked to <u>write</u> a quadratic equation to represent a problem.
Then you'll more than likely have to <u>solve</u> your quadratic equation to get the <u>answer</u>.

Example: "The width of a rectangular patio, W, is 3 m shorter than its length, L. Its area is 54 m². Find the length of the patio."

1) First write an <u>equation</u> in terms of L and get it into the form <u>$ax^2 + bx + c = 0$</u>.

   $W = L - 3$.   Area $= L \times W \Rightarrow 54 = L(L - 3) = L^2 - 3L$
   $\Rightarrow$ <u>$L^2 - 3L - 54 = 0$</u>

2) Now <u>solve it</u> using a suitable method.

   $L^2 - 3L - 54 = 0 \Rightarrow (L + 6)(L - 9) = 0$
   so <u>$L = -6$ or 9</u>

3) <u>Think</u> about your answer.

   You can't have a negative length, so −6 can't be a solution. 9 is the only possible solution, so the <u>length = 9 m</u>

Enough number crunches? Now it's time to work on your quads...

Learn the <u>3 crucial details</u> and the <u>4 steps of the method</u> for using the Quadratic Formula, then try these...

1) Find the solutions of these equations (to 2 d.p.): a) $x^2 + 10x - 4 = 0$ b) $3x^2 - 3x = 2$ c) $(2x + 3)^2 = 15$

Simultaneous Equations and Graphs

When you have <u>two graphs</u> which represent <u>two separate equations</u>, there are two ways the question can present it: <u>two simultaneous equations</u> or a <u>single merged equation</u>. In either case the solutions will simply be <u>where the two graphs cross</u>...

1) Two Graphs and Two Separate Equations

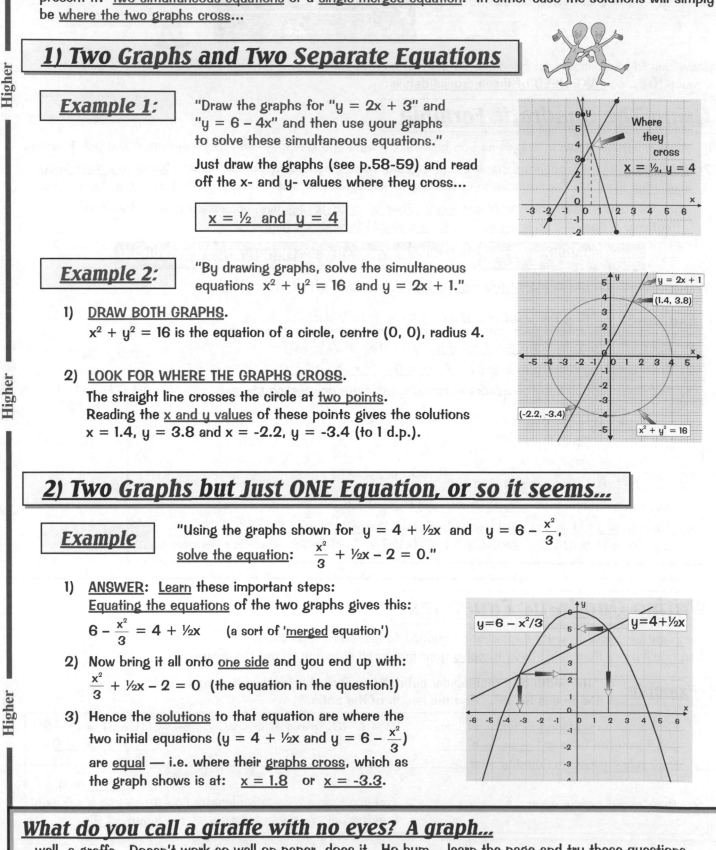

Example 1:

"Draw the graphs for "$y = 2x + 3$" and "$y = 6 - 4x$" and then use your graphs to solve these simultaneous equations."

Just draw the graphs (see p.58-59) and read off the x- and y- values where they cross...

$$\underline{x = \tfrac{1}{2} \text{ and } y = 4}$$

Where they cross
$$\underline{x = \tfrac{1}{2}, y = 4}$$

Example 2:

"By drawing graphs, solve the simultaneous equations $x^2 + y^2 = 16$ and $y = 2x + 1$."

1) <u>DRAW BOTH GRAPHS</u>.

$x^2 + y^2 = 16$ is the equation of a circle, centre (0, 0), radius 4.

2) <u>LOOK FOR WHERE THE GRAPHS CROSS</u>.

The straight line crosses the circle at <u>two points</u>.
Reading the <u>x and y values</u> of these points gives the solutions
$x = 1.4$, $y = 3.8$ and $x = -2.2$, $y = -3.4$ (to 1 d.p.).

$y = 2x + 1$
(1.4, 3.8)
(-2.2, -3.4)
$x^2 + y^2 = 16$

2) Two Graphs but Just ONE Equation, or so it seems...

Example

"Using the graphs shown for $y = 4 + \tfrac{1}{2}x$ and $y = 6 - \frac{x^2}{3}$, solve the equation: $\frac{x^2}{3} + \tfrac{1}{2}x - 2 = 0$."

1) <u>ANSWER</u>: <u>Learn</u> these important steps:
   <u>Equating the equations</u> of the two graphs gives this:

   $6 - \dfrac{x^2}{3} = 4 + \tfrac{1}{2}x$ (a sort of '<u>merged</u> equation')

2) Now bring it all onto <u>one side</u> and you end up with:

   $\dfrac{x^2}{3} + \tfrac{1}{2}x - 2 = 0$ (the equation in the question!)

3) Hence the <u>solutions</u> to that equation are where the two initial equations ($y = 4 + \tfrac{1}{2}x$ and $y = 6 - \dfrac{x^2}{3}$) are <u>equal</u> — i.e. where their <u>graphs cross</u>, which as the graph shows is at: <u>x = 1.8</u> or <u>x = -3.3</u>.

$y = 6 - x^2/3$
$y = 4 + \tfrac{1}{2}x$

What do you call a giraffe with no eyes? A graph...

...well, a graffe. Doesn't work so well on paper, does it. Ho hum... learn the page and try these questions.
1) Use graphs to find the solutions to these pairs of simultaneous equations:
   a) $y = 4x - 4$ and $y = 6 - x$ b) $y = 2x$ and $y = 6 - 2x$
2) Draw the graphs of $y = 2x^2 - 4$ and $y = 2 - x$ and hence solve $2x^2 + x = 6$.

Simultaneous Equations

This page is all about the thrilling world of <u>simultaneous equations</u>, and how to solve them using algebra methods. The rules are really quite simple, but <u>you must follow ALL the steps, in the right order, and treat them as a strict method</u>. (Alright, I might have been exaggerating a bit when I called it thrilling...)

There are two types of simultaneous equations you could get
— EASY ONES (where both equations are linear) and TRICKY ONES (where one's quadratic).

① $2x = 6 - 4y$ and $-3 - 3y = 4x$

② $7x + y = 1$ and $2x^2 - y = 3$

Only higher tier need to learn the 2nd type.

① Six Steps For EASY Simultaneous Equations

We'll use these two equations for our example: $2x = 6 - 4y$ and $-3 - 3y = 4x$

1) <u>Rearrange both equations</u> into the form <u>$ax + by = c$</u> where a, b, c are numbers, (which can be negative). Also label the two equations ① and ②

$$2x + 4y = 6 \quad - ①$$
$$-4x - 3y = 3 \quad - ②$$

2) You need to <u>match up the numbers in front</u> (the 'coefficients') of either the x's or y's in both equations. To do this you may need to multiply one or both equations by a suitable number. You should then relabel them: ③ and ④

$$① \times 2: \quad 4x + 8y = 12 \quad - ③$$
$$-4x - 3y = 3 \quad - ④$$

3) <u>Add or subtract the two equations</u> to eliminate the terms with the same coefficient
   If the <u>coefficients are the same</u> (both +ve or both −ve) then <u>SUBTRACT</u>
   If the <u>coefficients are opposite</u> (one +ve and one −ve) then <u>ADD</u>

$$③ + ④ \quad 0x + 5y = 15$$

4) <u>Solve the resulting equation</u> to find whichever letter is left in it.

$$5y = 15 \Rightarrow \underline{y = 3}$$

5) Substitute this value back into equation ① and solve it to find the other quantity.

Sub in ①: $\quad 2x + 4 \times 3 = 6 \Rightarrow 2x + 12 = 6 \Rightarrow 2x = -6 \Rightarrow \underline{x = -3}$

6) Then substitute both these values into equation ② to make sure it works.
   If it doesn't then you've done something wrong and you'll have to do it all again.

Sub x and y in ②: $\quad -4 \times -3 - 3 \times 3 = 12 - 9 = \underline{3}$, which is right, so it's worked.
So the solutions are: $\quad \underline{x = -3}, \quad \underline{y = 3}$

Sunday morning, lemon squeezy and simultaneous linear equations...

...all easy apparently. Easy or not, you need to learn the <u>6 steps</u> on this page. Remember, you only know them when you can write them all out from memory, so turn over the page and see if you can write down all six.

1) Apply the six steps to find F and G given that $2F - 10 = 4G$ and $3G = 4F - 15$

Simultaneous Equations

② Seven Steps For TRICKY Simultaneous Equations

Example: Solve these simultaneous equations: $7x + y = 1$ and $2x^2 - y = 3$

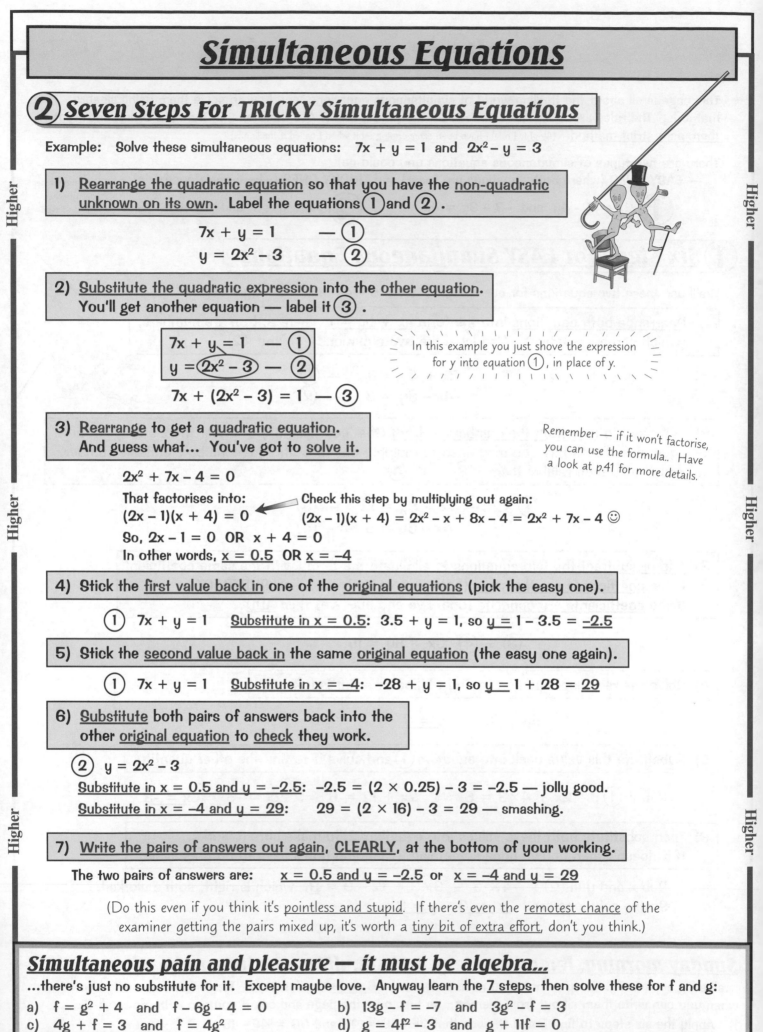

1) Rearrange the quadratic equation so that you have the non-quadratic unknown on its own. Label the equations ① and ②.

$$7x + y = 1 \quad — ①$$
$$y = 2x^2 - 3 \quad — ②$$

2) Substitute the quadratic expression into the other equation. You'll get another equation — label it ③.

$$7x + y = 1 \quad — ①$$
$$y = \boxed{2x^2 - 3} \quad — ②$$
$$7x + (2x^2 - 3) = 1 \quad — ③$$

In this example you just shove the expression for y into equation ①, in place of y.

3) Rearrange to get a quadratic equation. And guess what... You've got to solve it.

$$2x^2 + 7x - 4 = 0$$

That factorises into:
$$(2x - 1)(x + 4) = 0$$

Check this step by multiplying out again:
$(2x - 1)(x + 4) = 2x^2 - x + 8x - 4 = 2x^2 + 7x - 4$ ☺

So, $2x - 1 = 0$ OR $x + 4 = 0$
In other words, $\underline{x = 0.5}$ OR $\underline{x = -4}$

Remember — if it won't factorise, you can use the formula.. Have a look at p.41 for more details.

4) Stick the first value back in one of the original equations (pick the easy one).

① $7x + y = 1$ Substitute in $x = 0.5$: $3.5 + y = 1$, so $\underline{y = 1 - 3.5 = -2.5}$

5) Stick the second value back in the same original equation (the easy one again).

① $7x + y = 1$ Substitute in $x = -4$: $-28 + y = 1$, so $\underline{y = 1 + 28 = 29}$

6) Substitute both pairs of answers back into the other original equation to check they work.

② $y = 2x^2 - 3$

Substitute in $x = 0.5$ and $y = -2.5$: $-2.5 = (2 \times 0.25) - 3 = -2.5$ — jolly good.
Substitute in $x = -4$ and $y = 29$: $29 = (2 \times 16) - 3 = 29$ — smashing.

7) Write the pairs of answers out again, **CLEARLY**, at the bottom of your working.

The two pairs of answers are: $\underline{x = 0.5 \text{ and } y = -2.5}$ or $\underline{x = -4 \text{ and } y = 29}$

(Do this even if you think it's pointless and stupid. If there's even the remotest chance of the examiner getting the pairs mixed up, it's worth a tiny bit of extra effort, don't you think.)

Simultaneous pain and pleasure — it must be algebra...

...there's just no substitute for it. Except maybe love. Anyway learn the 7 steps, then solve these for f and g:

a) $f = g^2 + 4$ and $f - 6g - 4 = 0$ b) $13g - f = -7$ and $3g^2 - f = 3$
c) $4g + f = 3$ and $f = 4g^2$ d) $g = 4f^2 - 3$ and $g + 11f = 0$

Direct and Inverse Proportion

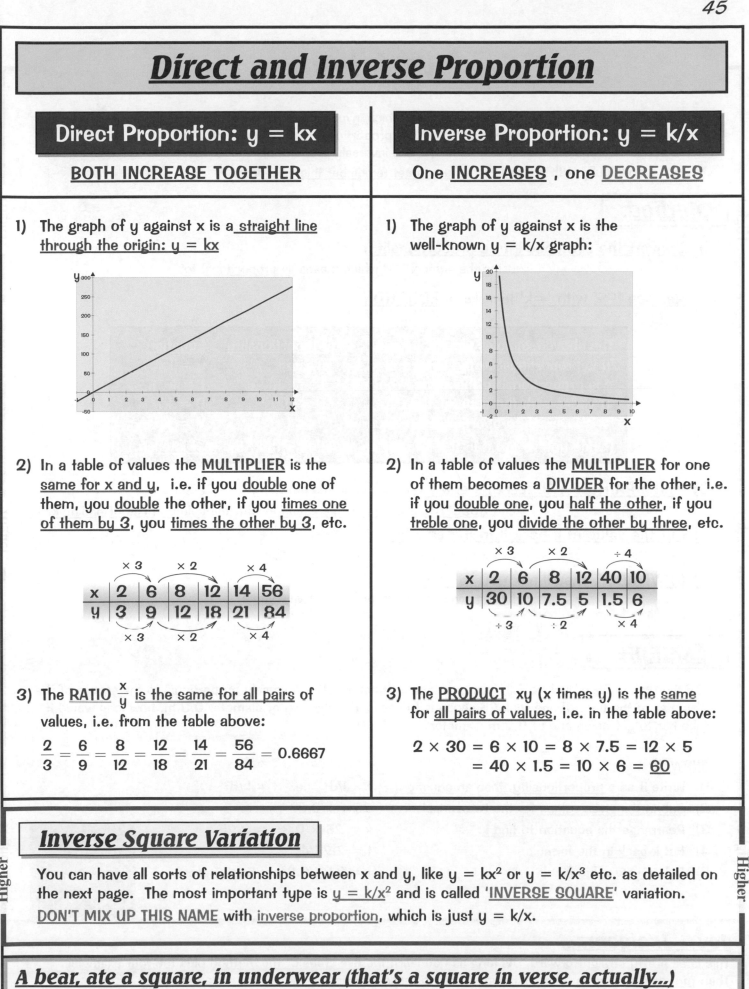

Direct Proportion: y = kx	Inverse Proportion: y = k/x
BOTH INCREASE TOGETHER	One **INCREASES** , one **DECREASES**

1) The graph of y against x is a straight line through the origin: y = kx

1) The graph of y against x is the well-known y = k/x graph:

2) In a table of values the **MULTIPLIER** is the same for x and y, i.e. if you double one of them, you double the other, if you times one of them by 3, you times the other by 3, etc.

× 3   × 2   × 4

x	2	6	8	12	14	56
y	3	9	12	18	21	84

× 3   × 2   × 4

2) In a table of values the **MULTIPLIER** for one of them becomes a **DIVIDER** for the other, i.e. if you double one, you half the other, if you treble one, you divide the other by three, etc.

× 3   × 2   ÷ 4

x	2	6	8	12	40	10
y	30	10	7.5	5	1.5	6

÷ 3   : 2   × 4

3) The **RATIO** $\frac{x}{y}$ is the same for all pairs of values, i.e. from the table above:

$$\frac{2}{3} = \frac{6}{9} = \frac{8}{12} = \frac{12}{18} = \frac{14}{21} = \frac{56}{84} = 0.6667$$

3) The **PRODUCT** xy (x times y) is the same for all pairs of values, i.e. in the table above:

$$2 \times 30 = 6 \times 10 = 8 \times 7.5 = 12 \times 5$$
$$= 40 \times 1.5 = 10 \times 6 = \underline{60}$$

Inverse Square Variation

You can have all sorts of relationships between x and y, like y = kx² or y = k/x³ etc. as detailed on the next page. The most important type is y = k/x² and is called 'INVERSE SQUARE' variation. DON'T MIX UP THIS NAME with inverse proportion, which is just y = k/x.

A bear, ate a square, in underwear (that's a square in verse, actually...)

Learn the 3 key features of both direct and inverse proportion. Then turn over and write them all down.
1) Give examples of 2 real quantities that exhibit: a) direct and b) inverse proportion.
2) Make up your own tables of values which show: a) direct proportion   b) inverse proportion

Variation

This page shows you how to deal with questions which involve statements like these:
  'y is proportional to the square of x'   't is proportional to the square root of h'
  'D varies with the cube of T'   'V is inversely proportional to r squared'
To deal successfully with things like this <u>you must remember this method</u>:

Method:

1) <u>Convert the sentence into a proportionality</u>,

   using the symbol '$\propto$' which means '<u>is proportional to</u>'.

2) <u>Replace '$\propto$' with '$=k$'</u> to make an <u>EQUATION</u>:

The above examples would become:	Proportionality	Equation
'y is proportional to the square of x'	$y \propto x^2$	$y = kx^2$
't is proportional to the square root of h'	$t \propto \sqrt{h}$	$t = k\sqrt{h}$
'D varies with the cube of T'	$D \propto T^3$	$D = kT^3$
'V is inversely proportional to r squared'	$V \propto 1/r^2$	$V = k/r^2$

(Once you've got it in the form of an equation with k, the <u>rest is easy</u>.)

3) <u>Find a PAIR OF VALUES</u> of x and y somewhere in the question,

   and <u>SUBSTITUTE</u> them into the equation with the <u>sole purpose of finding k</u>.

4) <u>Put the value of k back into the equation</u>

   and it's now ready to use, e.g. $y = 3x^2$.

5) <u>INEVITABLY, they'll ask you to find y</u>,

   having given you a value for x (or vice versa).

Example:

The time taken for a duck to fall down a chimney (it happens!) is inversely proportional to the square of the diameter of the flue. If she took 25 seconds to descend a chimney of diameter 0.3 m, how long would it take her to get down one of 0.2 m diameter?

<u>ANSWER</u>:

1) Write it as a <u>proportionality</u>, then an <u>equation</u>: $t \propto 1/d^2$ i.e. $t = k/d^2$

2) <u>Sub in the given values</u> for the two variables: $25 = k/0.3^2$

3) <u>Rearrange the equation to <u>find k</u></u>: $k = 25 \times 0.3^2 = 2.25$

4) Put k <u>back in</u> the formula: $t = 2.25/d^2$

5) <u>Sub in new value</u> for d: $t = 2.25/0.2^2 = \underline{56.25 \text{ secs}}$

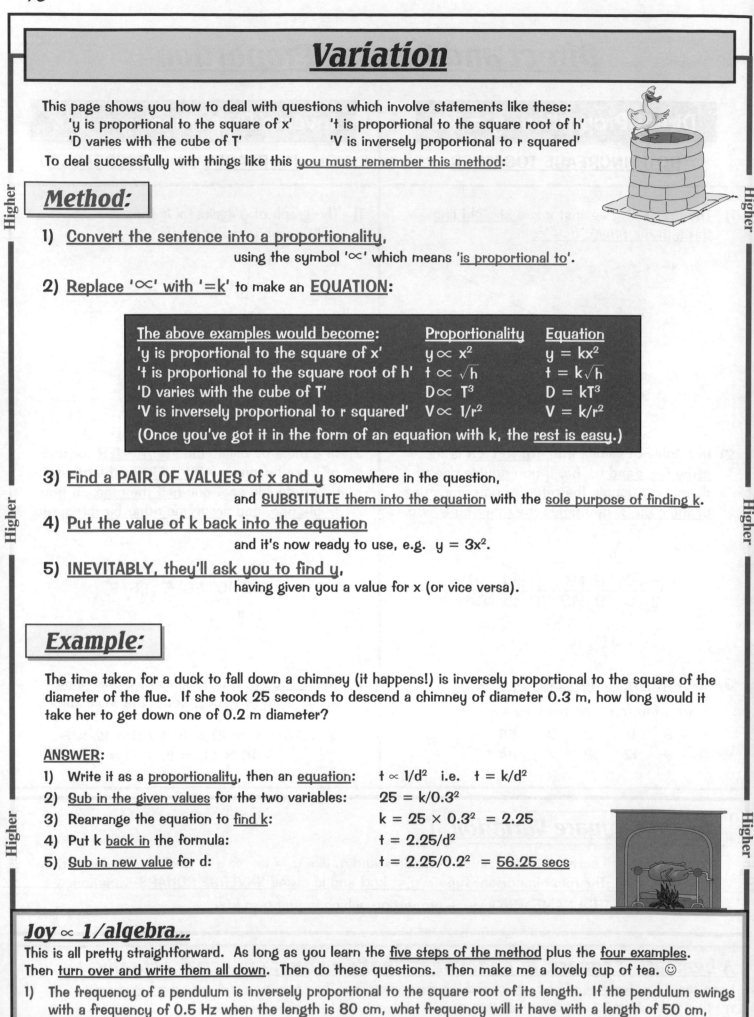

Joy $\propto$ 1/algebra...

This is all pretty straightforward. As long as you learn the <u>five steps of the method</u> plus the <u>four examples</u>. Then <u>turn over and write them all down</u>. Then do these questions. Then make me a lovely cup of tea. ☺

1) The frequency of a pendulum is inversely proportional to the square root of its length. If the pendulum swings with a frequency of 0.5 Hz when the length is 80 cm, what frequency will it have with a length of 50 cm, and what length will give a frequency of 0.7 Hz?

Revision Summary

Section 3 is the really nasty one — grisly grimsdike algebra. But grisly or not, you still have to learn it. Here's a simply spiffing set of questions to test what you know. Don't forget, you've got to keep trying these <u>over and over again</u>. Making sure that you can do these questions is the <u>best revision</u> you can possibly do. Just keep practising till you can glide through them all like a turtle or something.

KEEP LEARNING THESE BASIC FACTS UNTIL YOU KNOW THEM

1) Work out:
   a) $4a - -2a$ b) $4a \times -2a$ c) $4a + -2a$ d) $-4a \div -2a$

2) Write down 4 combinations of letters that regularly catch people out in algebra.

3) To find p you divide q by 6, cube the result, then add 4. Write a formula for p.

4) What are 'terms'?

5) What is the method for multiplying out brackets such as $3(2x + 4)$?

6) What is the method for multiplying pairs of brackets? What about squared brackets?

7) What are the three steps for factorising expressions such as $12x^2y^3z + 15x^3yz^2$?

8) Give details of the three techniques for dealing with algebraic fractions, with examples.

9) What are the six steps for solving equations or rearranging formulas? What's the 7th step?

10) What do you need to do if you divide an inequality by a negative number?

11) What do closed and open circles on a number line mean?

12) Solve these inequalities and show the solution on a number line.
    a) $2y + 3 > 9$ b) $3y^2 + 2 < 29$

13) What is the four-stage method for graphical inequalities?

14) What does 'factorising a quadratic' mean you have to do?

15) What check should you do to make sure you've done it right?

16) What difference does it make when factorising a quadratic if 'a' is not 1?

17) How exactly do you get solutions to a quadratic equation once you've factorised it?

18) Write down the formula for solving quadratics.

19) What are two main pitfalls that catch people out with the quadratic formula?

20) The difference between the length and width of a rectangle is 2 cm. The area of the rectangle is 63 cm². Find the dimensions of the rectangle.

21) Jacob stocks the tuck shop with chocolate bars each week. Last week he spent £4.20 buying 6 chocolate bars and 3 pints of milk for his mum. This week he spent £5.32 on 10 chocolate bars and 2 pints of milk (for his mum again). His receipts weren't itemised and he needs to know how much money to take back from the tuck shop for the chocolate bars (all the chocolate bars are the same price).
    a) Write simultaneous equations for Jacob's two receipts.
    b) Solve the equations to calculate how much money Jacob is owed.

22) List the three key features of both direct proportion and inverse proportion.

23) What sort of statements are involved in the subject of 'variation'?

24) What is the meaning of life? Why are we here? And why do we have to do so much algebra?

Number Patterns and Sequences

There are several different types of <u>number sequences</u> you could get in the Exam, each as pretty as the last. They're not difficult — <u>AS LONG AS YOU WRITE WHAT'S HAPPENING IN EACH GAP</u>.

1) 'Add or Subtract the Same Number'

The SECRET is to <u>write the differences in the gaps</u> between each pair of numbers:

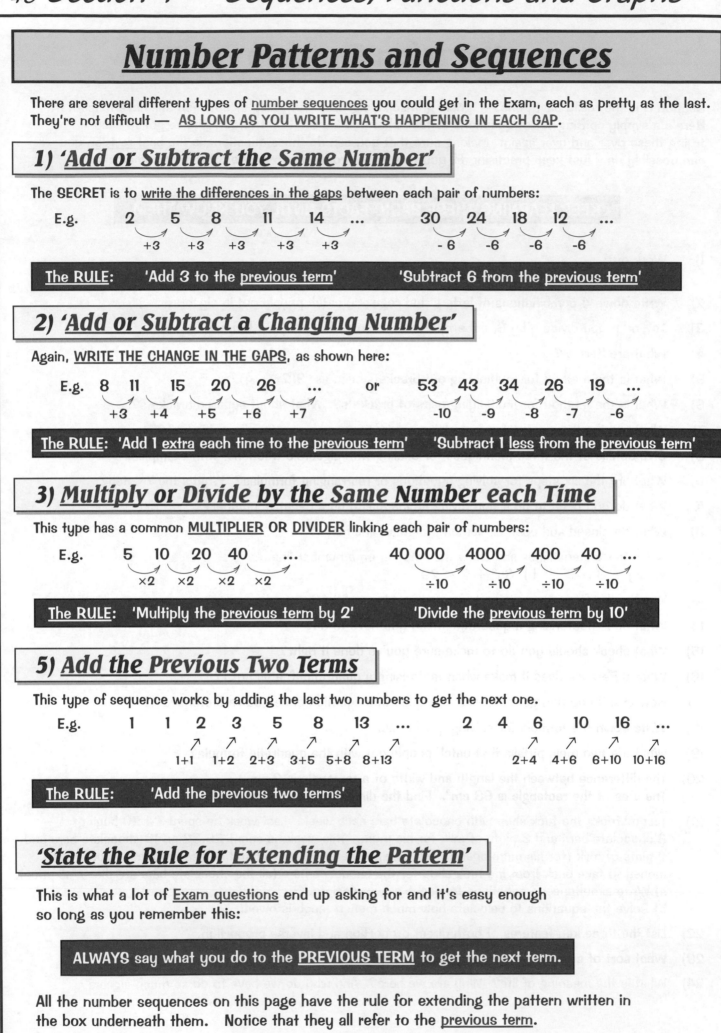

E.g.   2   5   8   11   14   ...   30   24   18   12   ...
       +3   +3   +3   +3   +3   -6   -6   -6   -6

| The RULE: | 'Add 3 to the <u>previous term</u>' | 'Subtract 6 from the <u>previous term</u>' |

2) 'Add or Subtract a Changing Number'

Again, <u>WRITE THE CHANGE IN THE GAPS</u>, as shown here:

E.g. 8   11   15   20   26   ...   or   53   43   34   26   19   ...
       +3   +4   +5   +6   +7   -10   -9   -8   -7   -6

| The RULE: | 'Add 1 <u>extra</u> each time to the <u>previous term</u>' | 'Subtract 1 <u>less</u> from the <u>previous term</u>' |

3) Multiply or Divide by the Same Number each Time

This type has a common <u>MULTIPLIER</u> OR <u>DIVIDER</u> linking each pair of numbers:

E.g.   5   10   20   40   ...   40 000   4000   400   40   ...
        ×2   ×2   ×2   ×2   ÷10   ÷10   ÷10   ÷10

| The RULE: | 'Multiply the <u>previous term</u> by 2' | 'Divide the <u>previous term</u> by 10' |

5) Add the Previous Two Terms

This type of sequence works by adding the last two numbers to get the next one.

E.g.   1   1   2   3   5   8   13   ...   2   4   6   10   16   ...
                1+1 1+2 2+3 3+5 5+8 8+13   2+4 4+6 6+10 10+16

| The RULE: | 'Add the previous two terms' |

'State the Rule for Extending the Pattern'

This is what a lot of <u>Exam questions</u> end up asking for and it's easy enough so long as you remember this:

| ALWAYS say what you do to the <u>PREVIOUS TERM</u> to get the next term. |

All the number sequences on this page have the rule for extending the pattern written in the box underneath them. Notice that they all refer to the <u>previous term</u>.

Number Patterns and Sequences

It's all very well being able to work out a term from the previous term, but if you're asked for the 100th term, well, it's going to take you a long time to get there. There are quicker ways though.

Find the Rule that Gives a Term from its Term Number

Some sequences are pretty easy to find a rule for — if you recognise the numbers that is. E.g.:

Example 1:

Terms	1	4	9	16	25	...
Term number	1	2	3	4	5	
(Term number)^2	1^2	2^2	3^2	4^2	5^2	

These are <u>square numbers</u>. The rule is (term number)^2.

Example 2:

Terms	2	4	8	16	32	...
Term number	1	2	3	4	5	
$2^{(\text{Term number})}$	2^1	2^2	2^3	2^4	2^5	

These are <u>powers of 2</u>. The rule is $2^{(\text{term number})}$.

Others are a trifle trickier. Here's how to deal with <u>common difference</u> sequences:

Example 3:

Terms	2	5	8	11	14	...
	+3	+3	+3	+3	+3	
Term number	1	2	3	4	5	
Term number × 3	3	6	9	12	15	
Difference	+1	+1	+1	+1	+1	

The difference is <u>3</u>, so multiply each term number by <u>3</u>.
Term number × 3 is always <u>1 more</u> than the actual term.
So the rule is <u>(term number × 3) – 1</u>.

Example 4:

Terms	30	24	18	12	6	...
	–6	–6	–6	–6	–6	
Term number	1	2	3	4	5	
Term number × –6	–6	–12	–18	–24	–30	
Difference	–36	–36	–36	–36	–36	

The difference is <u>–6</u>, so multiply each term number by <u>–6</u>.
Term number × –6 is always <u>36 less</u> than the actual term.
So the rule is <u>(term number × –6) + 36</u>.

To find, say, the 100th term, just <u>apply the rule</u>. E.g. for Example 4, the rule is (term number × –6) + 36
so 100th term = (100 × –6) + 36 = <u>–564</u>

Finding "the nth Term" for Common Difference Sequences

"The nth term" is a formula with "n" in it which gives you <u>any term in a sequence</u> when you put different values for n in. You need to know how to find 'the nth term' for a <u>common difference</u> formula.

For any sequence such as 3, 7, 11, 15, where there is a **COMMON DIFFERENCE**:

you can find 'the nth term' using the formula: **'nth term = dn + (a – d)'**

> 1) 'a' is simply the value of <u>THE FIRST TERM</u> in the sequence.
> 2) 'd' is simply the value of <u>THE COMMON DIFFERENCE</u> between the terms.
> 3) To get the <u>nth term</u>, you just find the values of '<u>a</u>' and '<u>d</u>' from the sequence and <u>stick them in the formula</u>. You don't replace n though — that wants to stay as n.
> 4) Of course <u>YOU HAVE TO LEARN THE FORMULA</u>, but life is like that.

Example: "Find the nth term of this sequence: 5, 8, 11, 14 ...."
1) The formula is dn + (a – d)
2) The <u>first term</u> is 5, so <u>a = 5</u>. The <u>common difference</u> is 3 so <u>d = 3</u>.
3) Putting these in the formula gives: 3n + (5 – 3) so the <u>nth term = 3n + 2</u>.

Look, if I've told you n times, I've told you n + 1 times — learn this page...

LEARN the <u>types of number patterns</u> and how to find <u>any term</u>, and you'll be ready to tackle sequence questions.
1) Find the next 2 numbers in these sequences: a) 2, 5, 9, 14 ....   b) 2, 20, 200 ....   c) 64, 32, 16, 8 ...
2) Find the 500th number in this sequence: 2, 4, 6, 8, 10 ...
3) Find the nth term of these sequences: a) 4, 7, 10, 13 ...   b) 3, 8, 13, 18 ...

Functions

...ook a bit scary-mathsy, but a function is really just another way of writing an equation.
...ng an <u>equation</u> like <u>y = 5x + 2</u>, you can write a <u>function</u> like <u>f(x) = 5x + 2</u> or <u>f : x → 5x + 2</u>.

Functions Map Numbers from One Set to Another

1) The definition of a function is a <u>rule</u> that <u>maps</u> each number from a set called the <u>domain</u>, to <u>exactly one number</u> of a second set called the <u>range</u>.

2) The diagram on the right shows the function <u>f(x) = 12/x</u>.

3) Sometimes you have to <u>exclude</u> values from the domain.
   For f(x) = 12/x, x <u>can't be 0</u>, because dividing by zero is <u>undefined</u>.

   Watch out for functions containing square roots too. You can only find the square root of a positive number, so for f(x) = √(x − 2) you'd have to exclude x < 2.

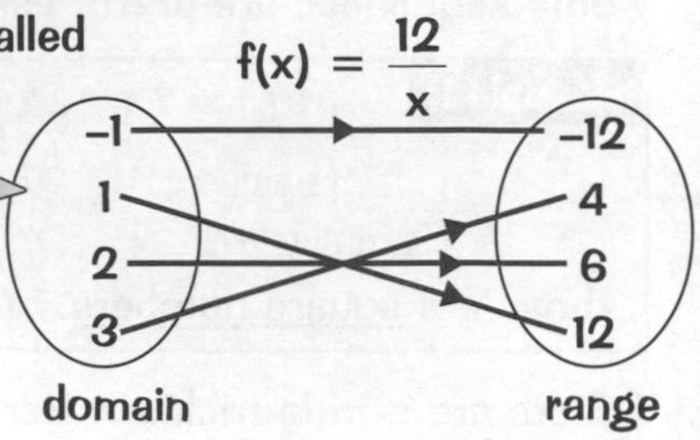

$$f(x) = \frac{12}{x}$$

−1 → −12
1 → 4
2 → 6
3 → 12

domain   range

Evaluating Functions

This is easy — just shove the numbers into the function and you're away.

> **EXAMPLE:** "If $f(x) = x^2 - x + 7$, find f(3)."
>
> **ANSWER:** $f(3) = 3^2 - 3 + 7 = 9 - 3 + 7 = \underline{13}$

Composite Functions

This is a bit more tricky. You might get a question with two functions, e.g. f(x) and g(x).
Then f(g(x)) and fg(x) both mean <u>exactly the same</u> — <u>replace</u> the <u>x</u> in f(x) with the <u>whole function</u> g(x).

> **EXAMPLE:** "If $f(x) = 2x - 10$ and $g(x) = -\dfrac{x}{2}$, find: a) fg(x) b) gf(x)."
>
> **ANSWER:** a) $fg(x) = f(-\dfrac{x}{2}) = 2(-\dfrac{x}{2}) - 10 = \underline{-x - 10}$
>
> b) $gf(x) = g(2x - 10) = -\left(\dfrac{2x - 10}{2}\right) = -(x - 5) = \underline{5 - x}$

Another way to think of this is that you have to do the function closest to x first. So for fg(x), you do g first, then f.

Inverse Functions

The <u>inverse</u> of a function f(x) is another function, f⁻¹(x), which <u>reverses</u> f(x).
Finding the inverse of a function is only slightly fiddly. Here's the <u>method</u>:

1) Write out the equation <u>x = f(y)</u>   f(y) is just the expression f(x), but with y's instead of x's

2) <u>Rearrange</u> the equation to <u>make y the subject</u>. This gives you the equation y = f⁻¹(x).

> **EXAMPLE:** "If $f(x) = \dfrac{12 + x}{3}$, find f⁻¹(x)."
>
> **ANSWER:** 1) Write out x = f(y): $x = \dfrac{12 + y}{3}$
>
> 2) Rearrange to make y the subject: $3x = 12 + y \Rightarrow y = 3x - 12$
>
> So $f^{-1}(x) = \underline{3x - 12}$

You can check your answer by seeing if f⁻¹(x) does reverse f(x): e.g. $f(9) = \dfrac{21}{3} = 7$, $f^{-1}(7) = 21 - 12 = 9$

This page has really put the 'fun' into 'functions'...

Sorry, that joke just had to be made. This is another topic where practice really does make perfect. Start here:

1) If $f(x) = 5x - 1$, $g(x) = 8 - 2x$ and $h(x) = x^2 + 3$, find:
   a) f(4)   b) h(−2)   c) gf(x)   d) fh(x)   e) gh(−3)   f) hf(2)   g) f⁻¹(x)   h) g⁻¹(f(x))

Travel Graphs

Ah, what could be better than a nice Distance-Time graph to kick things off? OK, so a picture of Keira Knightley might be better. Or Hugh Jackman. But the section isn't called 'Hollywood Hotties' is it...

1) Distance-Time Graphs

Just remember these 3 important points:

> 1) At any point, __GRADIENT = SPEED__, but watch out for the UNITS.
> 2) The __STEEPER__ the graph, the __FASTER__ it's going.
> 3) __FLAT SECTIONS__ are where it is __STOPPED__.

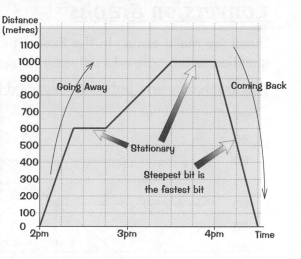

__EXAMPLE:__ "What is the speed of the return section on the graph shown?"

__ANSWER:__ Speed = gradient = 1000 m ÷ 30 mins = 33.33 __m/min__.
But m/min are naff units, so it's better to do it like this: 1 km ÷ 0.5 hrs = __2 km/h__

2) Speed-Time Graphs

A speed-time graph can __look__ just the same as a distance-time graph but it means something __completely different__. The graph shown here is exactly the same shape as the one above, but the actual motions are completely different.

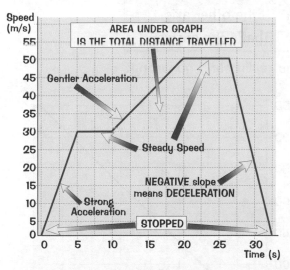

Remember these 4 important points:

> 1) At any point, __GRADIENT = ACCELERATION__, (The UNITS are m/s^2 don't forget).
> 2) __NEGATIVE SLOPE__ is __DECELERATION__.
> 3) __FLAT SECTIONS__ are __STEADY SPEED__.
> 4) __AREA UNDER GRAPH = DISTANCE TRAVELLED__

The D/T graph shows something __moving away__ and then __back again__ with __steady speeds__ and __long stops__, rather like an ocean liner. The __S/T graph__ on the other hand shows something that sets off from __rest__, __accelerates strongly__, __holds its speed__, then __accelerates__ again up to a __maximum speed__ which it holds for a while and then comes to a __dramatic halt__ at the end. More like a __Ferrari__ than an ocean liner...

Moan, moan, moan is all my slope ever does — he's just so negative...

It might not be the most exciting stuff, but it can be worth loads of marks in the Exam. Kerching. Learn the 7 important points and the two diagrams then turn over and write them all down. Then kick back with these...
1) For the D/T graph shown above, work out the speed of the middle section in km/h.
2) For the S/T graph, work out the three different accelerations and the two steady speeds.

Conversion Graphs

Yay, just what you wanted to see — some more graphs...

Conversion Graphs

These are really easy. In the Exam you're likely to get a Conversion Graph question which converts between things like £ → Dollars or mph → km/h, etc.

This graph converts between miles and kilometres

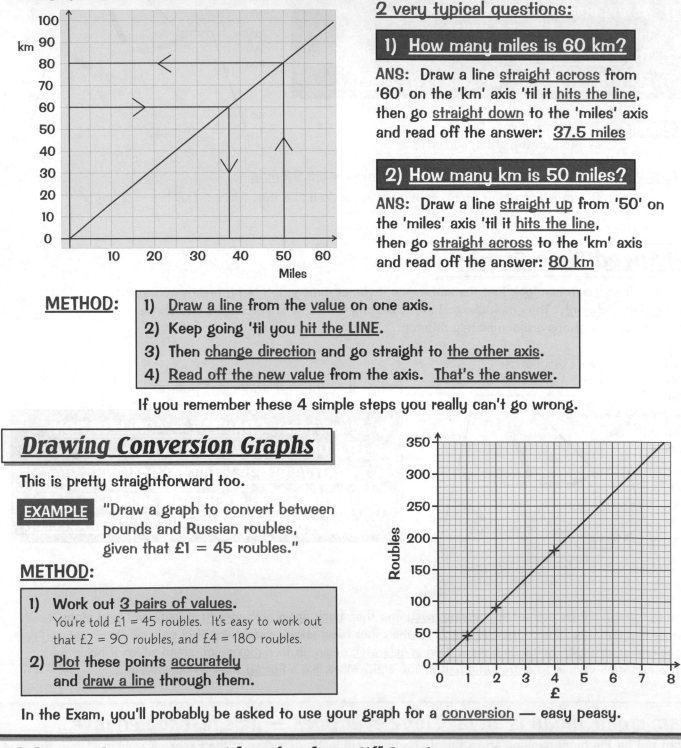

2 very typical questions:

1) How many miles is 60 km?

ANS: Draw a line <u>straight across</u> from '60' on the 'km' axis 'til it <u>hits the line</u>, then go <u>straight down</u> to the 'miles' axis and read off the answer: <u>37.5 miles</u>

2) How many km is 50 miles?

ANS: Draw a line <u>straight up</u> from '50' on the 'miles' axis 'til it <u>hits the line</u>, then go <u>straight across</u> to the 'km' axis and read off the answer: <u>80 km</u>

METHOD:
1) <u>Draw a line</u> from the <u>value</u> on one axis.
2) Keep going 'til you <u>hit the LINE</u>.
3) Then <u>change direction</u> and go straight to <u>the other axis</u>.
4) <u>Read off the new value</u> from the axis. <u>That's the answer</u>.

If you remember these 4 simple steps you really can't go wrong.

Drawing Conversion Graphs

This is pretty straightforward too.

EXAMPLE "Draw a graph to convert between pounds and Russian roubles, given that £1 = 45 roubles."

METHOD:

1) **Work out 3 pairs of values.**
You're told £1 = 45 roubles. It's easy to work out that £2 = 90 roubles, and £4 = 180 roubles.

2) **Plot these points accurately** and **draw a line** through them.

In the Exam, you'll probably be asked to use your graph for a <u>conversion</u> — easy peasy.

Right graph — we're not leaving here 'til I get some answers...

<u>Learn</u> the <u>2 simple methods above</u>. Then try these:
1) Use the conversion graph above to convert a) £3 to roubles, b) 300 roubles to pounds.

The Meaning of Area and Gradient

Ok, so it's not quite the meaning of life, but areas and gradients are still pretty darn useful...

The Area Under a Graph Represents the TOTAL SOMETHING

The secret here is the <u>unit</u> of the <u>vertical axis</u>, which will be a <u>RATE</u> of some sort,
i.e. '<u>SOMETHING per ANOTHER-THING</u>'.

To find the meaning of the area under the graph, all you do is remove the '<u>PER ANOTHER-THING</u>' from those units and the '<u>SOMETHING</u>' that's left is what the area under the graph represents.
The area is the '<u>TOTAL SOMETHING</u>' in fact.

Two Really Brilliant Examples:

1) If the vertical axis is <u>speed</u>, (measured in '<u>metres per second</u>'), then remove the 'per second' and the area must represent 'metres', or rather <u>total metres</u>, i.e. the <u>total distance travelled</u>.

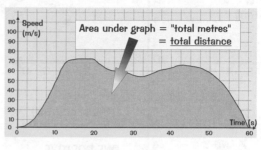

2) If the vertical axis was '<u>people per minute</u>' (entering a zoo, say), then remove the 'per minute' and the area under that graph would simply be <u>total people</u>.

(Easy peasy, don't you think?)

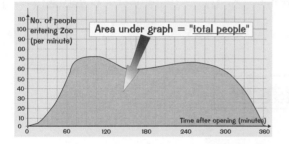

The Gradient of a Graph Represents the Rate

No matter what the graph may be, <u>the meaning of the gradient</u> is always simply:

(y-axis UNITS) PER (x-axis UNITS)

Once you've written 'something PER something' using the x- and y-axis <u>UNITS</u>, it's then pretty easy to work out what the gradient represents, as these four examples show.

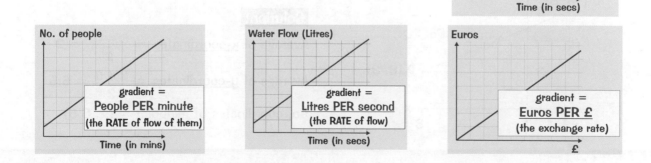

A rate that increases during revision — biscuits per hour...

Or so I'm told. I'm more of a Battenberg person myself. Make sure you learn <u>both</u> sections of this page, then produce a 4000 word essay on 'Area and Gradient — The Meaning'. If that seems <u>too extreme</u>, then try these:
1) On a graph of 'babies born per minute' vs 'time in minutes', what would the area represent?
2) If I drew a graph of 'kilometres travelled' up the y-axis and 'litres of fuel used' along the x-axis, and worked out the gradient, what would the value of it tell me?

Coordinates and Midpoints

What could be more fun than points in one quadrant? Points in <u>four quadrants</u> and <u>midpoints</u>, that's what...

The Four Quadrants

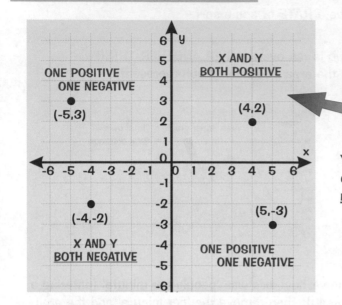

ONE POSITIVE ONE NEGATIVE (-5,3)

X AND Y BOTH POSITIVE (4,2)

(-4,-2) X AND Y BOTH NEGATIVE

(5,-3) ONE POSITIVE ONE NEGATIVE

A graph has <u>four different quadrants</u> (regions) where the x- and y- coordinates are either <u>positive</u> or <u>negative</u>.

This is the easiest region by far because here <u>all the coordinates are positive</u>.

You have to be careful in the <u>other regions</u> though, because either the x-coordinate, the y-coordinate or both will be <u>negative</u>, and that always makes life more difficult.

Coordinates are always written in brackets like this: (x, y) — remember x is <u>across</u>, and y is <u>up</u>.

Finding the Midpoint of a Line Segment

This regularly comes up in Exams and is really easy...

1) Find the <u>average</u> of the <u>two x-coordinates</u>, then do the same for the <u>y-coordinates</u>.
2) <u>These will be the coordinates of the midpoint.</u>

Example:

"Point P has coordinates (8, 3) and point Q has coordinates (-4, 8). Find the midpoint of the line PQ."

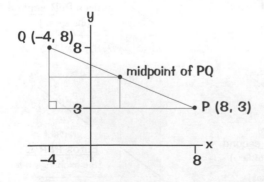

Q (-4, 8)
midpoint of PQ
P (8, 3)

Solution:

Average of <u>x-coordinates</u> $= \dfrac{8 + {}^{-}4}{2} = 2$

Average of <u>y-coordinates</u> $= \dfrac{8 + 3}{2} = 5.5$

So, coordinates of midpoint = (2, 5.5)

Plot some coordinates, or your graph will be pointless...

Learn how to find the <u>midpoint</u> of a <u>line segment</u> and use coordinates in <u>all four quadrants</u>.

1) Write down the coordinates of the points A to H on this graph:
2) Find the coordinates of the points exactly midway between:
   a) A and B   b) F and H   c) E and C
3) The points A, H and G are three corners of a parallelogram. What are the coordinates of the final corner of the parallelogram?

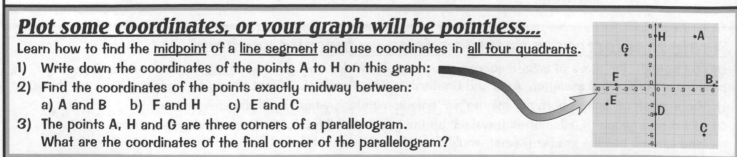

Straight Line Graphs

If you thought "I spy" was a fun game, wait 'til you play 'recognise the <u>straight line graph</u> from the <u>equation</u>'.

1) Horizontal and Vertical lines: 'x = a' and 'y = a'

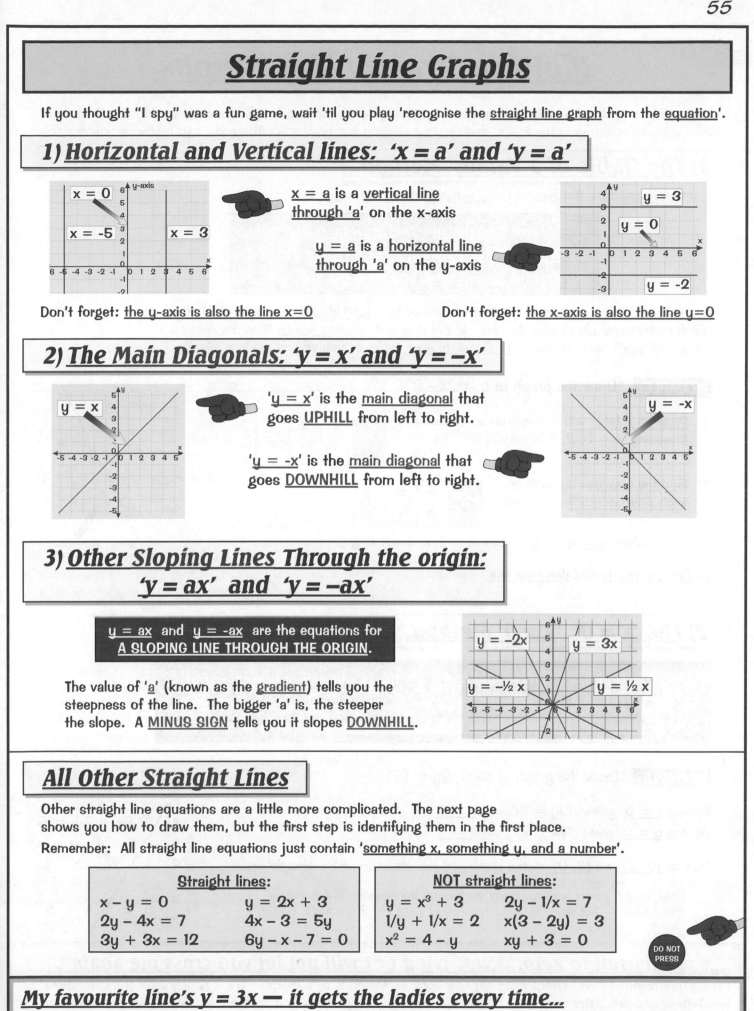

<u>x = a</u> is a <u>vertical line</u> through 'a' on the x-axis

<u>y = a</u> is a <u>horizontal line</u> through 'a' on the y-axis

Don't forget: <u>the y-axis is also the line x=0</u>

Don't forget: <u>the x-axis is also the line y=0</u>

2) The Main Diagonals; 'y = x' and 'y = –x'

'<u>y = x</u>' is the <u>main diagonal</u> that goes <u>UPHILL</u> from left to right.

'<u>y = -x</u>' is the <u>main diagonal</u> that goes <u>DOWNHILL</u> from left to right.

3) Other Sloping Lines Through the origin: 'y = ax' and 'y = –ax'

<u>y = ax</u> and <u>y = -ax</u> are the equations for **A SLOPING LINE THROUGH THE ORIGIN.**

The value of '<u>a</u>' (known as the <u>gradient</u>) tells you the steepness of the line. The bigger 'a' is, the steeper the slope. A <u>MINUS SIGN</u> tells you it slopes <u>DOWNHILL</u>.

All Other Straight Lines

Other straight line equations are a little more complicated. The next page shows you how to draw them, but the first step is identifying them in the first place.

Remember: All straight line equations just contain '<u>something x, something y, and a number</u>'.

<u>Straight lines:</u>		<u>NOT straight lines:</u>	
x – y = 0	y = 2x + 3	y = x³ + 3	2y – 1/x = 7
2y – 4x = 7	4x – 3 = 5y	1/y + 1/x = 2	x(3 – 2y) = 3
3y + 3x = 12	6y – x – 7 = 0	x² = 4 – y	xy + 3 = 0

DO NOT PRESS

My favourite line's y = 3x — it gets the ladies every time...

Ok, so I can't offer a guarantee with that. But it's still worth learning all the graphs on this page and how to identify straight line equations. Once you think you know it, turn over the page and try to write it all down.

Plotting Straight Line Graphs

Sadly, this isn't about a sinister gang of straight line graphs, plotting to take over the world. But then that isn't likely to come up in the Exam, and <u>drawing straight line graphs</u> is. There are <u>two</u> methods you can use:

1) The 'Table of 3 Values' Method

You can <u>easily</u> draw the graph of <u>any equation</u> using this <u>easy</u> method:

> 1) Choose <u>3 values of x</u> and <u>draw up a wee table</u>,
> 2) <u>Work out the y-values</u>,
> 3) <u>Plot the coordinates</u>, and <u>draw the line</u>.

If it's a <u>straight line equation</u>, the 3 points will be in a <u>dead straight line</u> with each other, which is the usual check you do when you've drawn it. <u>If they aren't</u>, then it's either a <u>curve</u> and you'll need to add <u>more values to your table</u>, or you've just made a <u>mistake</u>.

EXAMPLE: "Draw the graph of $y = 2x - 3$"

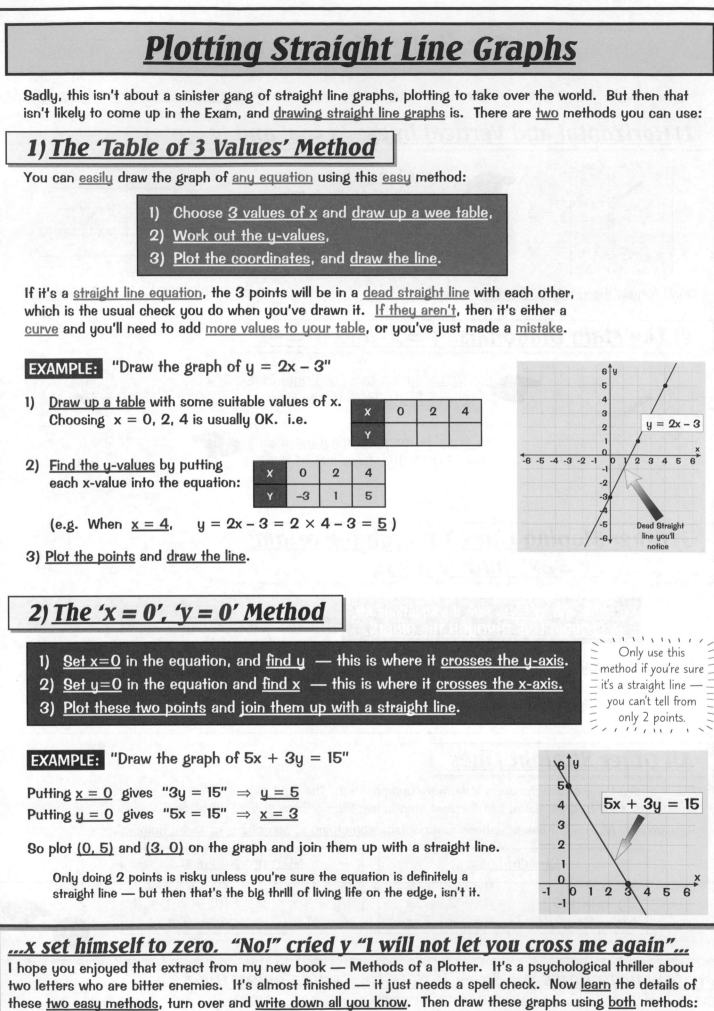

1) <u>Draw up a table</u> with some suitable values of x. Choosing x = 0, 2, 4 is usually OK. i.e.

x	0	2	4
Y			

2) <u>Find the y-values</u> by putting each x-value into the equation:

x	0	2	4
Y	−3	1	5

(e.g. When <u>x = 4</u>, $y = 2x - 3 = 2 \times 4 - 3 = \underline{5}$)

3) <u>Plot the points</u> and <u>draw the line</u>.

$y = 2x - 3$

Dead Straight line you'll notice

2) The 'x = 0', 'y = 0' Method

> 1) <u>Set x=0</u> in the equation, and <u>find y</u> — this is where it <u>crosses the y-axis</u>.
> 2) <u>Set y=0</u> in the equation and <u>find x</u> — this is where it <u>crosses the x-axis</u>.
> 3) <u>Plot these two points</u> and <u>join them up with a straight line</u>.

Only use this method if you're sure it's a straight line — you can't tell from only 2 points.

EXAMPLE: "Draw the graph of $5x + 3y = 15$"

Putting <u>x = 0</u> gives "$3y = 15$" $\Rightarrow$ <u>y = 5</u>
Putting <u>y = 0</u> gives "$5x = 15$" $\Rightarrow$ <u>x = 3</u>

So plot <u>(0, 5)</u> and <u>(3, 0)</u> on the graph and join them up with a straight line.

Only doing 2 points is risky unless you're sure the equation is definitely a straight line — but then that's the big thrill of living life on the edge, isn't it.

$5x + 3y = 15$

...x set himself to zero. "No!" cried y "I will not let you cross me again"...

I hope you enjoyed that extract from my new book — Methods of a Plotter. It's a psychological thriller about two letters who are bitter enemies. It's almost finished — it just needs a spell check. Now <u>learn</u> the details of these <u>two easy methods</u>, turn over and <u>write down all you know</u>. Then draw these graphs using <u>both</u> methods:
a) $y = 4 + x$ b) $4y + 3x = 12$ c) $y = 6 - 2x$

Finding the Gradient

Time to hit the slopes. Well, find them anyway...

Finding the Gradient

1) Find <u>TWO ACCURATE POINTS</u> and <u>COMPLETE THE TRIANGLE</u>

   Both points should be in the <u>upper right quadrant</u> if possible (to keep all the numbers positive).

2) Find the <u>CHANGE IN Y</u> and the <u>CHANGE IN X</u>

3) <u>LEARN</u> this formula, and use it:

   GRADIENT = CHANGE IN Y / CHANGE IN X

4) Check the <u>SIGN'S</u> right.

   If it slopes <u>UPHILL</u> left → right (⁄) <u>then it's positive</u>
   If it slopes <u>DOWNHILL</u> left → right (＼) <u>then it's negative</u>

① Two accurate Points — Change in y — Change in x

② Change in y = 50 – 10 = <u>40</u>
   Change in x = 8 – 1 = <u>7</u>

③ Gradient = $\frac{40}{7}$ = <u>5.7</u>

④ As the graph goes <u>UPHILL</u>, the gradient is positive. So <u>5.7 is correct</u>, not -5.7

Finding the Gradient from Coordinates

1) You can work out the gradient from just the <u>coordinates of two points</u> (you don't need to draw the graph).

2) Just find the <u>difference between the y-coordinates</u> and divide by the difference between the <u>x-coordinates</u>.

3) E.g. if the points (5, 2) and (3, 6) lie on a line:

   Gradient of line = $\frac{\text{change in y}}{\text{change in x}} = \frac{6-2}{3-5} = \frac{4}{-2} = \underline{-2}$

   Make sure you subtract the x coords the <u>same way round</u> as you do the y coords. E.g. y coord. of pt A − y coord. of pt B <u>and</u> x coord of pt A − x coord of pt B

Parallel Lines

1) The equation of a straight line is <u>y = mx + c</u> (see next page) where <u>m</u> is the <u>gradient</u> and c is the y-intercept.

2) Parallel lines have the <u>same value of m</u>, i.e. the <u>same gradient</u>. So the lines: y = 2x + 3, y = 2x and y = 2x – 4 are all parallel.

y = 2x + 3   y = 2x   y = 2x – 4

Gradients in Real Life

You do this in pretty much the same way —

GRADIENT = VERTICAL CHANGE / HORIZONTAL CHANGE

EXAMPLE:

"A ramp has a 1.25 m rise over a horizontal distance of 5 m. Calculate its gradient."

gradient = $\frac{\text{vertical change}}{\text{horizontal change}} = \frac{1.25\,\text{m}}{5\,\text{m}} = 0.25$

Finding gradients is often an uphill battle...

Learn the <u>four steps</u> for finding a gradient then <u>turn over</u> and <u>write them down</u> from memory. Fun times ahoy.

1) Plot these 3 points on a graph: (0,3) (2,0) (5,-4.5) and then join them up with a straight line. Now carefully apply the <u>four steps</u> to find the gradient of the line.

Higher

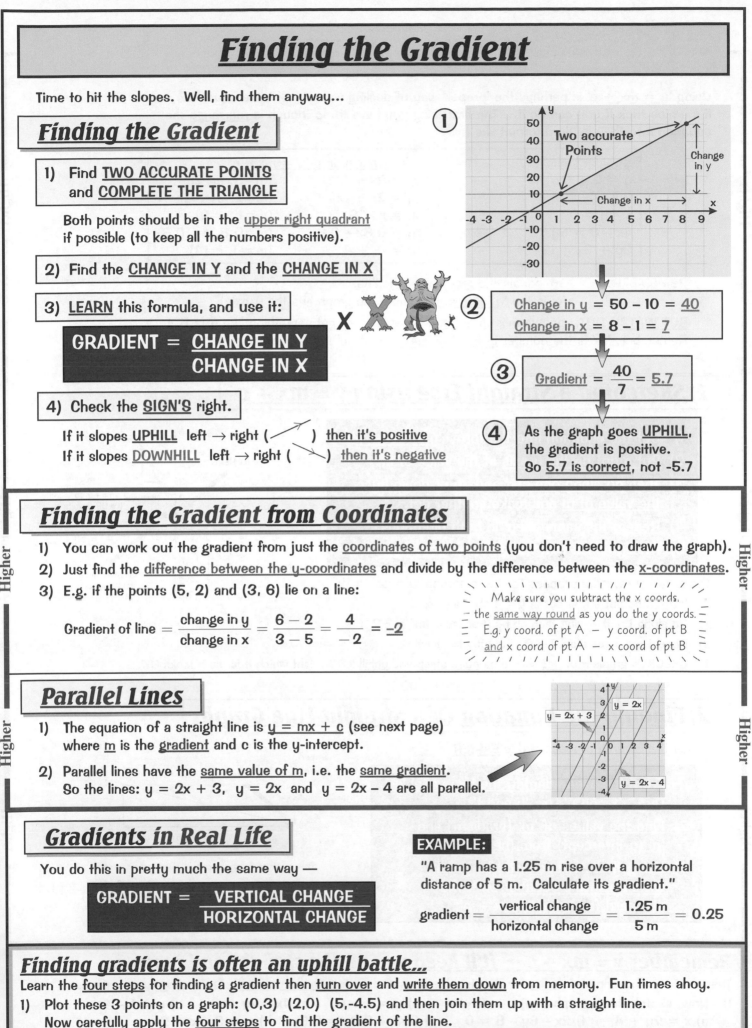

"y = mx + c"

Using 'y = mx + c' is perhaps the 'proper' way of dealing with straight line equations, and it's a nice trick if you can do it. The first thing you have to do though is <u>rearrange</u> the equation into the standard format like this:

Straight line:		Rearranged into 'y = mx + c'	
y = 2 + 3x	→	y = 3x + 2	(m=3, c=2)
2y – 4x = 7	→	y = 2x + 3½	(m=2, c=3½)
x – y = 0	→	y = x + 0	(m=1, c=0)
4x – 3 = 5y	→	y = 0.8x – 0.6	(m=0.8, c=-0.6)
3y + 3x = 12	→	y = -x + 4	(m=-1, c=4)

<u>REMEMBER</u>:   '<u>m</u>' equals the <u>gradient</u> of the line.

                    '<u>c</u>' is the '<u>y-intercept</u>' (where the graph hits the y-axis).

<u>BUT WATCH OUT</u>: people mix up 'm' and 'c' when they get something like y = 5 + 2x. Remember, 'm' is the number <u>in front of the 'x'</u> and 'c' is the number <u>on its own</u>.

1) Sketching a Straight Line using y = mx + c

1) Get the equation into the form '<u>y = mx + c</u>'.
2) <u>Put a dot on the y-axis</u> at the value of c.
3) Then go <u>along one unit</u> and <u>up or down by the value of m</u> and make another dot.
4) <u>Repeat</u> the same 'step' in <u>both directions</u>.
5) Finally check that the gradient <u>looks right</u>.

The graph shows the process for the equation 'y = 2x + 1':

1) 'c' = 1, so put a first dot at y = 1 on the y-axis.
2) Go along 1 unit → and then up by 2 because 'm' = +2.
3) Repeat the same step, 1→ 2↑ in both directions.
4) CHECK: a gradient of +2 should be <u>quite steep</u> and <u>uphill</u> left to right which it is, so it looks OK.

2) Finding the Equation Of a Straight Line Graph

This is the reverse process and is <u>EASIER</u>.

1) From the axes, <u>identify the two variables</u> (e.g. 'x and y' or 'h and t').
2) <u>Find the values</u> of '<u>m</u>' (gradient) and '<u>c</u>' (y-intercept) from the graph.
3) Using these values from the graph, <u>write down the equation</u> with the standard format 'y = mx + c'.

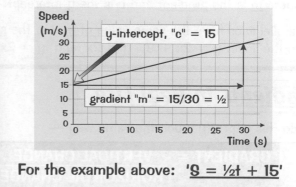

For the example above: '<u>S</u> = ½t + 15'

Remember y = mx + c — it'll keep you on the straight and narrow...

That, and remembering the <u>rules</u> for <u>drawing the lines</u> and <u>finding the equations</u>. And eating your greens.

1) Now, sketch these graphs: a) y = 2 + x   b) y = x + 6   c) 4x – 2y = 0   d) y = 1 – ½x
     e) x = 2y + 4   f) 2x – 6y – 8 = 0   g) 0.4x – 0.2y = 0.5   h) y = 3 – x + 2

Quadratic Graphs

Quadratic functions can sound pretty darn impressive — "What did you do in maths today, dear?", "Drawing quadratic functions and solving them graphically, mum." Have no fear, with a bit of practice you too can sound this... er... cool, as well as picking up lots of marks in your exams.

Plotting and Solving Quadratic Functions

Quadratic functions are of the form y = anything with x² (but not higher powers of x).
Notice that all these x² graphs have the same __SYMMETRICAL__ bucket shape.

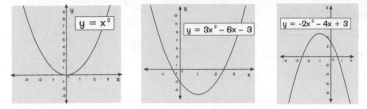

So when you plot a quadratic, remember that you're aiming for a __symmetrical bucket shape__ — anything else is a sure sign that you've gone wrong. Here's how to tackle questions on quadratics.

1) Fill in The Table of Values

__Example__ "Complete this table of values for the equation y = x² + 2x – 3 and draw the graph."

x	-5	-4	-3	-2	-1	0	1	2	3
y		5		-3	-4	-3	0		

x	-5	-4	-3	-2	-1	0	1	2	3
y	12	5	0	-3	-4	-3	0	5	12

Work out each point __very carefully__, writing down all your working. Don't just plug it all straight in your calculator — you'll make mistakes. To check you're __doing it right__, make sure you can __reproduce__ the y-values they've already given you.

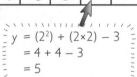

$$y = (2^2) + (2 \times 2) - 3$$
$$= 4 + 4 - 3$$
$$= 5$$

2) Draw the Curve

1) __PLOT THE POINTS CAREFULLY__, and don't mix up the x and y values.

2) The points should form a __COMPLETELY SMOOTH CURVE__. If they don't, they're __wrong__.

   __NEVER EVER__ let one point drag your line off in some ridiculous direction. When a graph is generated from an equation, you never get spikes or lumps — only __MISTAKES__.

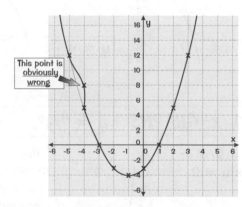

This point is obviously wrong

3) Read off the Solutions

__Example__ "Use your graph to solve the equation x² + 2x – 3 = 0."

1) Look — the equation you've been asked to solve is what you get when you put y=0 into the graph's equation, y = x² + 2x – 3.

2) To solve the equation, all you do is read the x-values where y = 0, i.e. where it crosses the x-axis.

3) So the solutions are __x = -3__ and __x = 1__. (Quadratic eqns usually have 2 solutions.)

4) Celebrate the only way graphs know how: line dancing.

How refreshing — a page on graphs. Not seen one of those in a while...

You know the deal by now — learn what's on this page, then treat yourself to answering the question below.
1) Plot the graph of y = x² – x – 6 (use x-values from -4 to 5).
   Use your graph to solve the equation x² – x – 6 = 0.

Higher

Some Harder Graphs to Learn

Graphs come in all sorts of shapes, sizes and wiggles — here are some more types you need to know:

1) 1/x GRAPHS: $y = \frac{A}{x}$, or $xy = A$ (A is any number — positive or negative)

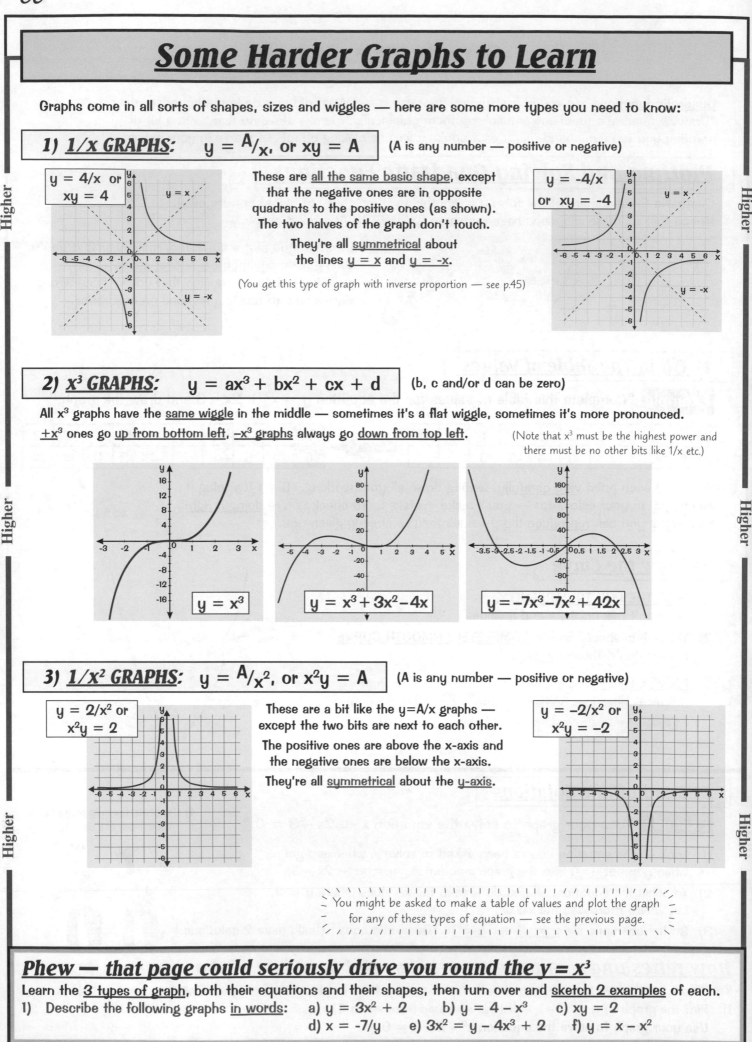

$y = 4/x$ or $xy = 4$

These are <u>all the same basic shape</u>, except that the negative ones are in opposite quadrants to the positive ones (as shown). The two halves of the graph don't touch.

They're all <u>symmetrical</u> about the lines <u>y = x</u> and <u>y = -x</u>.

(You get this type of graph with inverse proportion — see p.45)

$y = -4/x$ or $xy = -4$

2) x³ GRAPHS: $y = ax^3 + bx^2 + cx + d$ (b, c and/or d can be zero)

All x^3 graphs have the <u>same wiggle</u> in the middle — sometimes it's a flat wiggle, sometimes it's more pronounced.
$+x^3$ ones go <u>up from bottom left</u>, $-x^3$ graphs always go <u>down from top left</u>.

(Note that x^3 must be the highest power and there must be no other bits like 1/x etc.)

$y = x^3$

$y = x^3 + 3x^2 - 4x$

$y = -7x^3 - 7x^2 + 42x$

3) 1/x² GRAPHS: $y = \frac{A}{x^2}$, or $x^2 y = A$ (A is any number — positive or negative)

$y = 2/x^2$ or $x^2 y = 2$

These are a bit like the y=A/x graphs — except the two bits are next to each other.

The positive ones are above the x-axis and the negative ones are below the x-axis.

They're all <u>symmetrical</u> about the <u>y-axis</u>.

$y = -2/x^2$ or $x^2 y = -2$

You might be asked to make a table of values and plot the graph for any of these types of equation — see the previous page.

Phew — that page could seriously drive you round the y = x³

Learn the <u>3 types of graph</u>, both their equations and their shapes, then turn over and <u>sketch 2 examples</u> of each.

1) Describe the following graphs <u>in words</u>:   a) $y = 3x^2 + 2$ b) $y = 4 - x^3$ c) $xy = 2$
   d) $x = -7/y$ e) $3x^2 = y - 4x^3 + 2$ f) $y = x - x^2$

Differentiation

Differentiation looks like a bad one — it really does. Scary name, scary formula and all that.
But once you've learned it, it's not *that* difficult.

This means 'the result of differentiating the thing in the brackets'.

$$\frac{d}{dx}(x^n) = nx^{n-1}$$

If $y = x^n$, then you write: $\frac{dy}{dx}$

Use this Formula to Differentiate Powers of x

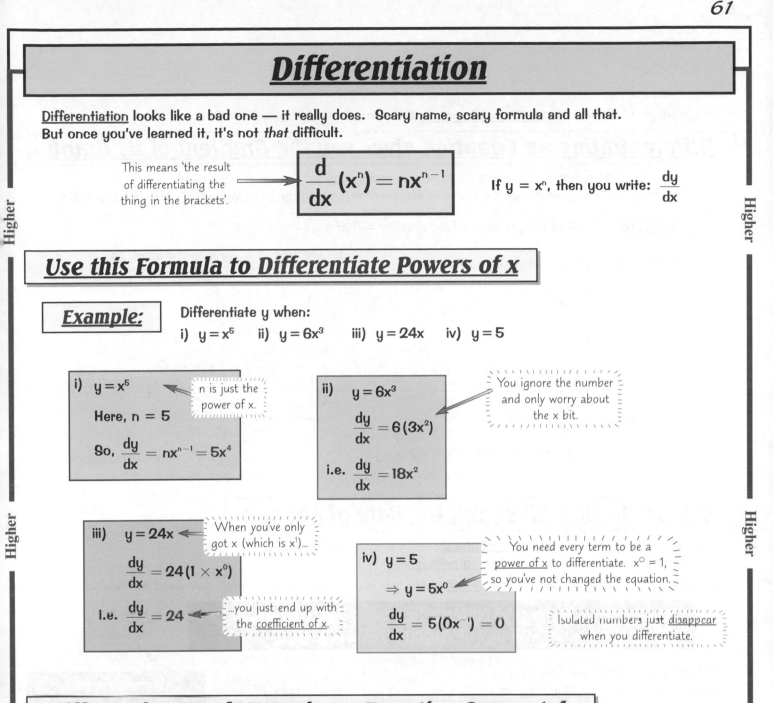

Example:

Differentiate y when:

i) $y = x^5$ ii) $y = 6x^3$ iii) $y = 24x$ iv) $y = 5$

i) $y = x^5$

    n is just the power of x.

Here, $n = 5$

So, $\frac{dy}{dx} = nx^{n-1} = 5x^4$

ii) $y = 6x^3$

    You ignore the number and only worry about the x bit.

$\frac{dy}{dx} = 6(3x^2)$

i.e. $\frac{dy}{dx} = 18x^2$

iii) $y = 24x$

    When you've only got x (which is x^1)...

$\frac{dy}{dx} = 24(1 \times x^0)$

I.e. $\frac{dy}{dx} = 24$

    ...you just end up with the coefficient of x.

iv) $y = 5$

    You need every term to be a power of x to differentiate. $x^0 = 1$, so you've not changed the equation.

$\Rightarrow y = 5x^0$

$\frac{dy}{dx} = 5(0x^{-1}) = 0$

    Isolated numbers just disappear when you differentiate.

Differentiate Each Term in an Equation Separately

Even if there are loads of terms in the equation, it doesn't matter.
Differentiate each bit separately and you'll be fine.

Example:

"Differentiate: $y = 6x^4 + 4x^3 - 2x + 1$."

$$\frac{dy}{dx} = 6(4x^3) + 4(3x^2) - 2(1x^0) + 0$$
$$= 24x^3 + 12x^2 - 2$$

Differentiate yourself from the crowd — wear your clothes backwards...

Luckily, once you can do the simple stuff, you should be all right. Longer equations are just made up of simple little terms, so they're not really that much harder. Learn the formula, and make sure you can use it by practising all day and all night forever. Then try these:

1) Differentiate   a) x^2 b) $y = 4x^3$ c) $y = 2$ d) $y = 3x^2 + 2$ e) $y = 4x - x^3$

Differentiation

The gradient of a curve is <u>constantly changing</u>. Differentiation helps you find what it is at any point.

Differentiating an Equation gives you the Gradient of its Graph

<u>Differentiating</u> the equation of a curve gives you an <u>expression</u> for the curve's gradient.
Then you can find the gradient of the curve at any point by <u>substituting the value for x</u> into the expression.

Example: *"Find the gradient of the graph $y = x^2$ at $x = 1$ and $x = -2$."*

<u>Differentiate</u> to get the gradient expression:

$$y = x^2 \Rightarrow \frac{dy}{dx} = 2x$$

Now when <u>x = 1</u>, $\frac{dy}{dx} = 2 \times 1 = 2$

So the gradient at $x = 1$ is <u>2</u>.

And when <u>x = -2</u>, $\frac{dy}{dx} = 2 \times -2 = -4$

So the gradient at $x = -2$ is <u>-4</u>.

The gradient of a <u>curve</u> is the same as
the gradient of the <u>tangent</u> at that point.

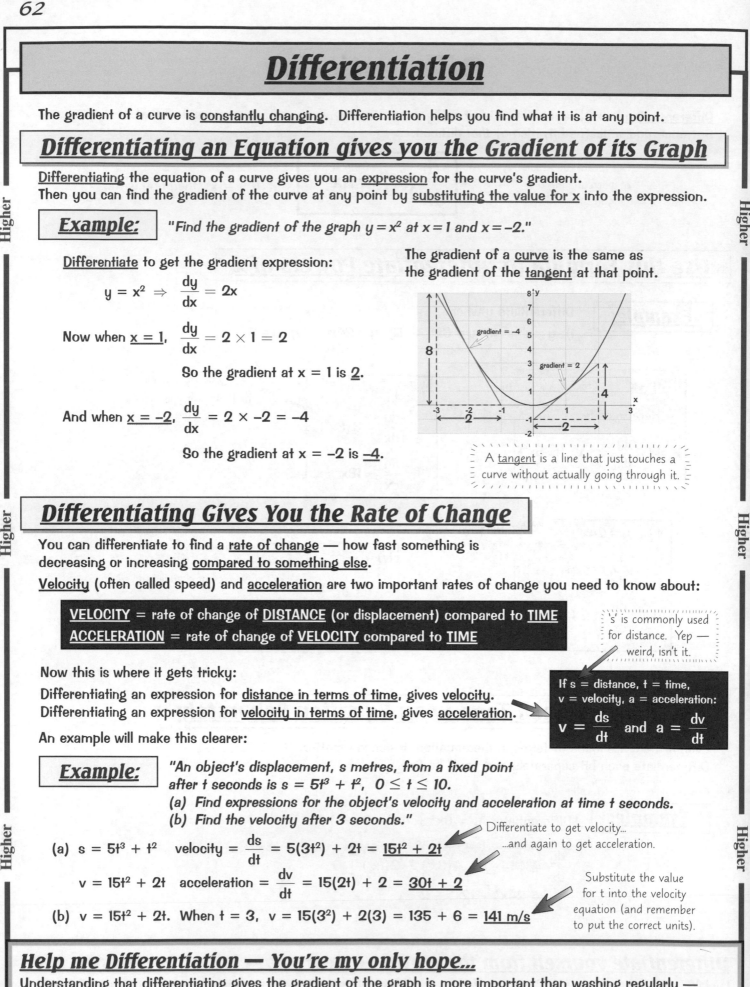

gradient = -4

gradient = 2

A <u>tangent</u> is a line that just touches a
curve without actually going through it.

Differentiating Gives You the Rate of Change

You can differentiate to find a <u>rate of change</u> — how fast something is
decreasing or increasing <u>compared to something else</u>.

<u>Velocity</u> (often called speed) and <u>acceleration</u> are two important rates of change you need to know about:

> **VELOCITY** = rate of change of <u>**DISTANCE**</u> (or displacement) compared to <u>**TIME**</u>
> **ACCELERATION** = rate of change of <u>**VELOCITY**</u> compared to <u>**TIME**</u>

Now this is where it gets tricky:

Differentiating an expression for <u>distance in terms of time</u>, gives <u>velocity</u>.
Differentiating an expression for <u>velocity in terms of time</u>, gives <u>acceleration</u>.

An example will make this clearer:

's' is commonly used
for distance. Yep —
weird, isn't it.

If s = distance, t = time,
v = velocity, a = acceleration:

$$v = \frac{ds}{dt} \quad \text{and} \quad a = \frac{dv}{dt}$$

Example: *"An object's displacement, s metres, from a fixed point
after t seconds is $s = 5t^3 + t^2$, $0 \leq t \leq 10$.
(a) Find expressions for the object's velocity and acceleration at time t seconds.
(b) Find the velocity after 3 seconds."*

(a) $s = 5t^3 + t^2$ velocity $= \frac{ds}{dt} = 5(3t^2) + 2t = \underline{15t^2 + 2t}$

$v = 15t^2 + 2t$ acceleration $= \frac{dv}{dt} = 15(2t) + 2 = \underline{30t + 2}$

(b) $v = 15t^2 + 2t$. When $t = 3$, $v = 15(3^2) + 2(3) = 135 + 6 = \underline{141 \text{ m/s}}$

Differentiate to get velocity...
...and again to get acceleration.

Substitute the value
for t into the velocity
equation (and remember
to put the correct units).

Help me Differentiation — You're my only hope...

Understanding that differentiating gives the gradient of the graph is more important than washing regularly —
and that's important. Now try these:
1) Find the gradient of the graph of $y = 6x^4 + 2x^3$ when $x = 2$.
2) If distance, $s = 3t(t^2 + t)$, where t = time, find expressions for velocity and acceleration.

Differentiation

Some graphs have <u>turning points</u> — places where the graph 'levels off' before going in the opposite direction.

Turning Points are when the Gradient is Zero

A turning point can be a <u>maximum</u> or a <u>minimum</u>
But whatever the type, the important thing to remember is that:

> Turning points have a gradient of <u>ZERO</u>.

So to find the turning points of a graph, you need to find the points where:

$$\frac{dy}{dx} = 0$$

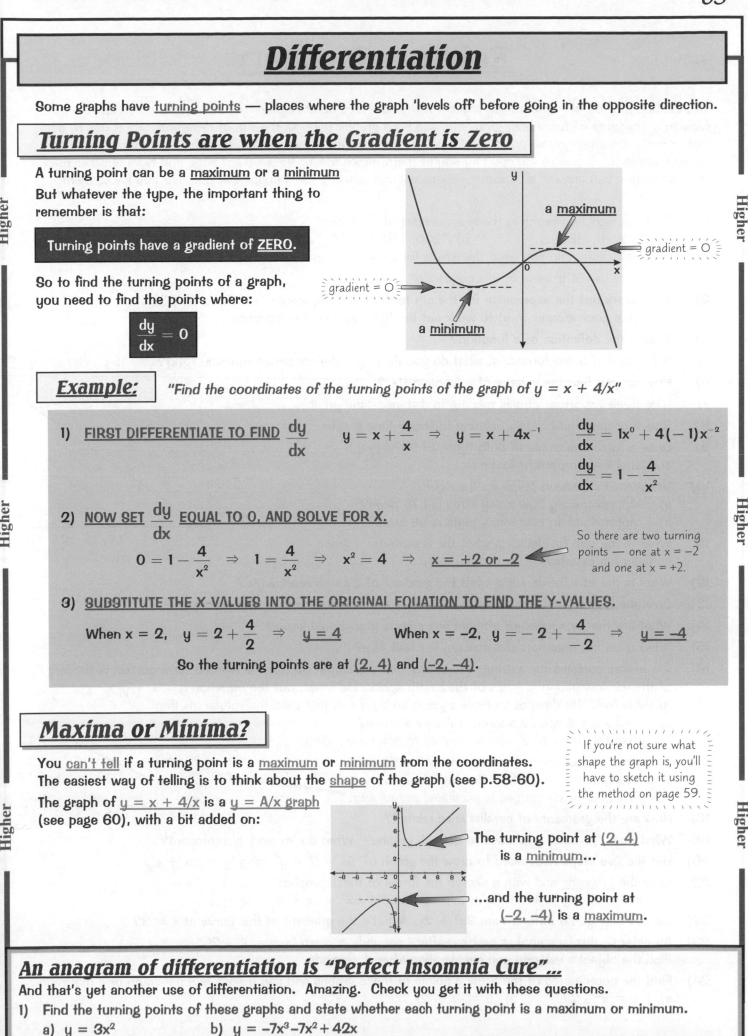

a <u>maximum</u>

gradient = 0

gradient = 0

a <u>minimum</u>

Example:
"Find the coordinates of the turning points of the graph of y = x + 4/x"

1) **FIRST DIFFERENTIATE TO FIND** $\frac{dy}{dx}$

$y = x + \dfrac{4}{x} \Rightarrow y = x + 4x^{-1}$

$\dfrac{dy}{dx} = 1x^0 + 4(-1)x^{-2}$

$\dfrac{dy}{dx} = 1 - \dfrac{4}{x^2}$

2) **NOW SET** $\frac{dy}{dx}$ **EQUAL TO 0, AND SOLVE FOR X.**

$0 = 1 - \dfrac{4}{x^2} \Rightarrow 1 = \dfrac{4}{x^2} \Rightarrow x^2 = 4 \Rightarrow \underline{x = +2 \text{ or } -2}$

So there are two turning points — one at x = −2 and one at x = +2.

3) **SUBSTITUTE THE X-VALUES INTO THE ORIGINAL EQUATION TO FIND THE Y-VALUES.**

When x = 2, $y = 2 + \dfrac{4}{2} \Rightarrow \underline{y = 4}$ When x = −2, $y = -2 + \dfrac{4}{-2} \Rightarrow \underline{y = -4}$

So the turning points are at <u>(2, 4)</u> and <u>(−2, −4)</u>.

Maxima or Minima?

You <u>can't tell</u> if a turning point is a <u>maximum</u> or <u>minimum</u> from the coordinates.
The easiest way of telling is to think about the <u>shape</u> of the graph (see p.58-60).

The graph of <u>y = x + 4/x</u> is a <u>y = A/x graph</u> (see page 60), with a bit added on:

If you're not sure what shape the graph is, you'll have to sketch it using the method on page 59.

The turning point at <u>(2, 4)</u> is a <u>minimum</u>...

...and the turning point at <u>(−2, −4)</u> is a <u>maximum</u>.

An anagram of differentiation is "Perfect Insomnia Cure"...

And that's yet another use of differentiation. Amazing. Check you get it with these questions.

1) Find the turning points of these graphs and state whether each turning point is a maximum or minimum.
   a) $y = 3x^2$ b) $y = -7x^3 - 7x^2 + 42x$

<u>Revision Summary</u>

This section started off reassuringly enough with some nice number patterns, but before much longer, you were in a quagmire of functions, gradients, and hard graphs (plus all the fun of differentiation if you're doing higher tier). So after you've got over all that, it's time to get the adrenaline pumping again by trying these lovely questions. If you're stumped by any of them, flick back to the relevant page and have another read. Only when you can answer all these questions without pausing for thought can you say you know them.

1) Find the next two terms in these sequences of numbers:
   a) 3, 7, 11, 15, ...   b) 1200, 600, 300, ...   c) 2, 5, 7, 12, 19, ...
   For each sequence, say what the rule is for extending the pattern.

2) Work out the 50th term in this sequence: 1, 5, 9, 13, ...

3) a) Work out the expression for the nth term in this sequence: –1, 5, 11, 17, 23, ...
   b) Use your answer to a) to work out the <u>10th term</u> in the sequence.

4) What's the definition of a function?

5) If f(x) and g(x) are functions, what do you do to get the combined function fg(x)?

6) How do you find the inverse of a function f(x)?

7) Give three important details relating to distance-time graphs.

8) Give four important details relating to speed-time graphs.

9) Draw a typical example of both types of travel graph and label their important features.

10) Using the conversion graph on the right:
    a) Approximately how many litres is 1.75 pints?
    b) Approximately how many pints is 1.6 litres?

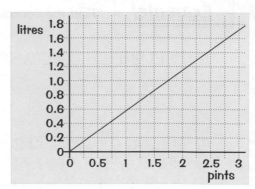

11) What is the rule for deciding what the area under a graph actually represents?

12) What is the rule for deciding what the gradient of a graph represents?

13) Describe how to find the midpoint of a line, given the coordinates of the endpoints.

14) What are the four types of straight line graphs you should know?

15) What does the equation of a straight line look like?

16) Joe makes curtains for a living. He knows that the length of material needed for a curtain is the length of the window plus one tenth of the length again. He works out the equation $y = x + \frac{1}{10}x$, to show this. He decides to draw a graph so staff can just read the values off that.
    a) Will Joe's graph be a straight line or a curve?
    b) Use the 'table of 3 values' method to draw Joe's graph.

17) Sarah has carried out an experiment to find the rate of photosynthesis at 30 °C. Use her graph to calculate how much oxygen is produced per minute.

18) How are the gradients of parallel lines related?

19) What does 'y = mx + c' have to do with graphs? What do 'm' and 'c' represent?

20) List the five steps necessary to draw the graph of '5x = 2 + y' using 'y = mx + c'.

21) Describe <u>in words</u> and with a sketch the forms of these graphs:
    $y = mx + c$; $y = ax^2 + bx + c$; $y = ax^3 + bx^2 + cx + d$; $xy = a$

22) Explain how you'd differentiate $3x^5 + 2x$. What's the gradient of this curve at x = 3?

23) An object's displacement, s metres, after t seconds is given by $s = t^2 - 2t$.
    Find the object's velocity and acceleration after 4 seconds.

24) Find the coordinates of the turning points of these graphs and say if each is a minimum or a maximum.
    a) $y = x^2 - 2x$ b) $y = -x^2 - 2x$

Maps and Scale Drawings

If maps were the same size as the place they were showing, then they'd be big... and a bit pointless. Thankfully maps are usually made using <u>scales</u>. The most usual map scale is '<u>1 cm = so many km</u>'. This just tells you <u>how many km in real life</u> it is for <u>1 cm measured on the map</u>.

1) Converting 'cm on a Map' into 'Real km'

This map shows the original Roman M6 Motorway built by the Emperor Hadrian in the year AD 120.

<u>Example:</u>

"The scale of the map is '1 cm to 12 000 m'
Work out the length of the section of M6 between Wigan and Preston."

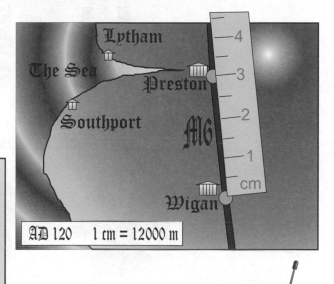

AD 120   1 cm = 12000 m

This is what you do:

1) <u>MEASURE</u> the distance on the map.
   The distance is 3 cm.

2) Use the 3-step <u>CONVERSION FACTOR METHOD</u> from page 21 to convert the distance.

   • Conversion Factor = 12 000

   • 3 cm × 12 000 = 36 000 m (looks OK)
     3 cm ÷ 12 000 = 0.00025 m (not good)

   • So <u>36 000 m</u> (or 36 km) is the answer.

Picture of 80's mobile.
Scale: 1 cm = 3.6 km

2) Converting 'Real m' into 'cm on a drawing'

Instead of a map, you might get a question about a <u>plan</u> in your Exam — like a plan of someone's <u>bedroom</u> or a <u>garden</u>. You do them in just the <u>same way</u>.

<u>Example:</u>

"A plan of a garden is being drawn at a scale of 1:50. If the patio is 4 metres wide, how wide should it be drawn on the plan?"

A scale of 1:50 means both units are the same. So it's 1 cm to 50 cm, or 1 m to 50 m.

<u>Answer:</u>

Use the 3-step <u>CONVERSION FACTOR METHOD</u> again:

• Conversion Factor = 50

• 4 m × 50 = 200 m (not good — bigger than in real life)
  4 m ÷ 50 = 0.08 m (looks OK)

• So <u>0.08 m</u> (or 8 cm) is the answer.

You might even be asked to <u>draw</u> something on a plan — just use the <u>method above</u> to work out how <u>big</u> it should be on the plan, then draw it <u>accurately</u>.

Symmetry

After you've finished this page, remind me that I need to pop out and buy some milk. There'll be none left for my breakfast otherwise. Anyway, sorry, symmetry... Right, yes, there are <u>TWO types</u> coming up:

1) Line Symmetry

This is where you can draw a <u>MIRROR LINE</u> (or more than one) across a picture and both sides will <u>fold exactly</u> together.

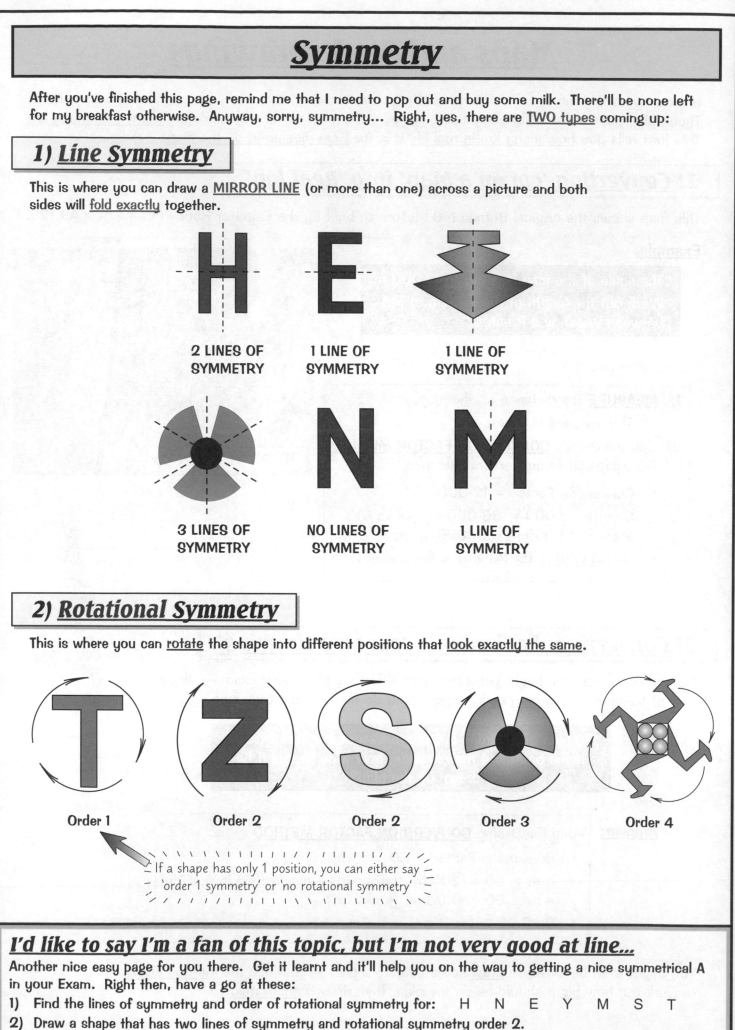

2 LINES OF SYMMETRY   **1 LINE OF SYMMETRY**   **1 LINE OF SYMMETRY**

3 LINES OF SYMMETRY   **NO LINES OF SYMMETRY**   **1 LINE OF SYMMETRY**

2) Rotational Symmetry

This is where you can <u>rotate</u> the shape into different positions that <u>look exactly the same</u>.

Order 1   Order 2   Order 2   Order 3   Order 4

If a shape has only 1 position, you can either say 'order 1 symmetry' or 'no rotational symmetry'

I'd like to say I'm a fan of this topic, but I'm not very good at line...

Another nice easy page for you there. Get it learnt and it'll help you on the way to getting a nice symmetrical A in your Exam. Right then, have a go at these:

1) Find the lines of symmetry and order of rotational symmetry for: H N E Y M S T
2) Draw a shape that has two lines of symmetry and rotational symmetry order 2.

The Shapes You Need to Know

Three-sided Shapes — Triangles
(just in case you didn't know...)

1) EQUILATERAL Triangle

60° 60° 60°

3 lines of symmetry.
Rotational symmetry order 3

2) RIGHT-ANGLED Triangle

No symmetry
(unless the other angles are 45°)

3) ISOSCELES Triangle

2 sides equal
2 angles equal

1 line of symmetry.
No rotational symmetry

Four-sided Shapes — Quadrilaterals

1) SQUARE

4 lines of symmetry.
Rotational symmetry order 4.

2) RECTANGLE

2 lines of symmetry.
Rotational symmetry order 2.

3) RHOMBUS (A square pushed over — so all sides are equal lengths)
(It's also a diamond)

2 lines of symmetry.
Rotational symmetry order 2.

4) PARALLELOGRAM
(A rectangle pushed over — two pairs of parallel sides of equal length)

NO lines of symmetry.
Rotational symmetry order 2.

5) TRAPEZIUM (One pair of parallel sides)

Only the isosceles trapezium has a line of symmetry.
None have rotational symmetry.

6) KITE

1 line of symmetry.
No rotational symmetry.

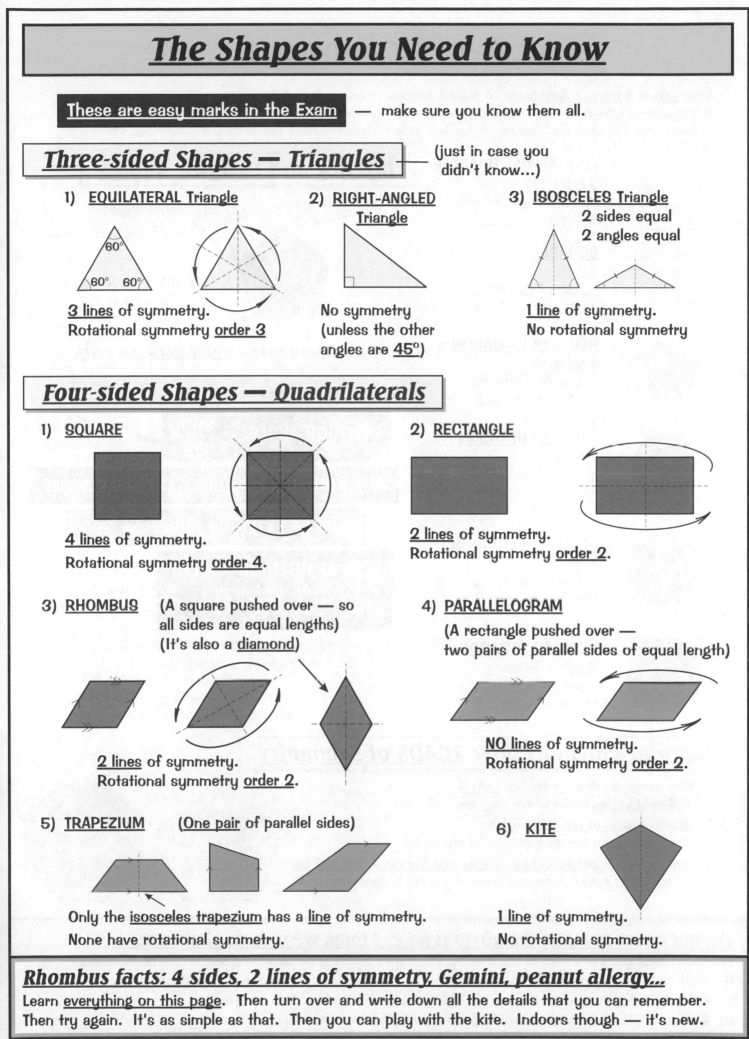

Rhombus facts: 4 sides, 2 lines of symmetry, Gemini, peanut allergy...
Learn everything on this page. Then turn over and write down all the details that you can remember.
Then try again. It's as simple as that. Then you can play with the kite. Indoors though — it's new.

Regular Polygons

A <u>polygon</u> is a <u>many-sided shape</u>. A <u>regular</u> polygon is one where all the <u>sides</u> and <u>angles</u> are the same. The regular polygons are a never-ending series of shapes with some fancy features. They're very easy to learn. Here are the first few but they don't stop — you can have one with 12 sides or 25, etc.

EQUILATERAL TRIANGLE
<u>3 sides</u>
<u>3 lines</u> of symmetry
Rotⁿˡ symm. <u>order 3</u>

SQUARE
<u>4 sides</u>
<u>4 lines</u> of symmetry
Rotⁿˡ symm. <u>order 4</u>

REGULAR PENTAGON
<u>5 sides</u>
<u>5 lines</u> of symmetry
Rotⁿˡ symm. <u>order 5</u>

REGULAR HEXAGON
<u>6 sides</u>
<u>6 lines</u> of symmetry
Rotⁿˡ symm. <u>order 6</u>

REGULAR HEPTAGON
<u>7 sides</u>
<u>7 lines</u> of symmetry
Rotⁿˡ symm. <u>order 7</u>

REGULAR OCTAGON
<u>8 sides</u>
<u>8 lines</u> of symmetry
Rotⁿˡ symm. <u>order 8</u>

Interior and Exterior Angles

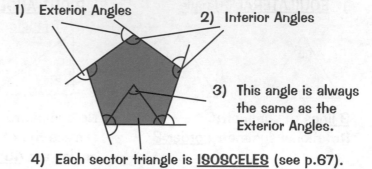

1) Exterior Angles
2) Interior Angles
3) This angle is always the same as the Exterior Angles.
4) Each sector triangle is <u>ISOSCELES</u> (see p.67).

There are 4 formulas to learn:

$$\text{EXTERIOR ANGLE} = \frac{360°}{n}$$
(n is the number of sides)

$$\text{INTERIOR ANGLE} = 180° - \text{EXTERIOR ANGLE}$$

$$\text{SUM OF EXTERIOR ANGLES} = 360°$$

SUM OF INTERIOR ANGLES
$= (2n - 4)$ right angles
$= (2n - 4) \times 90°$
(n is the number of sides again)

Note — the two <u>SUM</u> formulas above work for <u>any</u> polygons, not just regular ones.

Regular Polygons have LOADS of Symmetry

1) The pentagon shown here has <u>only 3 different angles</u> in the whole diagram.
2) This is <u>typical of regular polygons</u>. They display an amazing amount of symmetry.
3) With a regular polygon, <u>if two angles look the same</u>, <u>they will be</u>. (Which isn't a rule you should normally apply in geometry.)

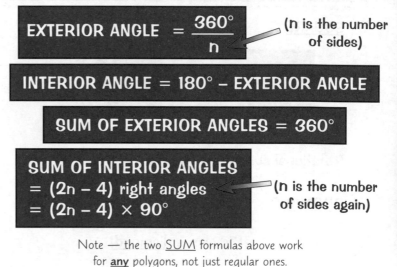

I'm not going to make the obvious joke. I think we're both above that...
You might think you know a lot of this already, but there's bound to be something new on the page, so <u>learn it all</u>.
1) Work out the two key angles for a regular pentagon. And for a 12-sided regular polygon.
2) A regular polygon has an interior angle of 156°. How many sides does it have?
3) Work out ALL the angles in the pentagon and octagon shown above.

Aww man, this was gonna be my big break an' everythin'.

Areas

Yes, I thought I could detect some groaning when you realised that this is a page of <u>formulas</u> that you need to learn to use. Well, I'm afraid it's tough — the sooner you get on with it, the <u>sooner</u> you'll have them sorted.

You must be able to use these Formulas:

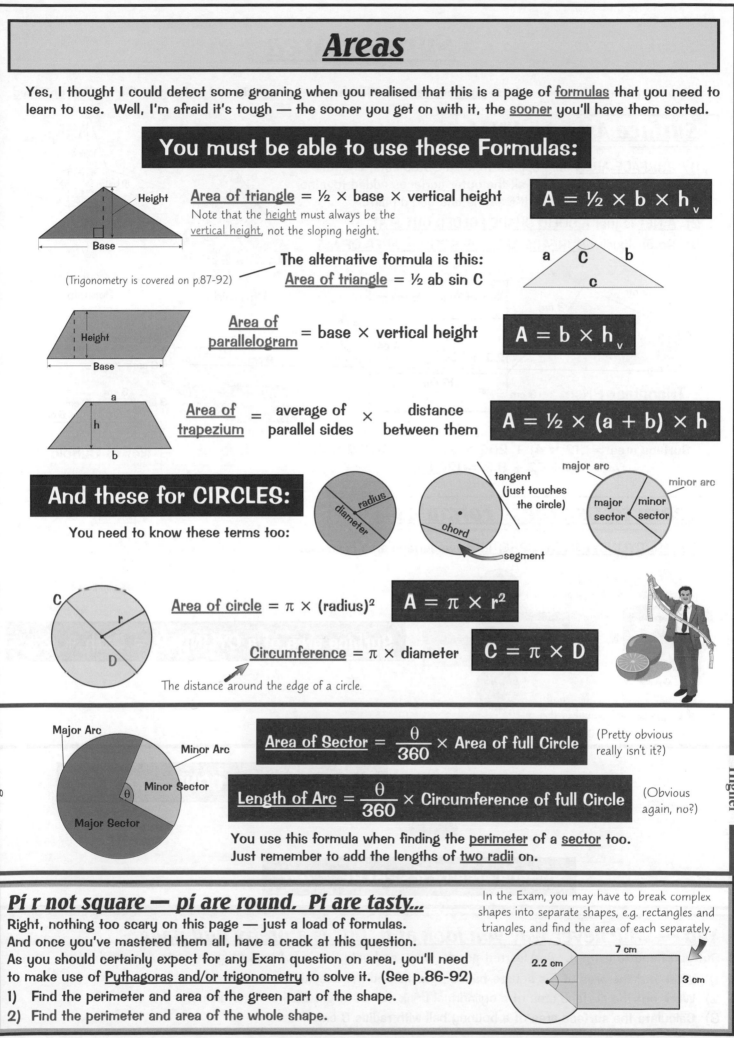

Height / **Base**

<u>Area of triangle</u> = ½ × base × vertical height

Note that the <u>height</u> must always be the <u>vertical height</u>, not the sloping height.

$A = \frac{1}{2} \times b \times h_v$

(Trigonometry is covered on p.87-92)

The alternative formula is this:
<u>Area of triangle</u> = ½ ab sin C

a   **C**   b
    c

Height / **Base**

$\dfrac{\text{Area of}}{\text{parallelogram}}$ = base × vertical height

$A = b \times h_v$

a / h / b

$\dfrac{\text{Area of}}{\text{trapezium}}$ = $\dfrac{\text{average of}}{\text{parallel sides}}$ × $\dfrac{\text{distance}}{\text{between them}}$

$A = \frac{1}{2} \times (a + b) \times h$

And these for CIRCLES:

You need to know these terms too:

radius / diameter

tangent (just touches the circle)

chord

segment

major arc / minor arc

major sector / minor sector

C / r / D

<u>Area of circle</u> = π × (radius)²

$A = \pi \times r^2$

<u>Circumference</u> = π × diameter

$C = \pi \times D$

The distance around the edge of a circle.

Major Arc

Minor Arc

Minor Sector

θ

Major Sector

<u>Area of Sector</u> = $\dfrac{\theta}{360}$ × Area of full Circle

(Pretty obvious really isn't it?)

<u>Length of Arc</u> = $\dfrac{\theta}{360}$ × Circumference of full Circle

(Obvious again, no?)

You use this formula when finding the <u>perimeter</u> of a <u>sector</u> too. Just remember to add the lengths of <u>two radii</u> on.

<u>Pi r not square — pi are round. Pi are tasty...</u>

Right, nothing too scary on this page — just a load of formulas.
And once you've mastered them all, have a crack at this question.
As you should certainly expect for any Exam question on area, you'll need to make use of <u>Pythagoras and/or trigonometry</u> to solve it. (See p.86-92)

1) Find the perimeter and area of the green part of the shape.
2) Find the perimeter and area of the whole shape.

In the Exam, you may have to break complex shapes into separate shapes, e.g. rectangles and triangles, and find the area of each separately.

2.2 cm   7 cm   3 cm

Surface Area

It's pretty simple to work out the <u>surface area</u> of a 3D shape — you just need to imagine the surface <u>unfolded</u>.

Surface Area and Nets

1) <u>SURFACE AREA</u> only applies to solid 3D objects, and it is simply <u>the total area</u> of all the <u>outer surfaces</u> added together. If you were painting it, it's all the bits you'd paint.

2) <u>A NET</u> is just <u>A SOLID SHAPE FOLDED OUT FLAT</u>.

3) So obviously: <u>SURFACE AREA OF SOLID = AREA OF NET</u>.

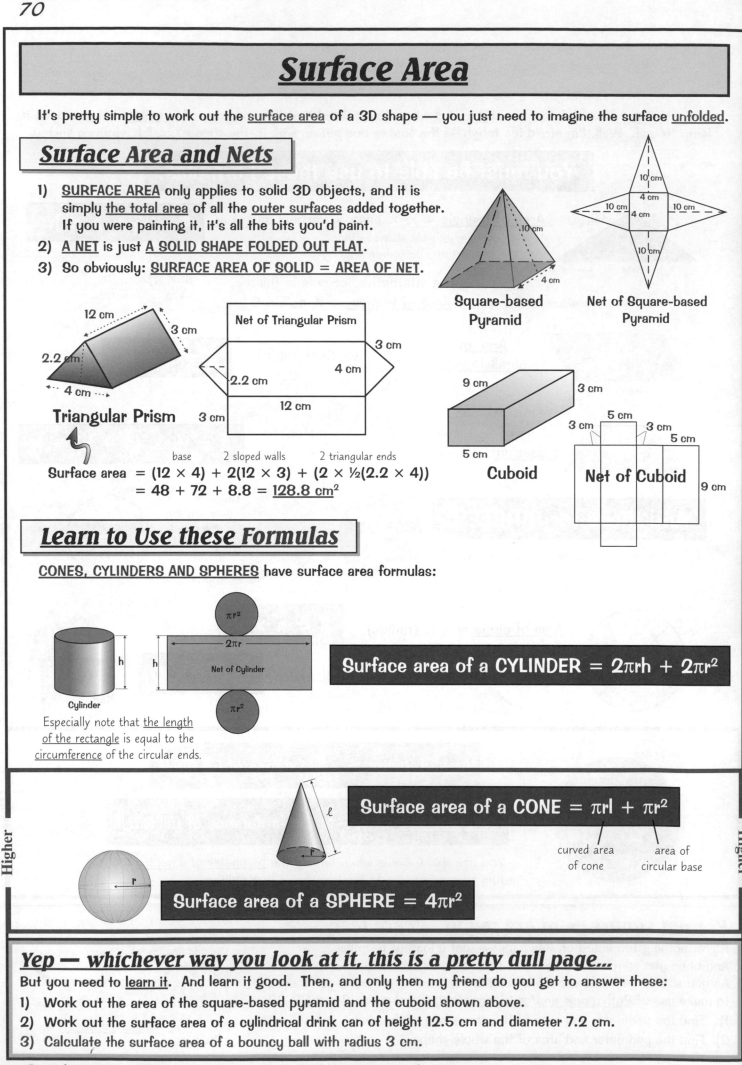

Square-based Pyramid

Net of Square-based Pyramid

Net of Triangular Prism

Triangular Prism

Cuboid

Net of Cuboid

Surface area = (12 × 4) + 2(12 × 3) + (2 × ½(2.2 × 4))
= 48 + 72 + 8.8 = <u>128.8 cm²</u>

Learn to Use these Formulas

<u>CONES, CYLINDERS AND SPHERES</u> have surface area formulas:

πr^2

$2\pi r$

Net of Cylinder

Cylinder

Especially note that <u>the length of the rectangle</u> is equal to the <u>circumference</u> of the circular ends.

Surface area of a CYLINDER = $2\pi rh + 2\pi r^2$

Surface area of a CONE = $\pi rl + \pi r^2$

curved area of cone

area of circular base

Surface area of a SPHERE = $4\pi r^2$

Yep — whichever way you look at it, this is a pretty dull page...

But you need to <u>learn it</u>. And learn it good. Then, and only then my friend do you get to answer these:

1) Work out the area of the square-based pyramid and the cuboid shown above.

2) Work out the surface area of a cylindrical drink can of height 12.5 cm and diameter 7.2 cm.

3) Calculate the surface area of a bouncy ball with radius 3 cm.

Section 5 — Shapes, Vectors and Transformations

Volume

I was going to make some pop-out <u>3D shapes</u> to put on this page, but I couldn't find the scissors and sticky tape. Sorry. Still, you need to know it all though — so chin up and learn the page.

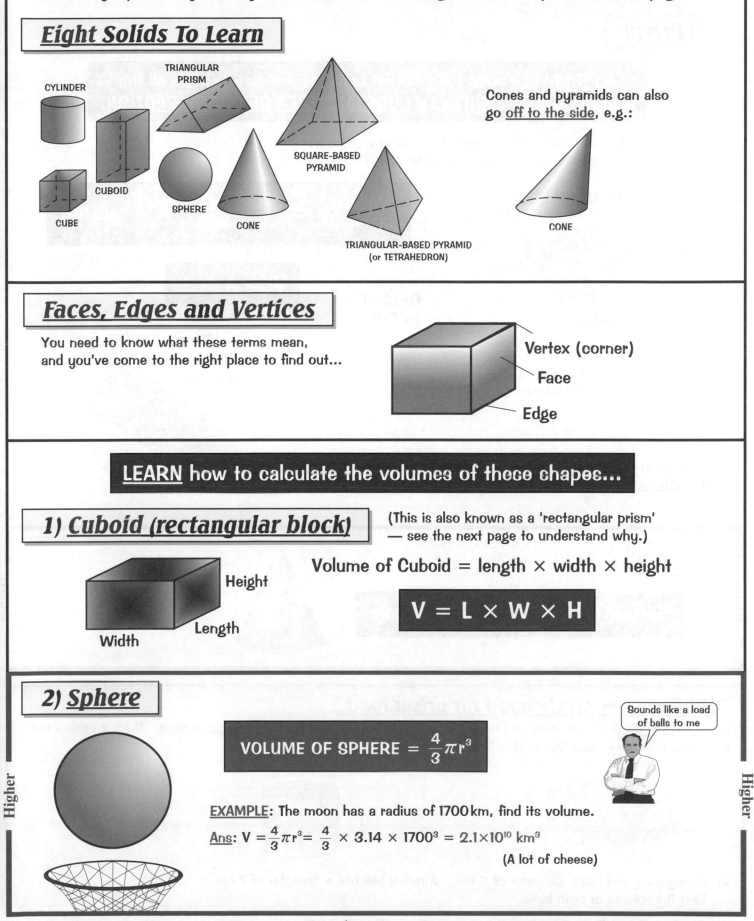

Eight Solids To Learn

CYLINDER

TRIANGULAR PRISM

CUBOID

CUBE

SPHERE

CONE

SQUARE-BASED PYRAMID

TRIANGULAR-BASED PYRAMID (or TETRAHEDRON)

Cones and pyramids can also go <u>off to the side</u>, e.g.:

CONE

Faces, Edges and Vertices

You need to know what these terms mean, and you've come to the right place to find out...

Vertex (corner)

Face

Edge

<u>LEARN</u> how to calculate the volumes of these shapes...

1) *Cuboid (rectangular block)*

(This is also known as a 'rectangular prism' — see the next page to understand why.)

Height

Length

Width

Volume of Cuboid = length × width × height

$$V = L \times W \times H$$

2) *Sphere*

$$\text{VOLUME OF SPHERE} = \frac{4}{3}\pi r^3$$

Sounds like a load of balls to me

<u>EXAMPLE</u>: The moon has a radius of 1700 km, find its volume.

<u>Ans</u>: $V = \frac{4}{3}\pi r^3 = \frac{4}{3} \times 3.14 \times 1700^3 = 2.1 \times 10^{10}$ km^3

(A lot of cheese)

Section 5 — Shapes, Vectors and Transformations

Volume

This page has a great bonus — once you've learnt it you can amaze people by calculating the volume of their ice cream cones. Who says revision isn't fun. I love it. I take exams just for fun.

3) Prism

> **A PRISM** is a solid (3D) object which is the same shape all the way through — i.e. it has a **CONSTANT AREA OF CROSS-SECTION**.

Now, for some reason, not a lot of people know what a prism is, but they come up all the time in Exams, so make sure YOU know.

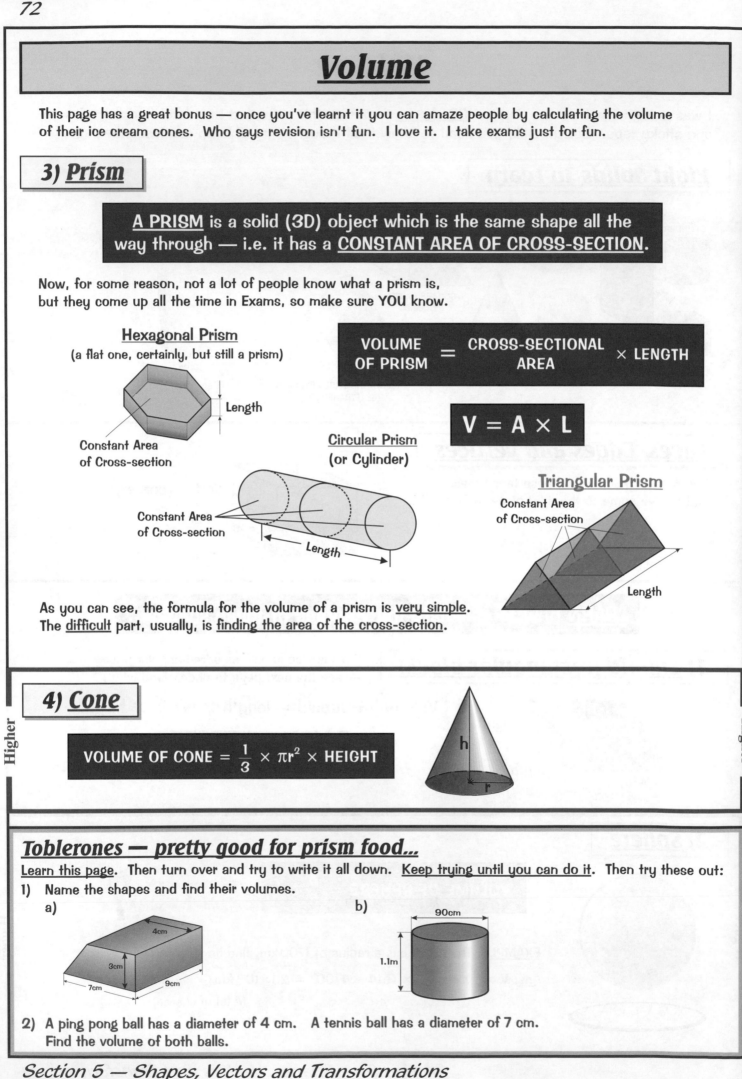

Hexagonal Prism
(a flat one, certainly, but still a prism)

Length

Constant Area of Cross-section

> **VOLUME OF PRISM** = **CROSS-SECTIONAL AREA** × **LENGTH**

> **V = A × L**

Circular Prism
(or Cylinder)

Constant Area of Cross-section

Length

Triangular Prism

Constant Area of Cross-section

Length

As you can see, the formula for the volume of a prism is <u>very simple</u>. The <u>difficult</u> part, usually, is <u>finding the area of the cross-section</u>.

4) Cone

> **VOLUME OF CONE** = $\frac{1}{3} \times \pi r^2 \times$ **HEIGHT**

h

r

Toblerones — pretty good for prism food...

<u>Learn this page.</u> Then turn over and try to write it all down. <u>Keep trying until you can do it</u>. Then try these out:

1) Name the shapes and find their volumes.

a)

4cm
3cm
7cm
9cm

b)

90cm
1.1m

2) A ping pong ball has a diameter of 4 cm. A tennis ball has a diameter of 7 cm. Find the volume of both balls.

Higher

Higher

Vectors

Some monstrously important things you need to know about <u>vectors</u>. Monsters... Aaaaaarrrrgggghhhh...

Vectors Have Size and Direction

Vectors are quantities that have MAGNITUDE (size or length) and DIRECTION.

1) <u>Displacement</u> and <u>velocity</u> (see page 62) are vectors. They have <u>size</u> and <u>direction</u>. (Distance and speed are similar to them, but <u>aren't</u> vectors — they <u>only</u> have size.)

2) If two vectors have the <u>same</u> magnitude and direction, they're <u>equal</u>.

So equal vectors are always <u>parallel</u>. E.g. $\overrightarrow{DA} = \overrightarrow{CB}$ and $\overrightarrow{AB} = \overrightarrow{DC}$.

The Three Notations

The vector shown here can be referred to as:

$\begin{pmatrix} 7 \\ 4 \end{pmatrix}$ or **a** (in bold type) or $\overrightarrow{AB}$

column vector

It's pretty obvious what these mean. Just make sure you know which number is which in the column vector ($x \rightarrow$ and $y \uparrow$) and what a negative value means in a column vector.

Magnitude of a Vector

1) If you get a vector question in the Exam, chances are it'll include a bit about <u>magnitude</u>.

2) $|\overrightarrow{AB}|$ means 'the <u>magnitude</u> of $\overrightarrow{AB}$' (it's sometimes called the <u>modulus</u>).

3) The magnitude of a vector is just its <u>length</u>.

4) You can usually work out the length of a vector using good old Pythagoras.

Example 1: "Find $|\overrightarrow{CD}|$."

$$\begin{aligned} |\overrightarrow{CD}| &= \sqrt{6^2 + 8^2} \\ &= \sqrt{36 + 64} \\ &= \sqrt{100} \\ &= 10 \end{aligned}$$

Example 2: "Find the magnitude of the vector $\begin{pmatrix} -7 \\ 10 \end{pmatrix}$."

$$\begin{aligned} \left| \begin{pmatrix} -7 \\ 10 \end{pmatrix} \right| &= \sqrt{(-7)^2 + 10^2} \\ &= \sqrt{49 + 100} \\ &= \sqrt{149} \\ &= 12.21 \end{aligned}$$

From numpty to vector king — via R, E, V, I, S, I, O and N...

I know it's dull, but make sure you know the vector basics (and that the page doesn't look like a bunch of randomly floating letters), then the next page won't seem so bad. Now try these:

1) $\overrightarrow{AB} = \begin{pmatrix} 2 \\ 5 \end{pmatrix}$ and $\overrightarrow{BC} = \begin{pmatrix} -3 \\ 3 \end{pmatrix}$. Find: a) $|\overrightarrow{AB}|$ b) $|\overrightarrow{BC}|$ c) $|\overrightarrow{AC}|$

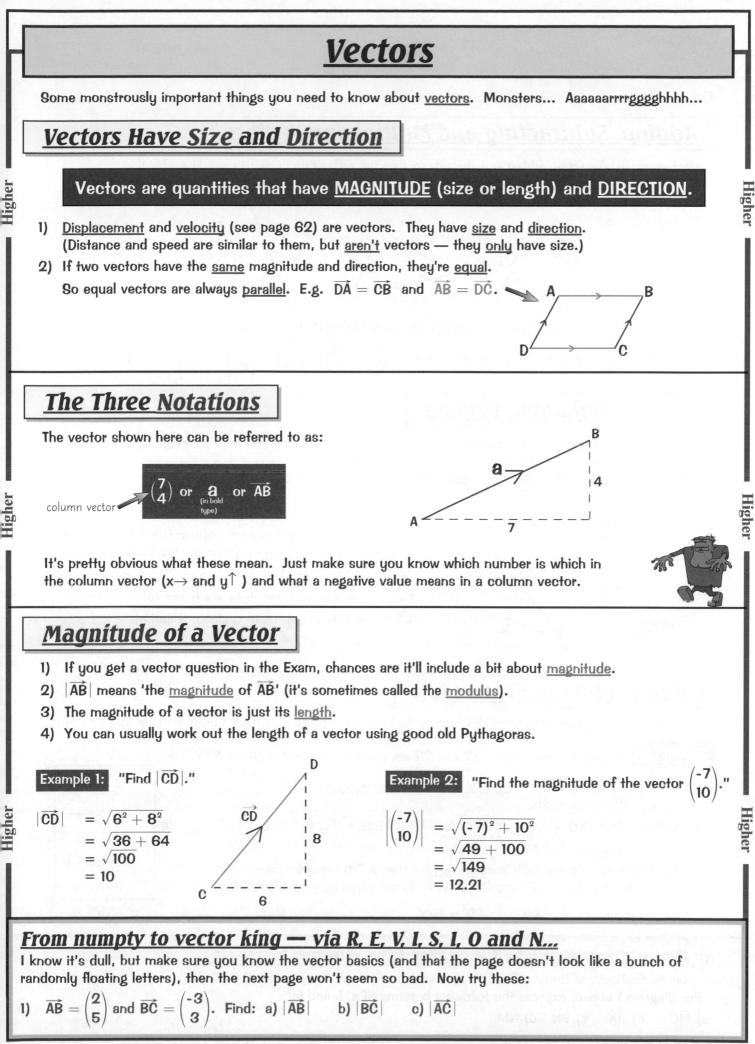

Vectors

And there's more. What fun, what fun.

Adding, Subtracting and Multiplying Vectors

Vectors must always be added <u>end to end</u>, so that the <u>arrows</u> don't point <u>against</u> each other.
The vector you get when you add vectors together is called the <u>resultant</u> vector.

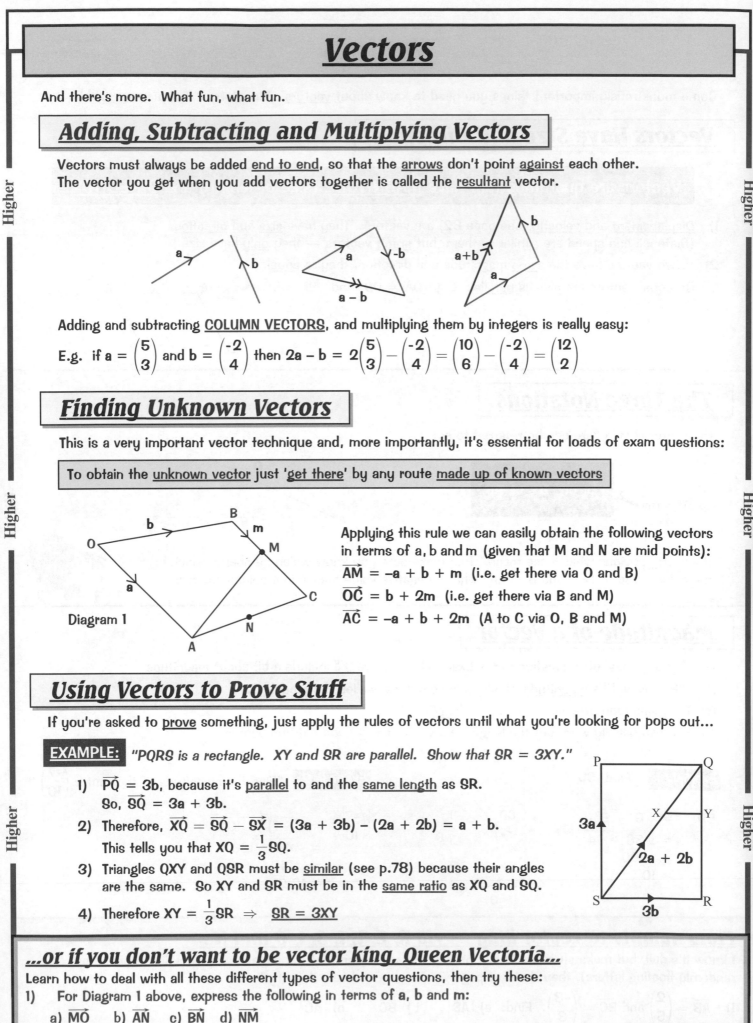

Adding and subtracting <u>COLUMN VECTORS</u>, and multiplying them by integers is really easy:

E.g. if $a = \begin{pmatrix} 5 \\ 3 \end{pmatrix}$ and $b = \begin{pmatrix} -2 \\ 4 \end{pmatrix}$ then $2a - b = 2\begin{pmatrix} 5 \\ 3 \end{pmatrix} - \begin{pmatrix} -2 \\ 4 \end{pmatrix} = \begin{pmatrix} 10 \\ 6 \end{pmatrix} - \begin{pmatrix} -2 \\ 4 \end{pmatrix} = \begin{pmatrix} 12 \\ 2 \end{pmatrix}$

Finding Unknown Vectors

This is a very important vector technique and, more importantly, it's essential for loads of exam questions:

To obtain the <u>unknown vector</u> just 'get there' by any route <u>made up of known vectors</u>

Applying this rule we can easily obtain the following vectors in terms of a, b and m (given that M and N are mid points):

$\overrightarrow{AM} = -a + b + m$ (i.e. get there via O and B)

$\overrightarrow{OC} = b + 2m$ (i.e. get there via B and M)

$\overrightarrow{AC} = -a + b + 2m$ (A to C via O, B and M)

Diagram 1

Using Vectors to Prove Stuff

If you're asked to <u>prove</u> something, just apply the rules of vectors until what you're looking for pops out...

EXAMPLE: *"PQRS is a rectangle. XY and SR are parallel. Show that SR = 3XY."*

1) $\overrightarrow{PQ} = 3b$, because it's <u>parallel</u> to and the <u>same length</u> as SR.
   So, $\overrightarrow{SQ} = 3a + 3b$.

2) Therefore, $\overrightarrow{XQ} = \overrightarrow{SQ} - \overrightarrow{SX} = (3a + 3b) - (2a + 2b) = a + b$.
   This tells you that $XQ = \frac{1}{3}SQ$.

3) Triangles QXY and QSR must be <u>similar</u> (see p.78) because their angles are the same. So XY and SR must be in the <u>same ratio</u> as XQ and SQ.

4) Therefore $XY = \frac{1}{3}SR \Rightarrow \underline{SR = 3XY}$

...or if you don't want to be vector king, Queen Victoria...

Learn how to deal with all these different types of vector questions, then try these:
1) For Diagram 1 above, express the following in terms of a, b and m:
   a) $\overrightarrow{MO}$ b) $\overrightarrow{AN}$ c) $\overrightarrow{BN}$ d) $\overrightarrow{NM}$

The Four Transformations

T	ranslation	— ONE Detail
E	nlargement	— TWO Details
R	otation	— THREE Details
R	eflection	— ONE Detail
Y		

1) Use the name <u>TERRY</u> to remember the 4 types.
2) You must always specify <u>all the details</u> for each type. And don't forget to state which <u>type</u> of <u>transformation</u> it is.
3) It'll help if you remember which properties remain <u>unchanged</u> in each transformation, too.

1) TRANSLATION

<u>You must specify this ONE detail:</u>

1) The distance <u>along</u> and <u>up</u>.
   OR
   The <u>VECTOR OF TRANSLATION</u> (Higher only) $\begin{pmatrix} x \to \\ \uparrow y \end{pmatrix}$

ABC to A'B'C' is a <u>translation</u> of <u>8 left and 6 up</u>.

ABC to A''B''C'' is a <u>translation</u> of <u>7 up</u>.

As vectors, the translations are: $\begin{pmatrix} -8 \\ 6 \end{pmatrix}$ and $\begin{pmatrix} 0 \\ 7 \end{pmatrix}$

All that changes in a translation is the POSITION of the object — <u>everything else</u> remains <u>unchanged</u>.

2) ENLARGEMENT

See page 78 for more on enlargements.

<u>You must specify these 2 details:</u>

1) The <u>SCALE FACTOR</u>
2) The <u>CENTRE</u> of Enlargement

From <u>A to B</u> is an enlargement of <u>scale factor 2</u>, and <u>centre (2,6)</u>

From <u>B to A</u> is an enlargement of <u>scale factor 1/2</u> and <u>centre (2,6)</u>

The ANGLES of the object and RATIOS of the lengths remain <u>unchanged</u>. The ORIENTATION is unchanged (if the scale factor is positive that is — which is all you need to know about).

3) ROTATION

<u>You must specify these 3 details:</u>

1) <u>ANGLE</u> turned
2) <u>DIRECTION</u> (Clockwise is negative, anticlockwise is positive.)
3) <u>CENTRE</u> of Rotation

ABC to A'B'C' is a Rotation of <u>+90°</u>, (<u>anticlockwise</u>), <u>ABOUT</u> the origin.

ABC to A''B''C'' is a Rotation of <u>−180°</u> (<u>clockwise</u>), <u>ABOUT</u> the origin.

+180° would have the same effect here.

The only things that change in a rotation are the POSITION and the ORIENTATION of the object. <u>Everything else</u> remains <u>unchanged</u>.

4) REFLECTION

<u>You must specify this ONE detail:</u>

1) The <u>MIRROR LINE</u>

A to B is a <u>reflection in the y-axis</u>.

A to C is a <u>reflection in the line y = x</u>

The line Y = X

With reflection, the POSITION and ORIENTATION of the object are the <u>only things that change</u>.

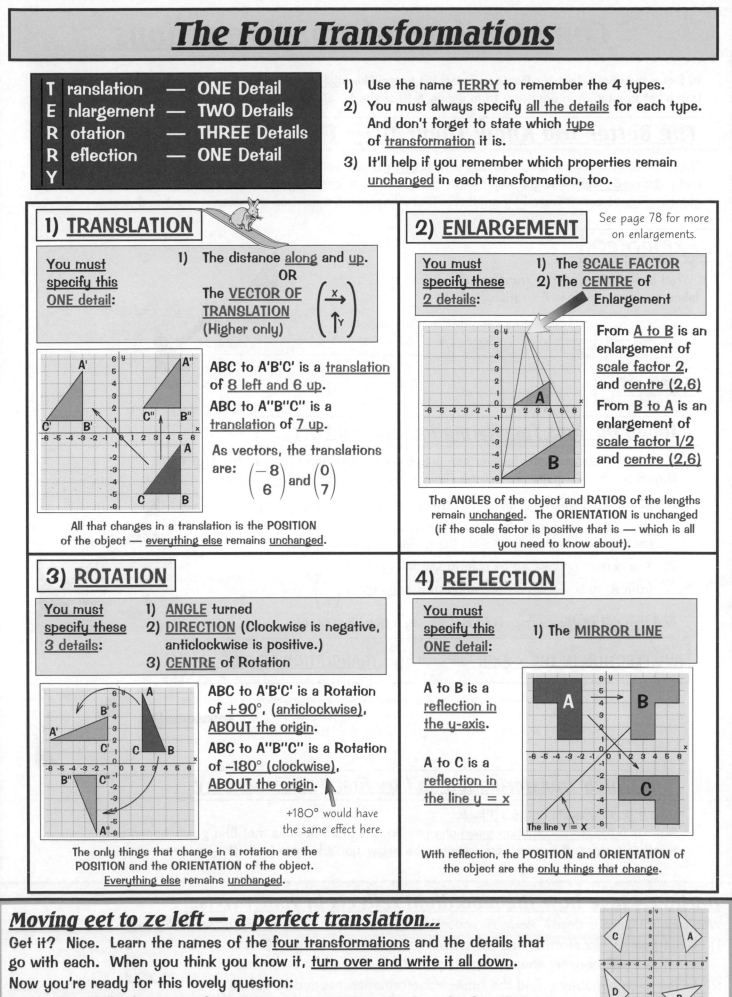

<u>Moving eet to ze left — a perfect translation...</u>

Get it? Nice. Learn the names of the <u>four transformations</u> and the details that go with each. When you think you know it, <u>turn over and write it all down</u>.

Now you're ready for this lovely question:

1) Describe <u>fully</u> these transformations: A → B, B → C, C → A, A → D.

Combinations of Transformations

In Exam questions they'll often do something <u>horrid</u> like <u>stick two transformations together</u> and then ask you what combination gets you from shape A to shape B. Be <u>ready</u> — those examiners are brutal.

The Better You Know Them All — The Easier it is

These kinds of question aren't so bad — but <u>ONLY</u> if you've <u>LEARNT</u> the <u>four transformations</u> on the last page <u>really well</u> — if you don't know them, then you certainly won't do too well at spotting a <u>combination</u> of one followed by another. That's because the method is basically <u>try it and see...</u>

Example:

"What combination of two transformations takes you from triangle A to triangle B?"

(There's usually a few different ways of getting from one shape to the other — but remember you only need to find <u>ONE</u> of them.)

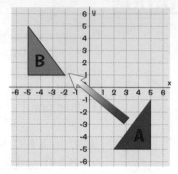

Method:

Try an Obvious Transformation first, and See...

If you <u>think</u> about it, the answer can <u>only</u> be a combination of two of the <u>four types</u> shown on the last page, so you can immediately start to <u>narrow it down</u>:

1) Since the shapes are the <u>same size</u> we can <u>rule out enlargements</u>.

2) Next, <u>try a reflection</u> (in either the x-axis or the y-axis). Here we've tried a reflection in the <u>y-axis</u>, to give shape A':

3) You should now easily be able to see the <u>final step</u> from A' to B — it's a <u>translation</u> of <u>6 units up</u> or $\begin{pmatrix} 0 \\ 6 \end{pmatrix}$.

And that's it <u>DONE</u> — from A to B is simply a combination of:

A <u>REFLECTION IN THE Y-AXIS</u> followed by a <u>TRANSLATION OF 6 UP</u> or $\begin{pmatrix} 0 \\ 6 \end{pmatrix}$

At least that's <u>one answer</u> anyway. If instead we decided to reflect it in the <u>x-axis</u> first (as shown here) then we'd get another answer (see question 2 below) — but both are right.

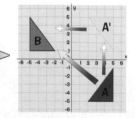

"But Which Transformation do I try first?" I hear you cry

Well it just depends on <u>how it looks</u>.
But the <u>more transformation questions</u> you do, the more obvious that first guess becomes.
In other words: the more you <u>practise</u>, the <u>easier</u> you'll be able to do it — surprise surprise...

Darling, I love how the moonlight reflects in your y-axis...

Who says romance is dead? Anyway, enough luvvy-duvvy stuff — crack on and learn this page.

1) What pair of transformations will convert shape C into shape D? What pair will convert shape D to shape C?

2) In the example above, find the other transformation needed to get to shape B after reflecting shape A in the x-axis.

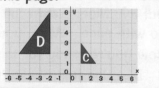

Congruence and Similarity

Congruence is another ridiculous maths word which sounds really complicated when it's not:
If two shapes are congruent, they are simply <u>the same</u> — the <u>same size</u> and the <u>same shape</u>.
That's all it is. They can however be <u>mirror images</u>.

CONGRUENT
— same size,
same shape

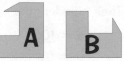

SIMILAR
— same shape,
different size

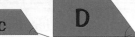

Note that the angles
are always unchanged

Congruent Triangles — are they or aren't they?

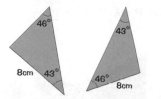

Probably the <u>trickiest area</u> of congruence is deciding whether
<u>two triangles</u>, like the ones shown here, are **CONGRUENT**.

In other words, from the skimpy information given, are the two going
to be the same or different. There are **THREE IMPORTANT STEPS**:

1) The Golden Rule is definitely to
   <u>draw them both</u> in the <u>same orientation</u>
   — only then can you compare them properly:

2) <u>Don't jump to hasty conclusions</u> — although the 8 cm sides are clearly in different positions,
   it's always possible that <u>both top sides are 8 cm</u>. In this case we can work out that they're <u>not</u>
   because the angles are different (so they can't be isosceles).

3) Now see if any of these <u>conditions are true</u>. If **ONE** of the conditions holds,
   the triangles are <u>congruent</u>.

1)	**SSS**	three sides are the same
2)	**AAS**	two angles and a side match up
3)	**SAS**	two sides and the angle between them match up
4)	**RHS**	a right angle, the hypotenuse (longest side) and one other side all match up

For two triangles to be congruent, **ONE OR MORE** of these four conditions must hold.

(<u>If none are true</u>, then you have proof
that the triangles <u>aren't congruent</u>.)

Congruence and Transformations

Remember <u>transformations</u>? (See page 75 if you don't), well...

**WHEN A SHAPE IS <u>TRANSLATED</u>, <u>ROTATED</u> OR <u>REFLECTED</u>,
THE IMAGE IS CONGRUENT TO THE ORIGINAL SHAPE.
<u>ENLARGEMENTS</u> DON'T FOLLOW THIS RULE.**

E.g.

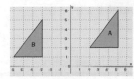

A to B is a <u>translation</u>
of 8 left and 1 down, or $\begin{pmatrix} -8 \\ -1 \end{pmatrix}$.
The lengths and angles
are unchanged, so <u>A is congruent to B</u>.

E.g.

A to B is an <u>enlargement</u> of scale
factor 2, and centre (2, 6).

The angles are unchanged
but not the lengths, so
<u>A is not congruent to B</u>.

Now, where did I put that cup of tea...

Ah there it is over there. Lovely. So here's the bad news — you need to know everything
on this page. And the good news — it'll all be great fun. What... you don't believe me?
<u>When you think you know it</u>, turn the page over and <u>write it all down</u> from <u>memory</u>,
including the sketches and examples.

They're my biscuits. Hands off.

Similarity and Enlargements

You'll be an expert in <u>similarity</u> and <u>scale factors</u> after this page — bet you can't wait.

Similar Shapes have the Same Angles

Similar shapes have <u>identical angles</u> but different <u>side lengths</u>. Their side lengths are in the <u>same ratio</u> though.

E.g. *"These triangles are similar.*
Find a, b and c."

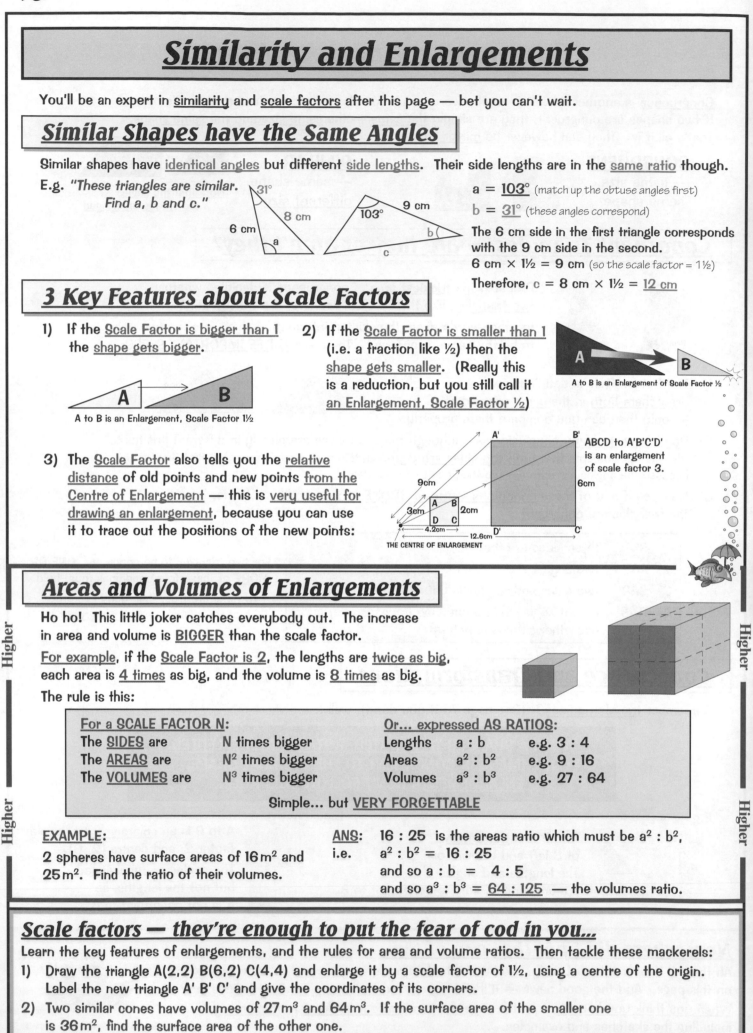

a = <u>**103°**</u> (match up the obtuse angles first)

b = <u>**31°**</u> (these angles correspond)

The 6 cm side in the first triangle corresponds with the 9 cm side in the second.

6 cm × 1½ = 9 cm (so the scale factor = 1½)

Therefore, c = 8 cm × 1½ = <u>12 cm</u>

3 Key Features about Scale Factors

1) If the <u>Scale Factor is bigger than 1</u> the <u>shape gets bigger</u>.

A to B is an Enlargement, Scale Factor 1½

2) If the <u>Scale Factor is smaller than 1</u> (i.e. a fraction like ½) then the <u>shape gets smaller</u>. (Really this is a reduction, but you still call it <u>an Enlargement, Scale Factor ½</u>)

A to B is an Enlargement of Scale Factor ½

3) The <u>Scale Factor</u> also tells you the <u>relative distance</u> of old points and new points <u>from the Centre of Enlargement</u> — this is <u>very useful for drawing an enlargement</u>, because you can use it to trace out the positions of the new points:

ABCD to A'B'C'D' is an enlargement of scale factor 3.

THE CENTRE OF ENLARGEMENT

Areas and Volumes of Enlargements

Ho ho! This little joker catches everybody out. The increase in area and volume is <u>BIGGER</u> than the scale factor.

<u>For example</u>, if the <u>Scale Factor is 2</u>, the lengths are <u>twice as big</u>, each area is <u>4 times</u> as big, and the volume is <u>8 times</u> as big.

The rule is this:

<u>For a SCALE FACTOR N</u>:		<u>Or... expressed AS RATIOS</u>:	
The <u>SIDES</u> are	N times bigger	Lengths a : b	e.g. 3 : 4
The <u>AREAS</u> are	N^2 times bigger	Areas $a^2 : b^2$	e.g. 9 : 16
The <u>VOLUMES</u> are	N^3 times bigger	Volumes $a^3 : b^3$	e.g. 27 : 64

Simple... but <u>VERY FORGETTABLE</u>

<u>EXAMPLE</u>:

2 spheres have surface areas of 16 m² and 25 m². Find the ratio of their volumes.

<u>ANS</u>: 16 : 25 is the areas ratio which must be $a^2 : b^2$,
i.e. $a^2 : b^2 = $ 16 : 25
and so a : b = 4 : 5
and so $a^3 : b^3 = $ <u>64 : 125</u> — the volumes ratio.

Scale factors — they're enough to put the fear of cod in you...

Learn the key features of enlargements, and the rules for area and volume ratios. Then tackle these mackerels:

1) Draw the triangle A(2,2) B(6,2) C(4,4) and enlarge it by a scale factor of 1½, using a centre of the origin. Label the new triangle A' B' C' and give the coordinates of its corners.

2) Two similar cones have volumes of 27 m³ and 64 m³. If the surface area of the smaller one is 36 m², find the surface area of the other one.

Section 5 — Shapes, Vectors and Transformations

Higher

Triangle Construction

I just know that you're dying to <u>draw some triangles</u> about now. And that's so weird, because that's exactly what's coming up next in this uber-exciting quest to master maths. Spooky.

Follow the Steps to Construct a Triangle

'<u>Construct</u>' means <u>draw accurately</u> using <u>pencil</u>, <u>ruler</u> and <u>compasses</u>.

If you're told to <u>construct a triangle</u> and you're told <u>how long the three sides are</u>, this is what to do.

> 1) Draw a <u>ROUGH SKETCH</u> and <u>LABEL THE LENGTHS</u> of the sides.
> 2) Draw the <u>BASE LINE</u> using a ruler.
> 3) Draw <u>TWO ARCS</u>, one from <u>EACH END</u> of the base line,
>   setting your compasses to the <u>LENGTHS OF THE SIDES</u>.
> 4) Draw lines from the <u>ENDS OF THE BASE LINE</u> to where the <u>TWO ARCS CROSS</u>.

Example: Construct the triangle ABC where AB = 6 cm, BC = 4 cm, AC = 5 cm.

ANSWER:

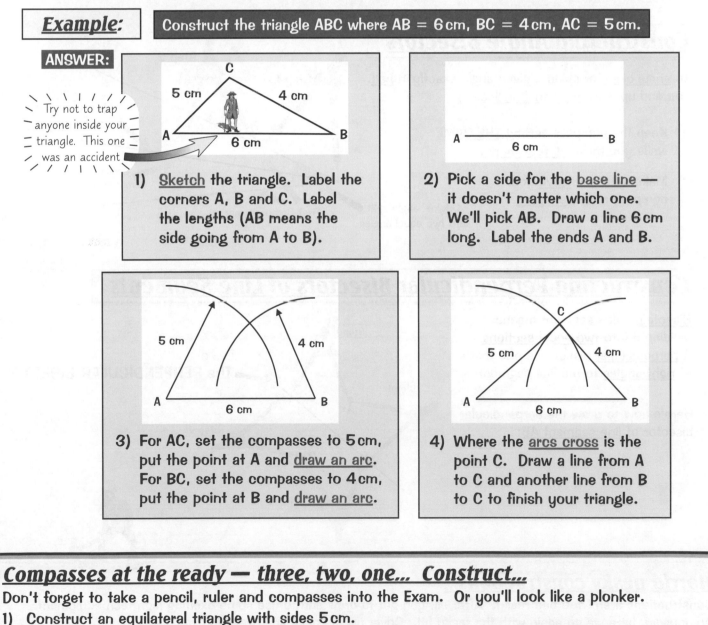

Try not to trap anyone inside your triangle. This one was an accident

1) <u>Sketch</u> the triangle. Label the corners A, B and C. Label the lengths (AB means the side going from A to B).

2) Pick a side for the <u>base line</u> — it doesn't matter which one. We'll pick AB. Draw a line 6 cm long. Label the ends A and B.

3) For AC, set the compasses to 5 cm, put the point at A and <u>draw an arc</u>. For BC, set the compasses to 4 cm, put the point at B and <u>draw an arc</u>.

4) Where the <u>arcs cross</u> is the point C. Draw a line from A to C and another line from B to C to finish your triangle.

Compasses at the ready — three, two, one... Construct...

Don't forget to take a pencil, ruler and compasses into the Exam. Or you'll look like a plonker.

1) Construct an equilateral triangle with sides 5 cm.

2) Construct a triangle with sides 3 cm, 4 cm and 5 cm. Check it by measuring the sides.

More Constructions

Don't put your compass away just yet. There's another page on constructions coming up.
The only way to master them is to practise lots and lots.

Constructing Accurate 90° Angles

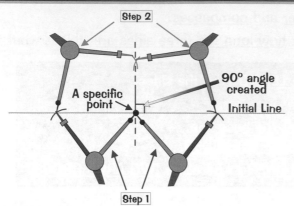

1) Being able to draw <u>accurate 90° angles</u> comes in handy for drawing squares or rectangles.

2) They won't accept it just done '<u>by eye</u>' or with a ruler — if you want the marks you've got to do it <u>the proper way</u> with <u>compasses</u> like I've shown you here.

3) Make sure you can <u>follow the method</u> shown in this diagram.

Constructing Angle Bisectors

An <u>angle bisector</u> splits a given angle exactly in <u>half</u>. You end up with <u>two equal angles</u>.

1) Keep the compass setting <u>THE SAME</u> while you make <u>all four marks</u>.

2) Make sure you <u>leave</u> your compass marks <u>showing</u>.

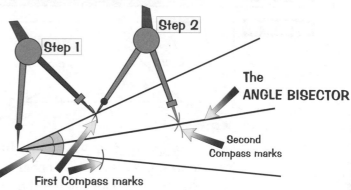

The ANGLE BISECTOR

Second Compass marks

Original angle split into two equal angles

First Compass marks

Constructing Perpendicular Bisectors of Line Segments

<u>Bisecting</u> a line segment means dividing it into <u>two equal sections</u>. A <u>perpendicular</u> bisector is one that's at <u>right angles</u> to the line segment.

Here's how to draw the perpendicular bisector of <u>line segment AB</u>:

Step 1

Step 1

Step 3

The PERPENDICULAR BISECTOR

A

Step 2

B

Step 2

Horrid pesky constructions...

Constructions aren't too bad really. After all, you get to draw and to use some exciting high tech equipment. So anyway, here we go again with the tasky bit. Cover up the page and draw an example of each of these constructions. Also, draw a square with accurate 90° angles.

Revision Summary

You've now well and truly broken the back of IGCSE Maths and are on your way out of it (assuming that you started at the beginning of the book that is). Section 5 was a pretty lengthy one, but on the bright side, there were lots of diagrams filling up the space. Try these questions and see what you know.

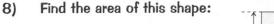

KEEP LEARNING THESE BASIC FACTS UNTIL YOU KNOW THEM

1) A map has a scale of 1:50 000. A lake is 3 cm long on the map. How many km long is the actual lake?

2) Name 6 quadrilaterals and describe their symmetry.

3) What are regular polygons? Name the first eight.

4) List the special features that regular polygons have.

5) What do you know about their symmetry?

6) There are five formulas for area you should know straight off. Write them all down.

7) Clive is re-carpeting his lounge, which is rectangular. The room is 12 m long and 7 m wide. The carpet he wants costs £12 per m². How much will it cost Clive to carpet his lounge?

8) Find the area of this shape:

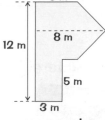

9) Draw a circle and show what an arc, a sector, a segment and a chord are.

10) What is the formula for the length of an arc? What is the formula for the area of a sector?

11) What is meant by a net? How is it related to surface area?

12) A confectionery company is designing the packaging for a new brand of biscuits. The packaging will be cylindrical, with a diameter of 4 cm and a height of 15 cm. Calculate the surface area of the packaging.

13) Calculate the surface area of a sphere with diameter 5 cm. (Watch out — this isn't quite as easy as it sounds.)

14) What is a prism? Sketch three different ones.

15) How do you calculate the volume of a prism?

16) A juice company makes apple squash in batches of 9000 cm³. The squash is sold in cylindrical cans that have a cross-sectional area of 12 cm² and a height of 6 cm. How many of these cans can the company fill from one batch of apple squash?

17) Explain what a vector is. Write down 3 different vector notations.

18) How do you do the following? Make up an example for each:
a) add column vectors   b) multiply a column vector by an integer

19) List the four types of transformation. What details must be specified for each type?

20) What do "congruent" and "similar" mean?

21) What are the rules for deciding if two triangles are congruent or not?

22) Draw a typical enlargement, showing the two important details.

23) What happens when you enlarge with a scale factor of between 0 and 1?

24) Geoff has built a scale model of a cuboid-shaped garden shed that he hopes to supply to garden centres. His model is 30 cm wide, 60 cm long and 50 cm high. He has used a scale factor of 0.2.
a) Give the width, length and height of the actual sheds.
b) Find the area of the base of the model shed and of the actual shed. Explain how they're related.
c) Find the volume of the model shed and of the actual shed. Explain how they're related.

25) Draw an accurate equilateral triangle.

26) Demonstrate how to draw accurate 90° angles. Draw an accurate square.

27) Demonstrate how to accurately draw the bisector of an angle.

28) Demonstrate how to accurately draw the perpendicular bisector of a line segment.

Angle Geometry

If you know <u>all</u> these rules <u>thoroughly</u>, you at least have a fighting chance of working out problems with lines and angles. If you don't — you've no chance. Sorry to break it to you like that.

7 Simple Rules — that's all:

1) Angles in a triangle

...ADD UP TO <u>180°</u>.

$$a+b+c=180°$$

2) Angles on a straight line

...ADD UP TO <u>180°</u>.

$$a+b+c=180°$$

3) Angles in a 4-sided shape   (a 'Quadrilateral')

...ADD UP TO <u>360°</u>.

$$a+b+c+d=360°$$

4) Angles round a point

...ADD UP TO <u>360°</u>.

$$a+b+c+d=360°$$

5) Exterior Angle of Triangle

<u>EXTERIOR ANGLE</u> of triangle
= <u>SUM OF OPPOSITE INTERIOR ANGLES</u>

Opposite Interior Angles

Exterior Angle

$$a+b=d$$

6) Isosceles triangles

2 sides the same
2 angles the same

These dashes indicate two sides the same length

In an isosceles triangle, you only need to know <u>one angle</u> to be able to find the other two:

a)
180° – 40° = 140°
<u>The two bottom angles are both the same</u> and they must add up to 140°, so each one must be half of 140°. So <u>x = 70°</u>.

b)
The <u>two bottom angles must be the same</u>, so 50° + 50° = 100°. All the angles add up to 180° so y = 180° – 100° = <u>80°</u>.

Angle Geometry

7) Parallel Lines

Whenever one line crosses two <u>parallel lines</u> then the two bunches of angles <u>are the same</u>, and <u>a + b = 180°</u>.

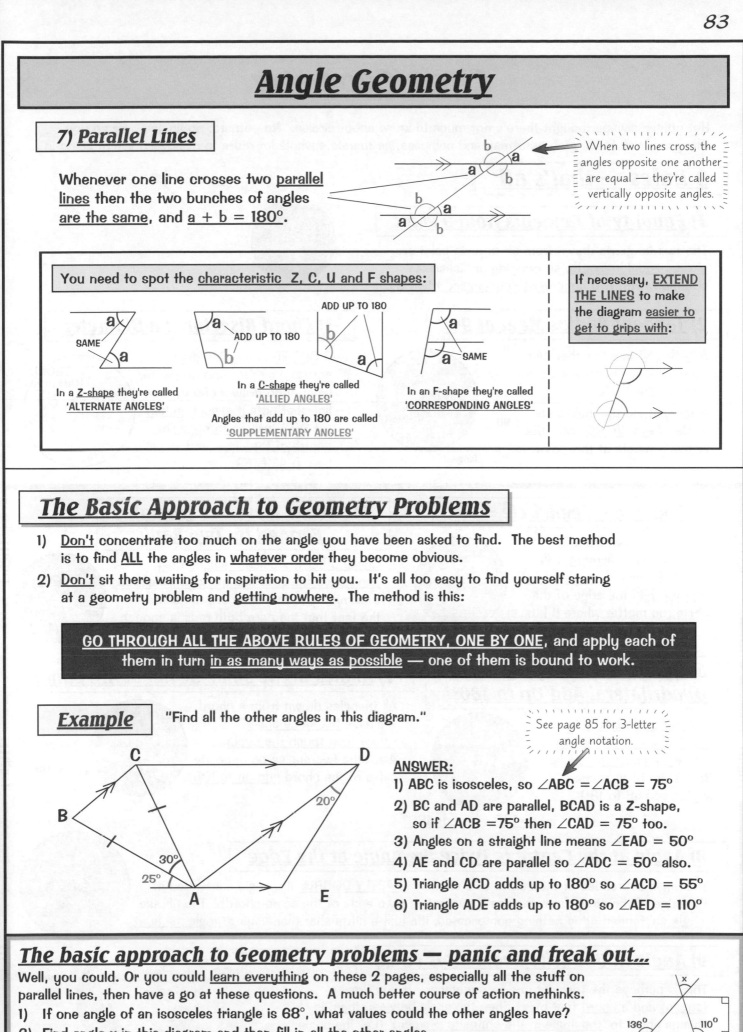

When two lines cross, the angles opposite one another are equal — they're called vertically opposite angles.

You need to spot the <u>characteristic Z, C, U and F shapes</u>:

ADD UP TO 180

SAME

ADD UP TO 180

In a <u>Z-shape</u> they're called
 'ALTERNATE ANGLES'

In a <u>C-shape</u> they're called
 'ALLIED ANGLES'

Angles that add up to 180 are called
 'SUPPLEMENTARY ANGLES'

SAME

In an F-shape they're called
 'CORRESPONDING ANGLES'

If necessary, <u>EXTEND THE LINES</u> to make the diagram <u>easier to get to grips with</u>:

The Basic Approach to Geometry Problems

1) <u>Don't</u> concentrate too much on the angle you have been asked to find. The best method is to find <u>ALL</u> the angles in <u>whatever order</u> they become obvious.

2) <u>Don't</u> sit there waiting for inspiration to hit you. It's all too easy to find yourself staring at a geometry problem and <u>getting nowhere</u>. The method is this:

> <u>GO THROUGH ALL THE ABOVE RULES OF GEOMETRY, ONE BY ONE</u>, and apply each of them in turn <u>in as many ways as possible</u> — one of them is bound to work.

Example

"Find all the other angles in this diagram."

See page 85 for 3-letter angle notation.

ANSWER:

1) ABC is isosceles, so ∠ABC = ∠ACB = 75°

2) BC and AD are parallel, BCAD is a Z-shape, so if ∠ACB = 75° then ∠CAD = 75° too.

3) Angles on a straight line means ∠EAD = 50°

4) AE and CD are parallel so ∠ADC = 50° also.

5) Triangle ACD adds up to 180° so ∠ACD = 55°

6) Triangle ADE adds up to 180° so ∠AED = 110°

The basic approach to Geometry problems — panic and freak out...

Well, you could. Or you could <u>learn everything</u> on these 2 pages, especially all the stuff on parallel lines, then have a go at these questions. A much better course of action methinks.

1) If one angle of an isosceles triangle is 68°, what values could the other angles have?

2) Find angle x in this diagram and then fill in all the other angles.

3) If the angles in a triangle are $(y + 30)°$, $(y + 5)°$ and $(y + 25)°$, what is the value of y?

Circle Geometry

Bet you've always thought there's not much to know about circles. No corners, no angles... or so you thought. Well folks, grab your map and compass, as there's a whole lot more to discover. We're going in...

9 Rules — that's all:

1) Equality of Tangents from a Point

The two tangents drawn from an outside point are <u>always equal in length</u>, so creating an 'isosceles' situation, with <u>two congruent</u> <u>right-angled triangles</u>.

2) Tangent-Radius Meet at 90°

A <u>TANGENT</u> is a line that just touches a single point on the edge of the circle.

A tangent always makes an angle of <u>exactly 90°</u> with the <u>radius</u> it meets at this point.

90°   Radius

Tangent

3) Chord Bisector is a Diameter

A <u>CHORD</u> is any line <u>drawn</u> <u>across a circle</u>. And no matter where you draw a chord, the line that <u>cuts it exactly in half</u> (at 90°), will <u>go through the</u> <u>centre of the circle</u> and so will be a <u>DIAMETER</u>.

CHORD
(Cut in two)
O

4) Angle in a Semicircle = 90°

A triangle drawn from the <u>two ends of a diameter</u> will ALWAYS make an <u>angle of 90°</u> <u>where it hits</u> the edge of the circle, no matter where it hits.

5) Sneaky Isosceles Triangles Formed by Two Radii

<u>Unlike other isosceles triangles</u> they <u>don't have the little tick marks on the sides</u> to remind you that they are the same — the fact that <u>they are both radii</u> is enough to make it an isosceles triangle.

6) Opposite Angles of a Cyclic Quadrilateral Add Up to 180°

A <u>cyclic quadrilateral</u> is a <u>4-sided shape with every</u> <u>corner touching the circle</u>. Both pairs of opposite angles add up to 180°.

a   b
d   c

<u>a+c=180°</u>   <u>b+d=180°</u>

7) Angles in the Same Segment Are Equal

All triangles drawn from a chord will have <u>the same angle</u> <u>where they touch the circle</u>. Also, the two angles on opposite sides of the chord <u>add up to 180°</u>.

b   b
b
Chord
a   a
a+b = 180°

8) Angle at the Centre is Twice the Angle at the Edge

The angle subtended at the centre of a circle is <u>EXACTLY DOUBLE</u> the angle subtended at the edge of the circle from the same two points (two ends of the same chord). The phrase <u>'angle subtended at'</u> is nothing complicated, it's just a bit posher than saying <u>'angle made at'</u>.

a
2a

9) Angle in Opposite Segment is Equal

Otherwise known as the Alternate Segment Theorem.

This is perhaps the trickiest one to remember. If you draw a <u>tangent</u> and a <u>chord</u> that meet, then <u>the angle between them</u> is always <u>equal</u> to '<u>the angle in the opposite segment</u>' (i.e. the angle made at the edge of the circle by two lines drawn from the chord).

The
Opposite Segment
(white)
The Chord
b
b
Angle in the
opposite segment
Angle between
chord and tangent

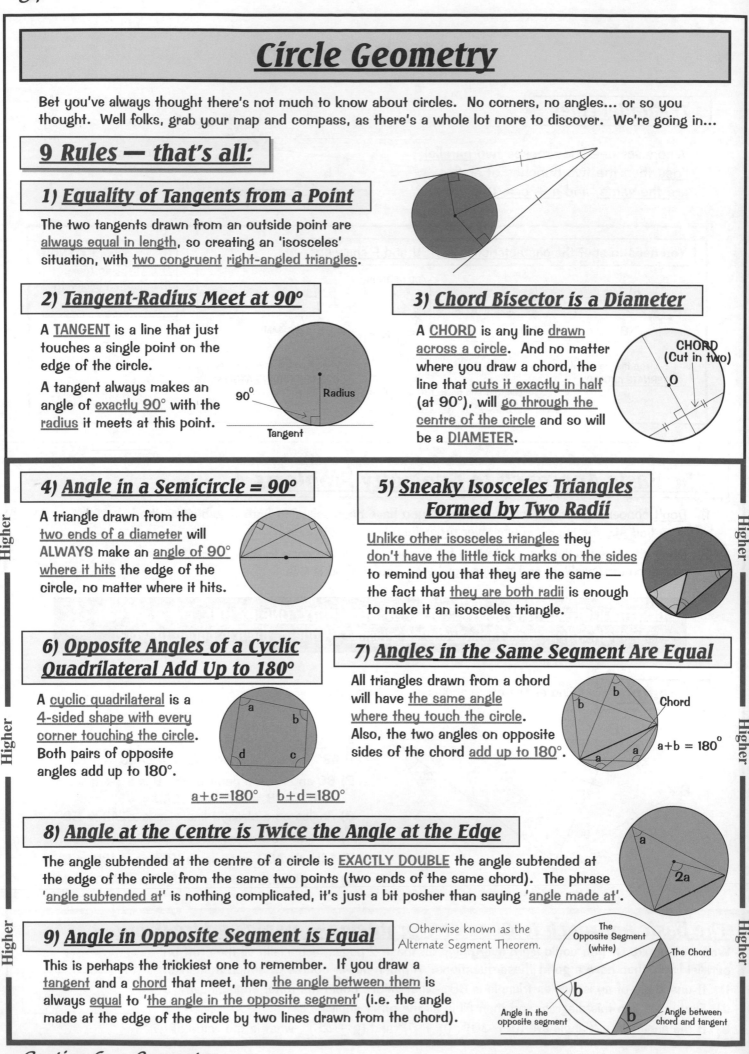

Higher

Circle Geometry

Intersecting Chord Properties

INTERNAL INTERSECTION: For any two chords that intersect inside a circle: <u>AO × OB = CO × OD</u>

EXTERNAL INTERSECTION: If two chords are extended and meet outside the circle: <u>OA × OB = OC × OD</u>

Watch out — all these lengths are measured from the point outside the circle.

EXAMPLE: "In the external intersection diagram above, OA = 22 mm, OB = 49 mm, and OD = 47 mm. Find the length of chord CD."

OA × OB = OC × OD. So: 22 × 49 = OC × 47 ⇒ OC = 22.9 mm

OD − OC = CD. So: 47 − 22.9 = 24.1 mm.

3-Letter Notation for Angles

1) <u>Angles are specified using 3 letters</u>, e.g. angle ODC = 48⁰

2) <u>THE MIDDLE LETTER IS WHERE THE ANGLE IS</u>

3) <u>THE OTHER TWO LETTERS</u> tell you <u>which lines enclose the angle</u>
   For example: Angle ODC is <u>at D</u> and <u>enclosed by the lines</u> going from <u>O to D</u> and from <u>D to C</u>.

Example

"Find all the angles in this diagram."

1) <u>PARALLEL LINES</u> — there are actually <u>4 different lines</u> crossing the 2 parallel ones, but the most useful one is ED which tells us that <u>EDC is 180 − 65 = 115°</u>

2) <u>ANGLE IN SAME SEGMENT</u> — there are potentially <u>eight different chords</u> where this rule could apply, but some are more useful than others:
   EAD = EBD, ADB = AEB (so AEB = <u>28°</u>)
   ABE = ADE, DAB = DEB (so DAB = <u>65°</u>)

3) <u>OPPOSITE ANGLES OF A CYCLIC QUADRILATERAL</u>
   — looking at BEDC gives:
   BCD = 180 − DEB = 180 − 65 = <u>115°</u>
   — looking at ABDE gives:
   ABD = 180 − AED = 180 − (28 + 65) = <u>87°</u>

4) <u>ANGLES IN A TRIANGLE ADD UP TO 180°</u> — this, the simplest of all the rules, will now find all the other angles for you.

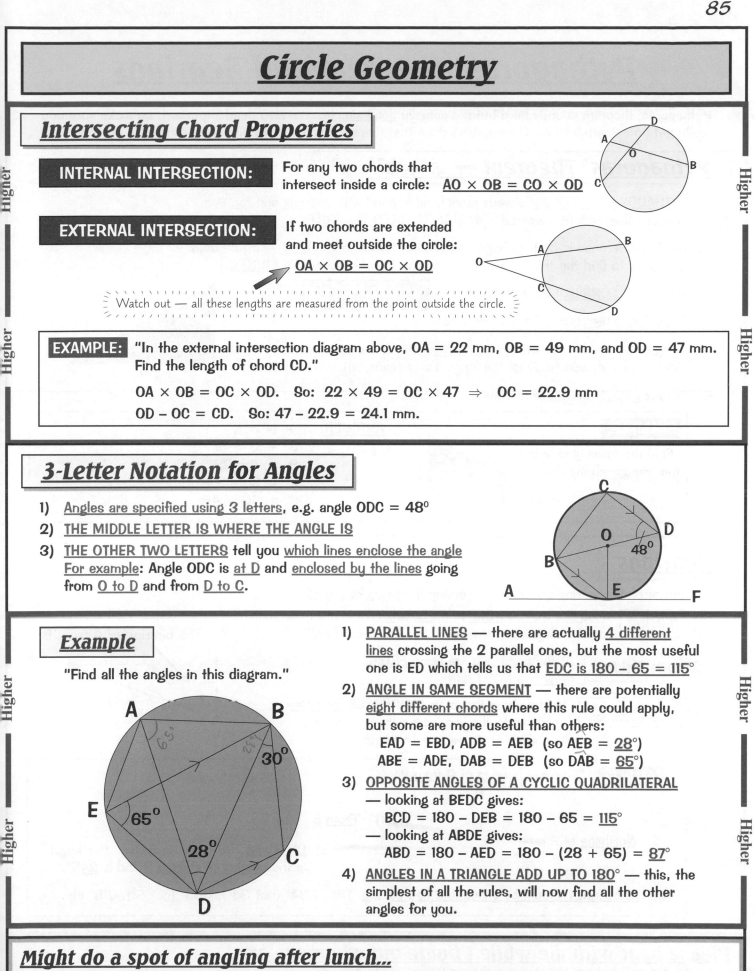

<u>Might do a spot of angling after lunch...</u>

You can join me if you like — but you need to learn all about circles first. Oh, and correctly answer these:

1) Find the angles **FEO** and **OBE** in the 3rd diagram above.
   Find the rest of the angles in this diagram.

2) <u>Practise the above example</u> till you <u>understand every step</u> and can do it easily without help.

Pythagoras' Theorem and Bearings

Pythagoras' theorem sounds hard but it's actually <u>dead simple</u>. It's also dead important, so make sure you really get your teeth into it. Once you've done that there are some tasty bites on <u>bearings</u> to chew on too.

Pythagoras' Theorem — $a^2 + b^2 = h^2$

1) <u>PYTHAGORAS' THEOREM</u> always goes hand in hand with <u>sin</u>, <u>cos</u> and <u>tan</u> because they're both involved with <u>RIGHT-ANGLED TRIANGLES</u>.

2) The big difference is that Pythagoras does not involve any <u>angles</u> — it just uses <u>two sides</u> to find the <u>third side</u>. (Sin, cos and tan always involve <u>ANGLES</u>.)

3) The <u>BASIC FORMULA</u> for Pythagoras is $a^2 + b^2 = h^2$

4) <u>PLUG THE NUMBERS IN</u> and work it out.

5) But get the numbers in the <u>RIGHT PLACE</u>. The 2 shorter sides (squared) add to equal the longest side (squared).

6) Always <u>CHECK</u> that your answer is <u>SENSIBLE</u>.

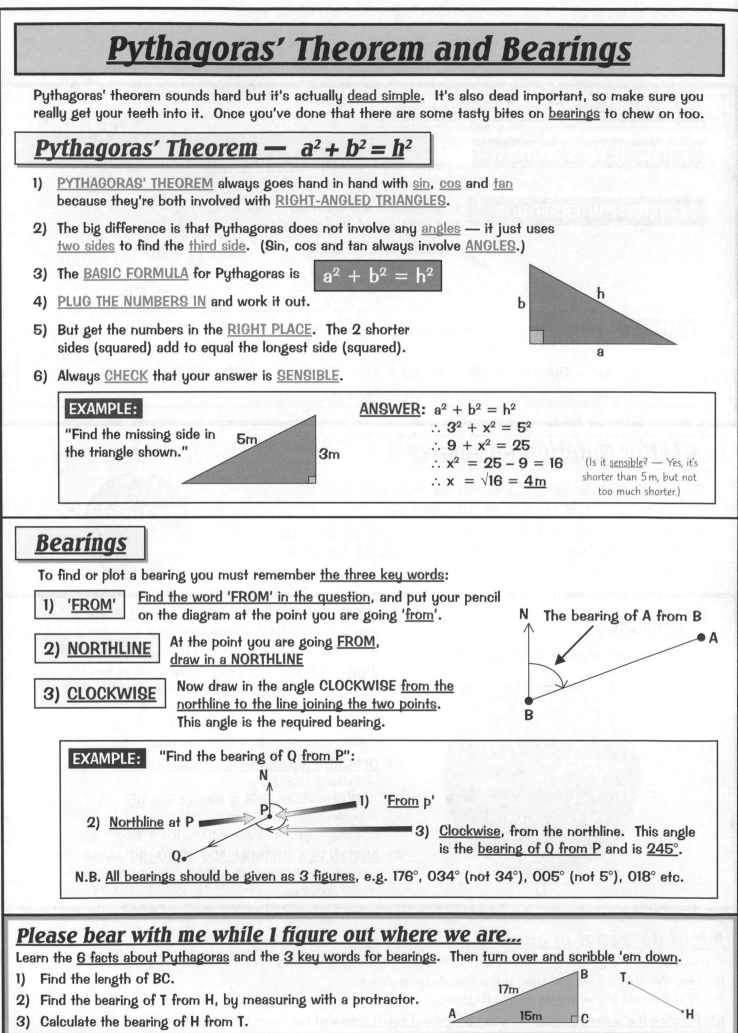

EXAMPLE:

"Find the missing side in the triangle shown."

5m

3m

<u>ANSWER</u>: $a^2 + b^2 = h^2$
$\therefore 3^2 + x^2 = 5^2$
$\therefore 9 + x^2 = 25$
$\therefore x^2 = 25 - 9 = 16$
$\therefore x = \sqrt{16} = \underline{4m}$

(Is it <u>sensible</u>? — Yes, it's shorter than 5m, but not too much shorter.)

Bearings

To find or plot a bearing you must remember <u>the three key words</u>:

1) 'FROM'   <u>Find the word 'FROM' in the question</u>, and put your pencil on the diagram at the point you are going '<u>from</u>'.

2) <u>NORTHLINE</u>   At the point you are going <u>FROM</u>, draw in a <u>NORTHLINE</u>

3) <u>CLOCKWISE</u>   Now draw in the angle CLOCKWISE <u>from the northline to the line joining the two points</u>. This angle is the required bearing.

N   The bearing of A from B

● A

B

EXAMPLE: "Find the bearing of Q <u>from P</u>":

N

P

Q

1) 'From p'

2) <u>Northline</u> at P

3) <u>Clockwise</u>, from the northline. This angle is the <u>bearing of Q from P</u> and is <u>245°</u>.

N.B. <u>All bearings should be given as 3 figures</u>, e.g. 176°, 034° (not 34°), 005° (not 5°), 018° etc.

Please bear with me while I figure out where we are...

Learn the <u>6 facts</u> about Pythagoras and the <u>3 key words</u> for bearings. Then <u>turn over and scribble 'em down</u>.

1) Find the length of BC.

2) Find the bearing of T from H, by measuring with a protractor.

3) Calculate the bearing of H from T.

B   T

17m

A   15m   C   H

Trigonometry — Sin, Cos, Tan

Trigonometry — it's a big scary word. But it's not a big scary topic. An <u>important</u> topic, yes. An <u>always cropping up</u> topic, definitely. But scary? Pur-lease. Takes more than a triangle to scare me. Read on...

Method

There are several methods for doing Trig and they're all pretty much the same. However, the method shown below has a number of advantages, mainly because the <u>formula triangles</u> mean the <u>same method</u> is used <u>every time</u> (no matter which side or angle is being asked for). This makes the whole topic a lot simpler, and you'll find that once you've learned this method, the answers automatically come out right every time.

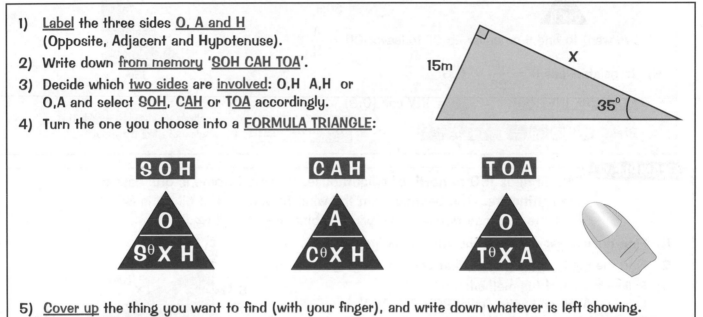

1) <u>Label</u> the three sides <u>O, A and H</u> (Opposite, Adjacent and Hypotenuse).

2) Write down <u>from memory</u> '<u>SOH CAH TOA</u>'.

3) Decide which <u>two sides</u> are <u>involved</u>: O,H A,H or O,A and select <u>SOH</u>, <u>CAH</u> or <u>TOA</u> accordingly.

4) Turn the one you choose into a <u>FORMULA TRIANGLE</u>:

5) <u>Cover up</u> the thing you want to find (with your finger), and write down whatever is left showing.

6) <u>Translate into numbers</u> and work it out.

7) Finally, <u>check</u> that your answer is <u>sensible</u>.

Four Important Details

1) The <u>Hypotenuse</u> is the <u>LONGEST SIDE</u>. The <u>Opposite</u> is the side <u>OPPOSITE</u> the angle being used (θ), and the <u>Adjacent</u> is the (other) side <u>NEXT TO</u> the angle <u>being used</u>.

2) In the formula triangles, Sθ represents sin θ, Cθ is cos θ, and Tθ is tan θ.

3) Remember, <u>TO FIND THE ANGLE — USE INVERSE</u>. i.e. press INV or SHIFT or 2nd, followed by <u>sin</u>, <u>cos</u> or <u>tan</u> (and make sure your calculator is in DEG mode).

4) You can only use sin, cos and tan on <u>RIGHT-ANGLED TRIANGLES</u> — you may have to add lines to the diagram to create one, especially with <u>isosceles triangles</u>.

Boo!

Charlie made one final attempt to preserve the scary reputation of the triangles.

SOH CAH TOA — the not-so-secret formula for success...

See — not scary at all. All you have to do is <u>learn</u> this one simple method and you'll be SOH-CAH-TOAing along with the best trigonometric minds around. Notice the strategic use of the word "learn" though. It doesn't say "All you have to do is skim briefly over this method and you'll be a trig whizz". No my friend, it doesn't say that, it says "learn". And I shall say it once more for good measure — "learn" this method. And the job's a good-un.

Trigonometry — Sin, Cos, Tan

Thought you'd been left with no lovely examples to help you through the trials of trig? Not on your nelly...

Examples:

EXAMPLE 1: "Find the angle θ in this triangle."

1) Label O, A, H
2) Write down 'SOH CAH TOA'
3) Two sides involved: A, H
4) So use

$$\frac{A}{C\theta \times H}$$

5) We want to find θ so cover up Cθ to leave: $C\theta = \dfrac{A}{H}$

6) Translate: $\cos \theta = \dfrac{15}{25} = 0.6$

   NOW USE INVERSE: θ = INV cos (0.6)

   Press [INV][COS][0.6][=]   [53.130102]

   So ans. = <u>53.1°</u>

25m   25m

θ

30m

Note the usual way of dealing with an **ISOSCELES TRIANGLE**: split it <u>down the middle</u> to get a <u>RIGHT ANGLE</u>:

Hyp
25m   Opp
θ   Adj
15m

Finally, is it sensible? — Yes, the angle looks like it's about 50°.

EXAMPLE 2: "An oil rig is 150 m north of a lighthouse. A wind turbine is due east of the lighthouse. The bearing from the wind turbine to the oil rig is 305°. Find the distance between the wind turbine and the oil rig."

1) First draw a <u>diagram</u> using the information you're given.
2) Find the <u>right-angled triangle</u> that you can use trigonometry on.
3) Follow the usual trig method:
   Label O, A, H, and write down 'SOH CAH TOA'
   Two sides involved: O, H. So use:

   $$\frac{O}{S\theta \times H}$$

4) We want to find H so cover it up to leave: $H = \dfrac{O}{S\theta}$

5) Translate: $x = \dfrac{150}{\sin 35}$

150 m
Opp   Hyp
x

Adj
305° − 270° = 35°   305°

Press: [150][÷][SIN][35][=]   [261.51702]   So ans = <u>261.5 m</u>

Angles of Elevation And Depression

A sad donkey.
Poor donkey.

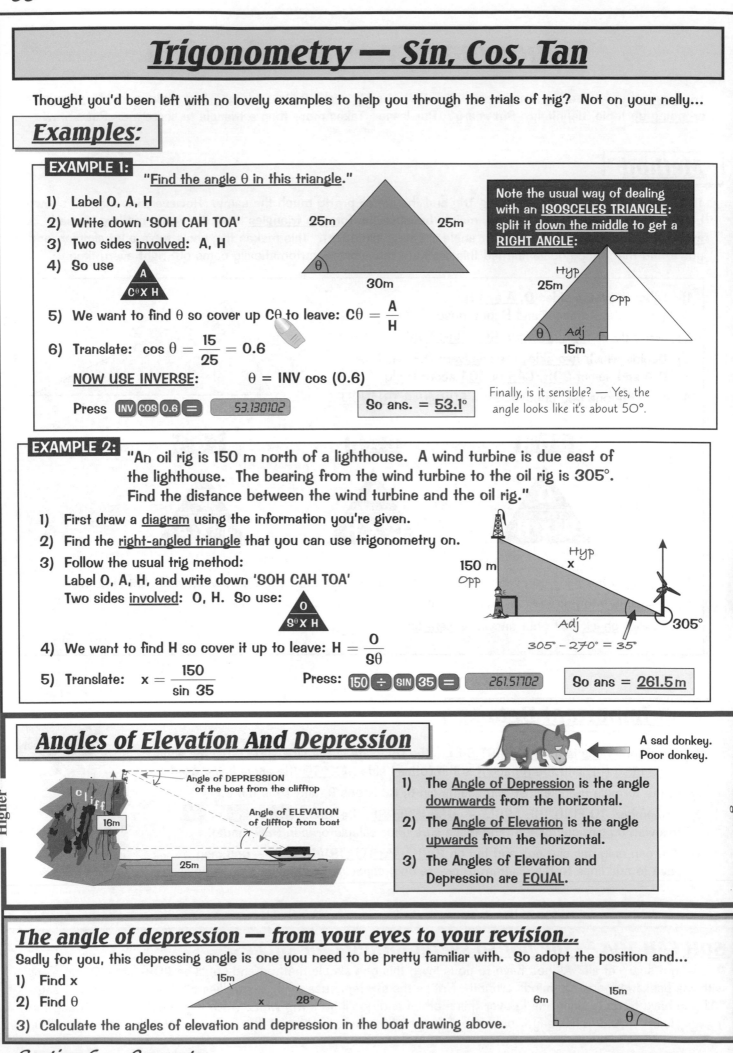

Angle of DEPRESSION
of the boat from the clifftop

Angle of ELEVATION
of clifftop from boat

cliff

16m

25m

1) The <u>Angle of Depression</u> is the angle <u>downwards</u> from the horizontal.
2) The <u>Angle of Elevation</u> is the angle <u>upwards</u> from the horizontal.
3) The Angles of Elevation and Depression are <u>EQUAL</u>.

Higher

The angle of depression — from your eyes to your revision...

Sadly for you, this depressing angle is one you need to be pretty familiar with. So adopt the position and...

1) Find x
2) Find θ
3) Calculate the angles of elevation and depression in the boat drawing above.

15m
x   28°

15m
6m
θ

3D Pythagoras and Trigonometry

3D questions on Pythagoras and trig are a bit tricky. Or should that be a bit of a trick... for whilst they might <u>seem</u> fiendishly difficult, they're actually mild as a poor quality cheddar. All you need is the same old rules.

Angle Between Line and Plane — Use a Diagram

Learn The 3-Step Method

1) Make a <u>RIGHT-ANGLED</u> triangle using <u>the line</u>, <u>a line in the plane</u> and <u>a line between the two</u>.

2) <u>Draw</u> this right-angled triangle again so that you can see it <u>clearly</u>. <u>Label</u> the sides. You might have to use <u>Pythagoras</u> to work out the length of one of the sides.

3) Use <u>trigonometry</u> to calculate the angle.

EXAMPLE:

"ABCDE is a square-based pyramid. It is 12 cm high and the square base has sides of length 7 cm. Find the angle the edge AE makes with the base."

X is the centre of the square base.

1) First draw a <u>right-angled triangle</u> using the <u>edge AE</u>, the <u>base</u> and <u>a line between the two</u> (in this case the central height). Call the angle you're trying to find <u>θ</u>.

2) Now draw this triangle <u>clearly</u> and label it.

To find θ, you need to know the length of side EX.

So, using <u>Pythagoras</u> — $EX^2 = 3.5^2 + 3.5^2 = 24.5 \Rightarrow EX = \sqrt{24.5}$ cm

You know the lengths of the <u>opposite</u> and <u>adjacent</u> sides, so use <u>tan</u>.

3) Now use <u>trigonometry</u> to find the angle θ:

$$\tan\theta = \frac{12}{\sqrt{24.5}} = 2.4... \quad \theta = \underline{67.6°} \text{ (1 d.p.)}$$

Use Right-Angled Triangles To Find Lengths too

EXAMPLE: "Find the lengths FH and BH shown in the diagram."

1) First use <u>Pythagoras</u> to find the length <u>FH</u>.
$FH^2 = 3^2 + 3^2 = 18 \Rightarrow FH = \sqrt{18}$ cm $= \underline{4.2 \text{ cm}}$ (1 decimal place)

2) Now use <u>Pythagoras</u> again to find the length <u>BH</u>.
$BH^2 = 3^2 + (\sqrt{18})^2 = 27 \Rightarrow BH = \sqrt{27}$ cm $= \underline{5.2 \text{ cm}}$ (1 decimal place)

Wow — just what can't right-angled triangles do?

Well, they can't learn this for you. Or bake a victoria sponge. Or answer any of these rather splendid questions. You'll just have to do it yourself.

1) Calculate the angle that the line AG makes with the base of this cuboid.
2) Calculate the length of AG.

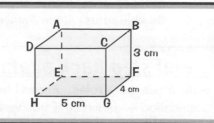

The Sine and Cosine Rules

Normal trigonometry using SOH CAH TOA etc. can only be applied to <u>right-angled</u> triangles. Which leaves us with the question of what to do with other-angled triangles. Step forward the <u>Sine and Cosine Rules</u>...

Labelling The Triangle

This is very important. You must label the sides and angles properly so that the letters for the sides and angles correspond with each other:

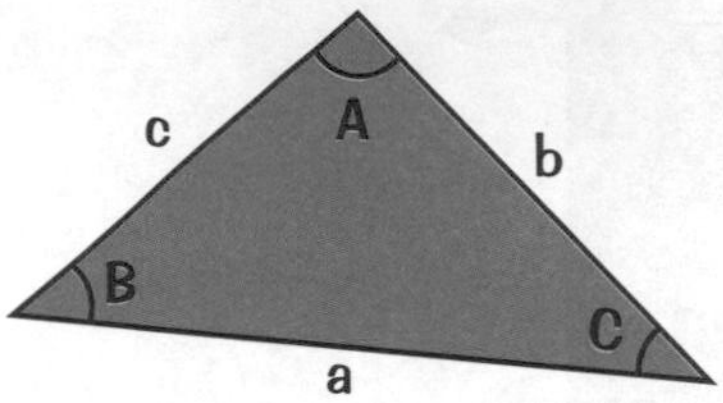

Remember, <u>side 'a' is opposite angle A</u> etc.

It doesn't matter which sides you decide to call a, b, and c, just as long as the angles are then labelled properly.

Three Formulas to Learn:

These first two formulas let you work out <u>sides</u> and <u>angles</u>:

The Sine Rule

You don't use the whole thing with both '=' signs of course, so it's not half as bad as it looks — you just choose the two bits that you want:

$$\frac{a}{\sin A} = \frac{b}{\sin B} = \frac{c}{\sin C}$$

e.g. $\frac{b}{\sin B} = \frac{c}{\sin C}$ or $\frac{a}{\sin A} = \frac{b}{\sin B}$

The Cosine Rule

$$a^2 = b^2 + c^2 - 2bc \cos A$$

or $\cos A = \frac{b^2+c^2-a^2}{2bc}$

Area of the Triangle

Of course, you already know the simple formula when you have the <u>base</u> and <u>vertical height</u>:

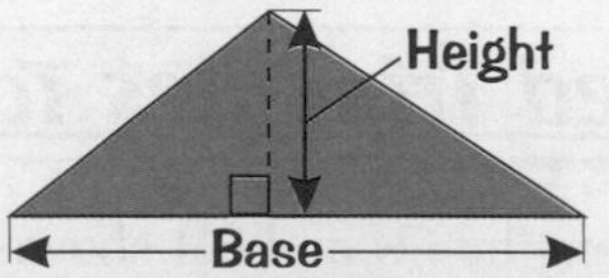

Area = ½ base × height

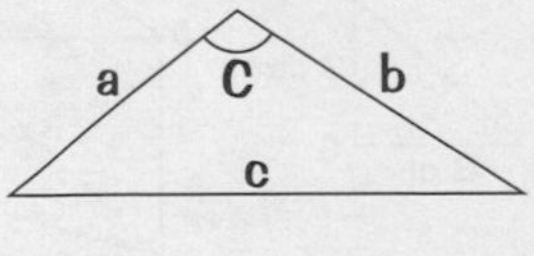

Well, here's a fancier formula that you can use when you know <u>two sides</u> and the angle <u>between them</u>:

Area of triangle = ½ ab sin C

Yes, these formulas will be given to you in the exam. But you should still <u>**LEARN**</u> them off by heart and practise using them. If you don't, you'll spend all your time flicking to the front of the paper, and won't be able to use them anyway.

...and step back again. Hope you enjoyed your moment in the spotlight...

With these extra rules, you will be able to conquer any triangles you come across. The next step is surely world domination — but only if you've learnt the formulas on this page and know how to properly label a triangle.

The Sine and Cosine Rules

Amazingly, there are only FOUR question types where you have to apply the Sine and Cosine rules. So learn the exact details of these four examples and you'll be laughing. WARNING: if you laugh too much people will think you're crazy.

The Four Examples

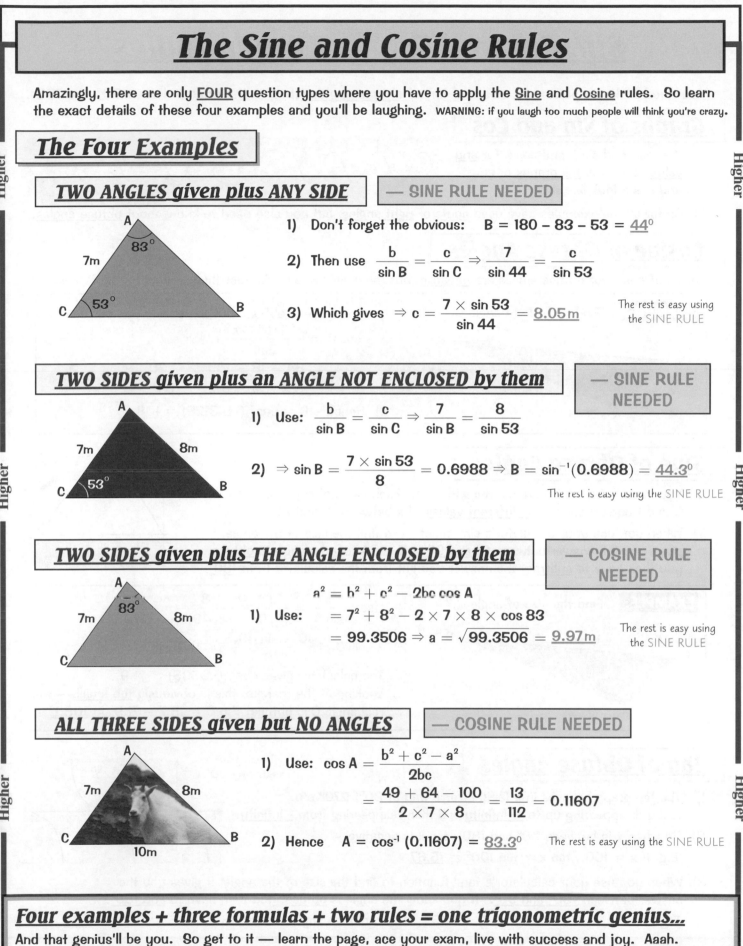

TWO ANGLES given plus ANY SIDE — SINE RULE NEEDED

1) Don't forget the obvious: B = 180 − 83 − 53 = 44°

2) Then use $\frac{b}{\sin B} = \frac{c}{\sin C} \Rightarrow \frac{7}{\sin 44} = \frac{c}{\sin 53}$

3) Which gives $\Rightarrow c = \frac{7 \times \sin 53}{\sin 44} = 8.05\,m$

The rest is easy using the SINE RULE

TWO SIDES given plus an ANGLE NOT ENCLOSED by them — SINE RULE NEEDED

1) Use: $\frac{b}{\sin B} = \frac{c}{\sin C} \Rightarrow \frac{7}{\sin B} = \frac{8}{\sin 53}$

2) $\Rightarrow \sin B = \frac{7 \times \sin 53}{8} = 0.6988 \Rightarrow B = \sin^{-1}(0.6988) = 44.3°$

The rest is easy using the SINE RULE

TWO SIDES given plus THE ANGLE ENCLOSED by them — COSINE RULE NEEDED

1) Use: $a^2 = b^2 + c^2 - 2bc \cos A$
   $= 7^2 + 8^2 - 2 \times 7 \times 8 \times \cos 83$
   $= 99.3506 \Rightarrow a = \sqrt{99.3506} = 9.97\,m$

The rest is easy using the SINE RULE

ALL THREE SIDES given but NO ANGLES — COSINE RULE NEEDED

1) Use: $\cos A = \frac{b^2 + c^2 - a^2}{2bc}$
   $= \frac{49 + 64 - 100}{2 \times 7 \times 8} = \frac{13}{112} = 0.11607$

2) Hence $A = \cos^{-1}(0.11607) = 83.3°$

The rest is easy using the SINE RULE

Four examples + three formulas + two rules = one trigonometric genius...

And that genius'll be you. So get to it — learn the page, ace your exam, live with success and joy. Aaah.

1) Write down a new version of each of the 4 examples above and then use the SINE and COSINE RULES to find ALL of the sides and angles for each one.

2) A triangle has two sides of 12m and 17m with an angle of 70° between them. Find all the other sides and angles in the triangle. (A sketch is essential, of course).

Sin, Cos and Tan for Larger Angles

You need to know about sin, cos and tan of <u>obtuse angles</u> (they're the ones between 90° and 180°.)

Graphs of Sin and Cos

1) You can find sin x and cos x for <u>any</u> value of x. The <u>full graphs</u> of sin x and cos x look like this:

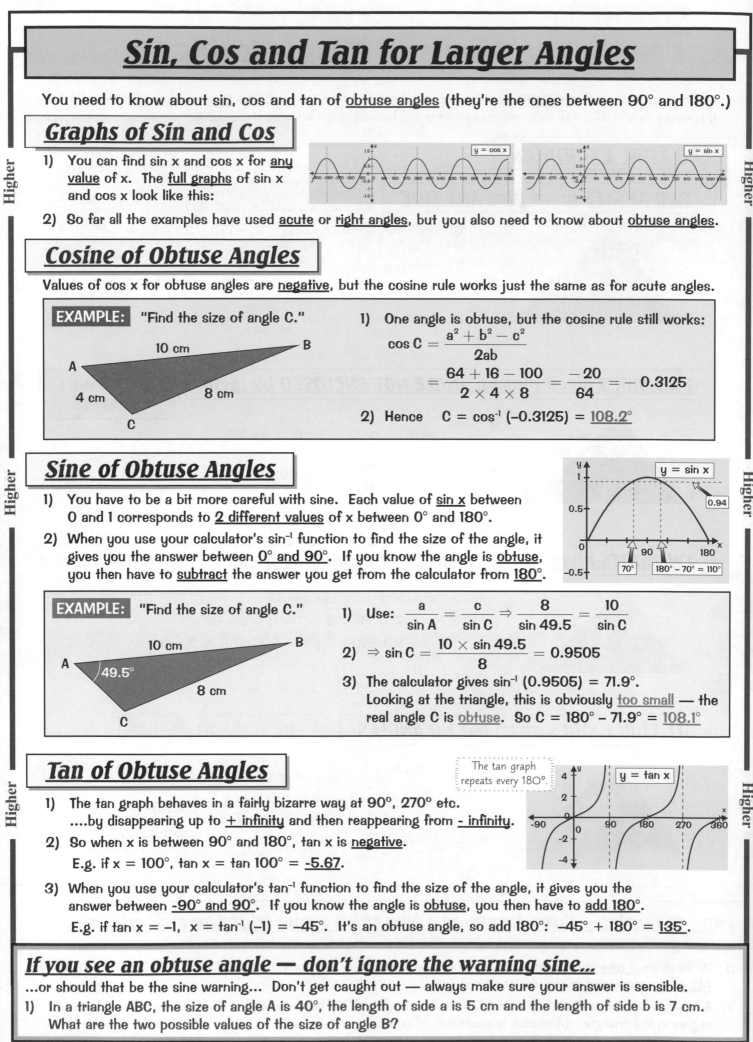

2) So far all the examples have used <u>acute</u> or <u>right angles</u>, but you also need to know about <u>obtuse angles</u>.

Cosine of Obtuse Angles

Values of cos x for obtuse angles are <u>negative</u>, but the cosine rule works just the same as for acute angles.

EXAMPLE: "Find the size of angle C."

10 cm
A
4 cm
8 cm
C
B

1) One angle is obtuse, but the cosine rule still works:
$$\cos C = \frac{a^2 + b^2 - c^2}{2ab}$$
$$= \frac{64 + 16 - 100}{2 \times 4 \times 8} = \frac{-20}{64} = -0.3125$$

2) Hence $C = \cos^{-1}(-0.3125) = \underline{108.2°}$

Sine of Obtuse Angles

1) You have to be a bit more careful with sine. Each value of <u>sin x</u> between 0 and 1 corresponds to <u>2 different values</u> of x between 0° and 180°.

2) When you use your calculator's sin⁻¹ function to find the size of the angle, it gives you the answer between <u>0° and 90°</u>. If you know the angle is <u>obtuse</u>, you then have to <u>subtract</u> the answer you get from the calculator from <u>180°</u>.

EXAMPLE: "Find the size of angle C."

10 cm
A
49.5°
8 cm
C
B

1) Use: $\frac{a}{\sin A} = \frac{c}{\sin C} \Rightarrow \frac{8}{\sin 49.5} = \frac{10}{\sin C}$

2) $\Rightarrow \sin C = \frac{10 \times \sin 49.5}{8} = 0.9505$

3) The calculator gives sin⁻¹ (0.9505) = 71.9°. Looking at the triangle, this is obviously <u>too small</u> — the real angle C is <u>obtuse</u>. So C = 180° − 71.9° = <u>108.1°</u>

Tan of Obtuse Angles

The tan graph repeats every 180°.

1) The tan graph behaves in a fairly bizarre way at 90°, 270° etc. ....by disappearing up to + infinity and then reappearing from - infinity.

2) So when x is between 90° and 180°, tan x is <u>negative</u>.
   E.g. if x = 100°, tan x = tan 100° = <u>-5.67</u>.

3) When you use your calculator's tan⁻¹ function to find the size of the angle, it gives you the answer between <u>-90° and 90°</u>. If you know the angle is <u>obtuse</u>, you then have to <u>add 180°</u>.
   E.g. if tan x = −1, x = tan⁻¹ (−1) = −45°. It's an obtuse angle, so add 180°: −45° + 180° = <u>135°</u>.

<u>If you see an obtuse angle — don't ignore the warning sine...</u>

...or should that be the sine warning... Don't get caught out — always make sure your answer is sensible.

1) In a triangle ABC, the size of angle A is 40°, the length of side a is 5 cm and the length of side b is 7 cm. What are the two possible values of the size of angle B?

Revision Summary

Here we are again — more lovely questions for you to test yourself with.

Remember you have to keep practising these questions <u>over and over again</u> until you can answer them <u>all</u>. Seriously, you do. That's the best kind of revision there is because the whole idea is to find out what you <u>don't know</u> and then learn it <u>until you do</u>.   Enjoy.

KEEP LEARNING THESE BASIC FACTS UNTIL YOU KNOW THEM

1) Write down seven easy rules of geometry.
2) Write down three simple rules for circle geometry.
3) Write down six more circle geometry rules.
4) Write down the two chord intersection properties.
5) Find the length of line segment AB in this circle:

16 cm / A / 12 cm / 18 cm / B

6) What is three-letter angle notation? Give an example.
7) What is the formula for Pythagoras' theorem? Where can you use Pythagoras' Theorem?
8) How do you decide where each side length goes in the formula? What final check do you make?
9) A museum has a flight of stairs up to its front door (see diagram).
A ramp is to be put over the top of the steps for wheelchair users.
Calculate the length that the ramp would need to be.

ramp / 2.5m / 4m

10) What are the three key words for bearings? How must bearings be written?
11) Write down the important steps of a good solid method for doing **TRIGONOMETRY**.
12) What are the advantages of using formula triangles to do trig?
13) Most avalanches happen on slopes that are at angles of between 15° and 60°. Jane decided to estimate the angle of the slope she was on to see whether she was at high risk from an avalanche. She created a right-angled triangle using two ice axes and estimated the measurements shown. Calculate angle x — the angle of the slope.

0.4m / x / 0.35m

14) Draw a diagram to illustrate angles of elevation and depression.
15) What three steps allow you to find the angle between a line and a plane?
16) Write down the **SINE** and **COSINE RULES** and draw a properly labelled triangle.
17) List the 4 different types of sine/cosine rule questions and which rule you need for each.
18) Find the other two angles and the other side length in this triangle.

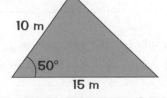

10 m / 50° / 15 m

19) What is the formula (involving sin) for the area of any triangle? Demonstrate its use.
20) If x is an obtuse angle, are the following positive or negative?
a) cos x   b) sin x   c) tan x
21) If 90° < x < 180°, find x when:
a) sin x = 0.5   b) sin x = 0.125   c) sin x = 0.98
22) If 90° < x < 180°, find x when:
a) tan x = –1.73   b) tan x = –57.3   c) tan x = –0.26

Mean, Median, Mode and Range

If you don't manage to <u>learn these 4 basic definitions</u> then you'll be passing up on some of the easiest marks in the whole Exam. It can't be that difficult can it?

> 1) <u>MODE</u> = <u>MOST</u> common
>
> 2) <u>MEDIAN</u> = <u>MIDDLE</u> value
>
> 3) <u>MEAN</u> = <u>TOTAL</u> of items ÷ <u>NUMBER</u> of items
>
> 4) <u>RANGE</u> = How far from the smallest to the biggest

The Golden Rule

Mean, median and mode should be <u>easy marks</u> but even people who've gone to the incredible extent of learning them still manage to lose marks in the Exam because they don't do <u>this one vital step</u>:

Always REARRANGE the data in ASCENDING ORDER

(and check you have the same number of entries!)

Example

> "Find the mean, median, mode and range of these numbers:"
> 2, 5, 3, 2, 6, -4, 0, 9, -3, 1, 6, 3, -2, 3   (14)

1) FIRST... rearrange them: -4, -3, -2, 0, 1, 2, 2, 3, 3, 3, 5, 6, 6, 9   (14) ✓

2) MEAN = $\dfrac{\text{total}}{\text{number}}$ = $\dfrac{-4-3-2+0+1+2+2+3+3+3+5+6+6+9}{14}$

   = 31 ÷ 14 = <u>2.21</u>

3) MEDIAN = <u>the middle value</u> (only when they are <u>arranged in order of size</u> though!).

   When there are two middle numbers as in this case, then the median is **HALFWAY BETWEEN THE TWO MIDDLE NUMBERS**.

   -4, -3, -2, 0, 1, 2, 2, 3, 3, 3, 5, 6, 6, 9
   ← seven numbers this side   ↑   seven numbers this side →
   Median = <u>2.5</u>

4) MODE = <u>most</u> common value, which is simply <u>3</u>. (Or you can say, "The <u>modal</u> value is 3.")

5) RANGE = distance from lowest to highest value, i.e. from -4 up to 9 = <u>13</u>

> REMEMBER:
> <u>Mode</u> = <u>most</u> (emphasise the 'o' in each when you say them)
> <u>Median</u> = <u>mid</u> (emphasise the m*d in each when you say them)
> <u>Mean</u> is just the <u>average</u>, but it's <u>mean</u> 'cos you have to work it out.

Strike a pose, there's nothing to it — mode...

Learn the <u>four definitions</u> and the <u>golden rule</u>... then turn this page over and write them down from memory. Then apply all that you have <u>learnt</u> to this set of data: 1, 3, 14, -5, 6, -12, 18, 7, 23, 10, -5, -14, 0, 25, 8.

Frequency Tables

Frequency tables can either be done in <u>rows</u> or in <u>columns</u> of numbers and they can be quite confusing, <u>but not if you learn these seven key points</u>:

Seven Key Points

1) The word <u>FREQUENCY</u> just means <u>HOW MANY</u>, so a frequency table is nothing more than a '<u>How many in each group</u>' table.

2) The <u>FIRST ROW</u> (or column) just gives the <u>GROUP LABELS</u>.

3) The <u>SECOND ROW</u> (or column) gives the <u>ACTUAL DATA</u>.

4) You have to <u>WORK OUT A THIRD ROW</u> (or column) <u>yourself</u>.

5) The <u>MEAN</u> is always found using: 3rd Row total ÷ 2nd Row Total

6) The <u>MEDIAN</u> is found from the <u>MIDDLE VALUE</u> in the 2nd row.

7) The <u>RANGE</u> is found from <u>the extremes of the first row</u>.

Example

Here is a typical frequency table shown in both <u>ROW FORM</u> and <u>COLUMN FORM</u>:

No. of Sisters	Frequency
0	7
1	15
2	12
3	8
4	3
5	1
6	0

No. of Sisters	0	1	2	3	4	5	6
Frequency	7	15	12	8	3	1	0

Column Form

Row Form

There's no real difference between these two forms and you could get either one in your Exam. Whichever you get, make sure you remember these <u>THREE IMPORTANT FACTS</u>:

1) <u>THE 1ST ROW</u> (or column) gives us the <u>GROUP LABELS</u> for <u>the different categories</u> : i.e. 'no sisters', 'one sister', 'two sisters', etc.

2) <u>THE 2ND ROW</u> (or column) <u>is the ACTUAL DATA</u> and tells us <u>HOW MANY (people) THERE ARE in each category</u> i.e. 7 people had 'no sisters', 15 people had 'one sister', etc.

3) <u>BUT YOU SHOULD SEE THE TABLE AS UNFINISHED</u> because it still needs <u>A THIRD ROW</u> (or column) and <u>TOTALS</u> for the <u>2nd and 3rd rows</u>, as shown on the next page...

Frequency Tables

And here they are — the <u>completed tables</u> you've been eagerly awaiting...

This is what the two types of table look like when they're completed:

No. of Sisters	0	1	2	3	4	5	6	Totals	
Frequency	7	15	12	8	3	1	0	46	(People asked)
No. × Frequency	0	15	24	24	12	5	0	80	(Sisters)

No. of Sisters	Frequency	No. × Frequency
0	7	0
1	15	15
2	12	24
3	8	24
4	3	12
5	1	5
6	0	0
Totals	46	80
	(People asked)	(Sisters)

"WHERE DOES THE THIRD ROW COME FROM?"

....I hear you cry!

<u>THE THIRD ROW</u> (or column) is <u>ALWAYS</u> obtained by <u>MULTIPLYING</u> the numbers from the <u>FIRST 2 ROWS</u> (or columns).

> **THIRD ROW = 1ST ROW × 2ND ROW**

Once the table is complete, you can easily find the <u>MEAN, MEDIAN, MODE AND RANGE</u> (see p.94) which is what they usually demand in the Exam:

Mean, Median, Mode and Range:

This is easy enough <u>if you learn it</u>. If you don't, you'll drown in a sea of numbers.

MEAN $= \dfrac{\text{3rd Row Total}}{\text{2nd Row Total}} = \dfrac{80}{46} = 1.74$ (sisters per person)

Mean sisters

MEDIAN — imagine the original data <u>SET OUT IN ASCENDING ORDER</u>:

0000000 111111111111111 222222222222 33333333 444 5

and the median is just the middle number which is between the 23rd and 24th digits. So for this data <u>THE MEDIAN IS 2</u>. (Of course, when you get slick at this you can easily find the position of the middle value straight from the table)

The MODE is very easy — it's just <u>THE GROUP WITH THE MOST ENTRIES</u>: in this case, <u>1</u>.

The RANGE is 5 − 0 = 5 The 2nd row tells us there are people with anything from 'no sisters' right up to 'five sisters' (but not 6 sisters). (Always give it as a <u>single number</u>.)

What's this? No gag? Yes well I thought you might appreciate being able to reach the end of one page without having to endure a pathetic attempt at humour. See, I really do care. Normal service will be resumed on p.97. Now learn the <u>7 rules</u> for frequency tables, then turn over and write them down to see what you know.

Using the methods you have just learned and this frequency table, find the MEAN, MEDIAN, MODE and RANGE of the no. of phones that people have.

No. of phones	0	1	2	3	4	5	6
Frequency	1	25	53	34	22	5	1

Grouped Frequency Tables

These are a bit <u>trickier</u>. The table below shows the distribution of weights of 60 school kids:

Weight (kg)	$30 \leq w < 40$	$40 \leq w < 50$	$50 \leq w < 60$	$60 \leq w < 70$	$70 \leq w < 80$
Frequency	8	16	18	12	6

What does $30 \leq w < 40$ mean?

Don't get confused by the notation used for the intervals.

1) The $\leq$ symbol means w can be <u>greater than or equal to 30</u>.
2) The $<$ symbol means w must be <u>less than 40</u> (but not equal to it).
3) So <u>a value of 30</u> will go in this group, but <u>a value of 40</u> will have to go in the next group: $40 \leq w < 50$.

'Estimating' The Mean using Mid-Interval Values

Just like with ordinary frequency tables you have to <u>add extra rows and find totals</u> to be able to work anything out.   Also notice <u>you can only 'ESTIMATE' the mean from grouped data tables</u> — you can't find it exactly unless you know all the original values.

1) <u>Add a 3rd row</u> and enter <u>MID-INTERVAL VALUES</u> for each group.

2) <u>Add a 4th row</u> and <u>multiply FREQUENCY × MID-INTERVAL VALUE</u> for each group.

Weight (kg)	$30 \leq w < 40$	$40 \leq w < 50$	$50 \leq w < 60$	$60 \leq w < 70$	$70 \leq w < 80$	Totals
Frequency	8	16	18	12	6	60
Mid-Interval Value	35	45	55	65	75	—
Frequency × Mid-Interval Value	280	720	990	780	450	3220

<u>ESTIMATING THE MEAN</u> is then the usual thing of <u>DIVIDING THE TOTALS</u>:

$$\text{Mean} = \frac{\text{Overall Total (Last Row)}}{\text{Frequency Total (2nd Row)}} = \frac{3220}{60} = 53.7$$

Finding The Mode and Median

1) <u>THE MODE</u> is still nice'n'easy: the modal group (or modal class) is $50 \leq w < 60$ kg.

2) <u>THE MEDIAN</u> can't be found exactly but you can say <u>which group it's in</u>.
    If all the data were put in order, the 30th/31st entries would be in the $50 \leq w < 60$ kg group.

There are Two Types of Data — Continuous and Discrete

<u>CONTINUOUS DATA</u> can take any value in a certain range. E.g. height, weight, time.

<u>DISCRETE DATA</u> can only take specific values. E.g. the number of pupils in a school, number of eggs laid, favourite lesson.

For discrete data where only <u>whole numbers</u> are possible, you can use intervals of say, $5 \leq x \leq 10$, $11 \leq x \leq 15$, ... You can't have the value 10.5, so it doesn't matter that it's not included in any group. You <u>can't</u> do this with continuous data, like weight, in the example above.

Mid-interval value — cheap ice-creams...

Learn all the details on this page, then turn over and write down <u>everything</u> you've learned. Good clean fun.

1) Estimate the mean for this table:

2) Also state the modal group and the approximate value of the median.

Length L (cm)	$15.5 \leq L < 16.5$	$16.5 \leq L < 17.5$	$17.5 \leq L < 18.5$	$18.5 \leq L < 19.5$
Frequency	12	18	23	8

Quartiles and the Interquartile Range

Now we're getting to the good stuff. And by good stuff, I mean <u>quartiles</u> and <u>interquartile</u> range...

Finding the Quartiles is just like Finding the Median

1) <u>Quartiles</u> divide the data into <u>four equal groups</u>.
2) The quartiles are the <u>lower quartile Q_1</u>, the <u>median Q_2</u> and the <u>upper quartile Q_3</u>.
3) If you put the data in ascending order, the quartiles are 25% (¼), 50% (½) and 75% (¾) of the way through the list.

> **EXAMPLE** Find the value of Q_1, Q_2 and Q_3 for this set of numbers: 7, 12, 5, 4, 3, 9, 5, 11, 6
>
> *This is discrete data (see p.97).*
>
> 1) Put the data in **ASCENDING ORDER** — 3, 4, 5, 5, 6, 7, 9, 11, 12
>
> 2) Work out where the **QUARTILES** come in the list using the following formulas:
>
> $$Q_1 \text{ position number} = (n+1)/4$$
> $$Q_2 \text{ position number} = 2(n+1)/4$$
> $$Q_3 \text{ position number} = 3(n+1)/4$$
>
> *n is just the total number of values.*
>
> Step 1: n = 9 so Q_1 position no. = (9+1)/4 = 2.5
> Q_2 position no. = 2(9+1)/4 = 5
> Q_3 position no. = 3(9+1)/4 = 7.5
>
> *If you get "half values", like in this example, find the halfway point of the two numbers either side of this position. This is just like finding the median of an even number of values.*
>
> Step 2: 3 4 5 5 6 7 9 11 12
> position 1 Q_1 (4+5)/2 = 4.5 Q_2 Q_3 (9+11)/2 = 10   position 9
>
> 3) So, the lower quartile $Q_1 = 4.5$, the median $Q_2 = 6$ and the upper quartile $Q_3 = 10$.

Interquartile means "Between Quartiles"

The <u>interquartile range</u> is the <u>difference</u> between the <u>upper quartile</u> and the <u>lower quartile</u>.

> **EXAMPLE** Find the <u>interquartile range</u> of the following set of numbers:
> *Put the data in ascending order.*
> 3 4 ④ 5 5 6 7 7 ⑨ 11 12
> Upper quartile = 9   Lower quartile = 4   Interquartile range = 9 − 4 = 5

And for non-grouped data that's all there is to it, but with grouped data it's a bit trickier. You can estimate the interquartile range using a cumulative frequency graph (see p.99).

The interquartile ranger — fighting crime between quartiles...

This page is really important, so make sure you understand it, then have a go at this question:
1) For the list of integers from 1 to 999 inclusive:
   a) What is the value of the lower quartile?
   b) What is the value of the upper quartile?
2) Write down the odd numbers between 1 and 13 inclusive. What is the interquartile range?

Cumulative Frequency

Four Key Points

1) <u>CUMULATIVE FREQUENCY</u> just means <u>ADDING IT UP AS YOU GO ALONG</u>.

2) You have to <u>ADD A THIRD ROW</u> to the table — the <u>RUNNING TOTAL</u> of the 2nd row.

3) <u>When plotting the graph</u>, always plot points <u>using the HIGHEST VALUE in each group</u> (of row 1) with the value from <u>row 3</u>. i.e. plot 13 at <u>160</u>, etc. (see below).

4) Cumulative Frequency is always plotted <u>up the side</u> of a graph, not across.

Example

Height (cm)	$140 \leq x < 150$	$150 \leq x < 160$	$160 \leq x < 170$	$170 \leq x < 180$	$180 \leq x < 190$	$190 \leq x < 200$	$200 \leq x < 210$
Frequency	4	9	20	33	36	15	3
Cumulative frequency	4 (at 150)	13 (at 160)	33 (at 170)	66 (at 180)	102 (at 190)	117 (at 200)	120 (at 210)

The graph is plotted from these pairs: (150, 4) (160, 13) (170, 33) (180, 66) etc.

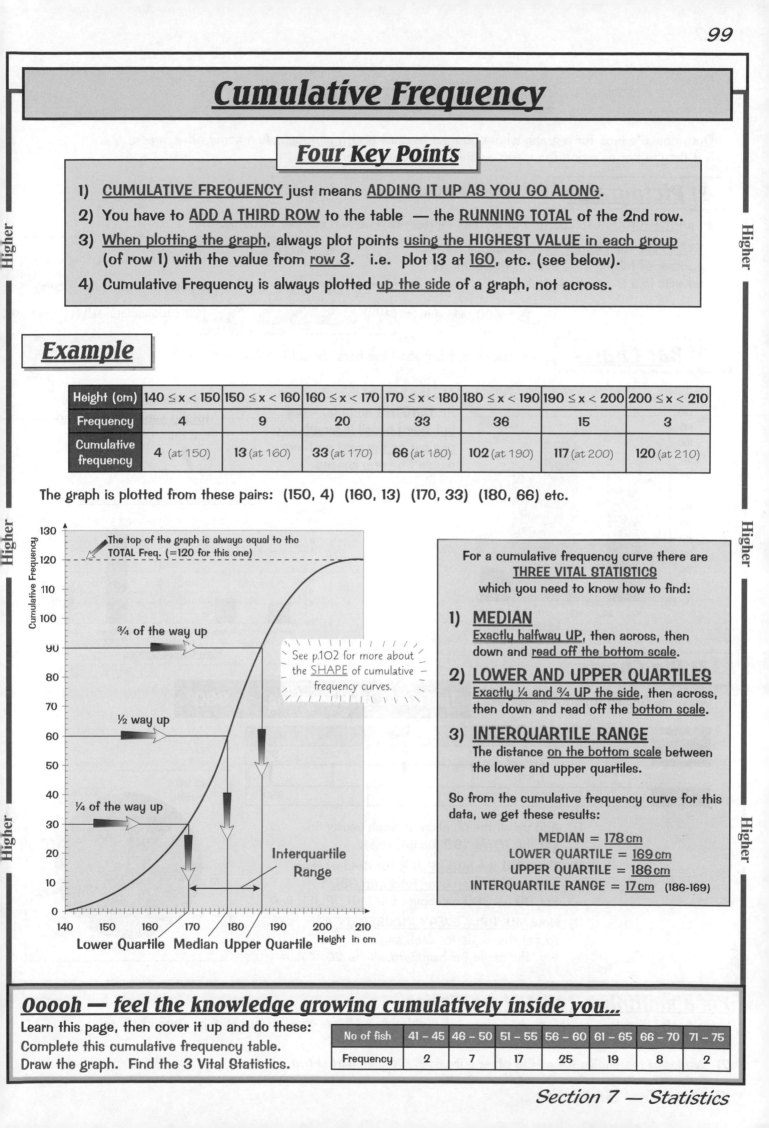

The top of the graph is always equal to the TOTAL Freq. (=120 for this one)

¾ of the way up

½ way up

¼ of the way up

See p.102 for more about the <u>SHAPE</u> of cumulative frequency curves.

Interquartile Range

Lower Quartile   Median   Upper Quartile   Height in cm

For a cumulative frequency curve there are **THREE VITAL STATISTICS** which you need to know how to find:

1) **MEDIAN**
<u>Exactly halfway UP</u>, then across, then down and <u>read off the bottom scale</u>.

2) **LOWER AND UPPER QUARTILES**
<u>Exactly ¼ and ¾ UP the side</u>, then across, then down and read off the <u>bottom scale</u>.

3) **INTERQUARTILE RANGE**
The distance <u>on the bottom scale</u> between the lower and upper quartiles.

So from the cumulative frequency curve for this data, we get these results:

MEDIAN = <u>178 cm</u>
LOWER QUARTILE = <u>169 cm</u>
UPPER QUARTILE = <u>186 cm</u>
INTERQUARTILE RANGE = <u>17 cm</u> (186-169)

Ooooh — feel the knowledge growing cumulatively inside you...

Learn this page, then cover it up and do these:
Complete this cumulative frequency table.
Draw the graph. Find the 3 Vital Statistics.

No of fish	41 – 45	46 – 50	51 – 55	56 – 60	61 – 65	66 – 70	71 – 75
Frequency	2	7	17	25	19	8	2

More Graphs and Charts

Ooo, now it's time for a graph where you get to draw pretty pictures. And some other types, but they're not as much fun. You've still got to know them though.

1) Pictograms — these use pictures instead of numbers.

In a PICTOGRAM each picture or symbol represents a certain number of items.

EXAMPLE: The pictogram opposite shows the number of talking cats used in ridiculous TV adverts in a 3-month period:

🐱 = 500 talking cats

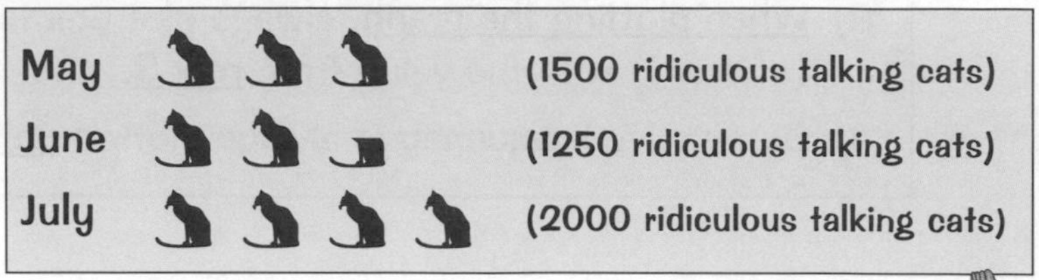

May	🐱 🐱 🐱	(1500 ridiculous talking cats)
June	🐱 🐱 🐱	(1250 ridiculous talking cats)
July	🐱 🐱 🐱 🐱	(2000 ridiculous talking cats)

2) Bar Charts — Just watch out for when the bars should touch or not touch:

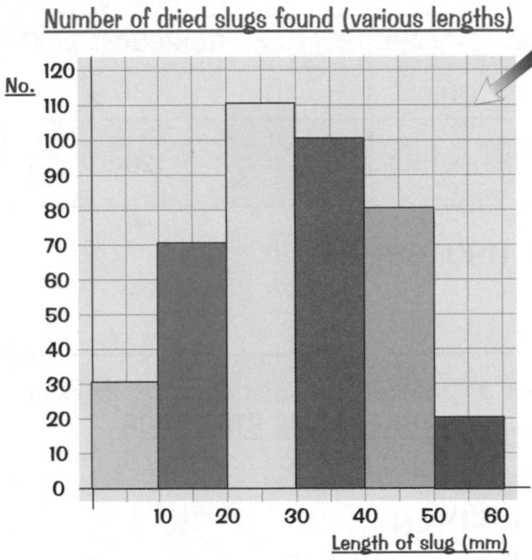

Number of dried slugs found (various lengths)

ALL the bars in this chart are for LENGTHS and you must put every possible length into one bar or the next so there mustn't be any spaces.

This bar chart compares totally separate items so the bars are separate.

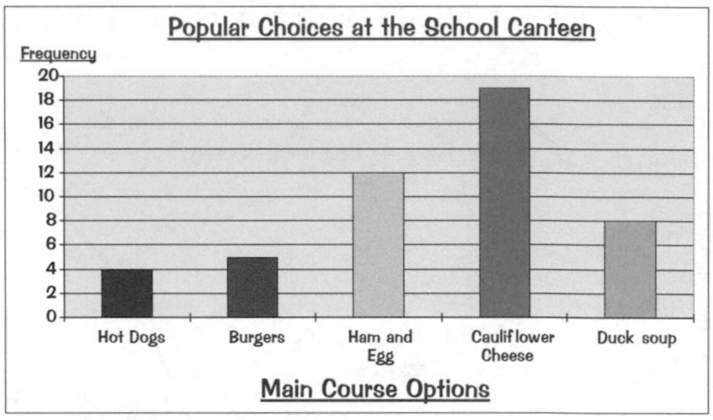

Popular Choices at the School Canteen

Main Course Options

3) Pie Charts

Learn the Golden Rule for Pie Charts: **The TOTAL of Everything = 360°**

Creature	Stick insects	Hamsters	Guinea pigs	Rabbits	Ducks	Total
Number	12	20	17	15	26	90
Angle		80°				360°

×4 ... ×4

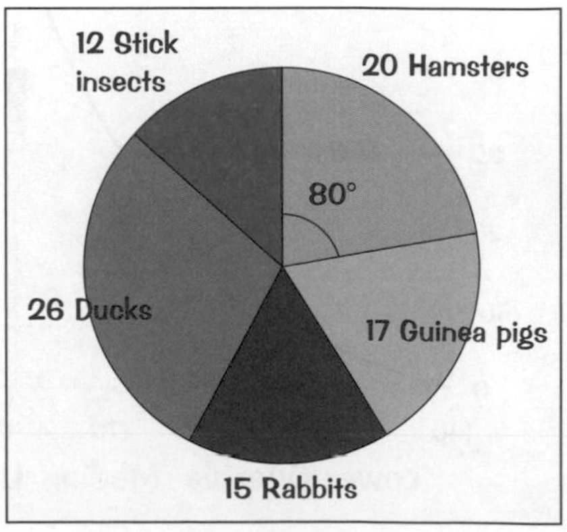

1) Add up all the numbers in each sector to get the TOTAL (90 for this one).
2) Then find the MULTIPLIER (or divider) that you need to turn your total into 360°: For 90 → 360 as above, the MULTIPLIER is 4.
3) Now MULTIPLY EVERY NUMBER BY 4 to get the angle for each sector. E.g. the angle for hamsters will be 20 × 4 = 80°.

12 Stick insects · 20 Hamsters · 80° · 17 Guinea pigs · 15 Rabbits · 26 Ducks

I'm a multiplier, twisted multiplier...

Lotsa useful diagrams on this page — learn all the details of these charts. Got all that stored? Good...
1) Turn over the page and draw an example of each chart.
2) Work out the angles for all the other animals in the pie chart shown above.

Histograms and Frequency Density

You'll be pleased to know that <u>histograms</u> are used to show frequency distributions for <u>continuous data</u>...

Histograms Can Have Equal Class Widths...

Histograms are similar to bar charts — they also show <u>frequency</u> using bars. Drawing a histogram for data with equal class widths is easy... you put <u>frequency</u> on the <u>y-axis</u> and a <u>suitable scale</u> for your data on the <u>x-axis</u> — then you draw a <u>bar</u> for each <u>class</u>. But remember, in histograms there are <u>no gaps</u> between the bars and the <u>x-axis</u> is <u>continuous</u>.

This squiggle is used to show that some of the x-axis is missing.

...Or Unequal Class Widths

Drawing histograms for data with <u>unequal</u> class widths is trickier. The key thing to remember is that <u>frequency</u> is represented by the <u>AREA</u> of the bars instead of the <u>height</u>.

1) To work out the <u>heights</u> of the bars you need to calculate the <u>frequency density</u> for each data class:

   ### FREQUENCY DENSITY = FREQUENCY ÷ CLASS WIDTH

2) Then, draw the axes with <u>frequency density</u> on the <u>y-axis</u> and the <u>variable values</u> on the <u>x-axis</u>.

3) Now draw <u>bars</u> for each class — the <u>height</u> is the <u>frequency density</u> and the <u>width</u> is the <u>class width</u>.

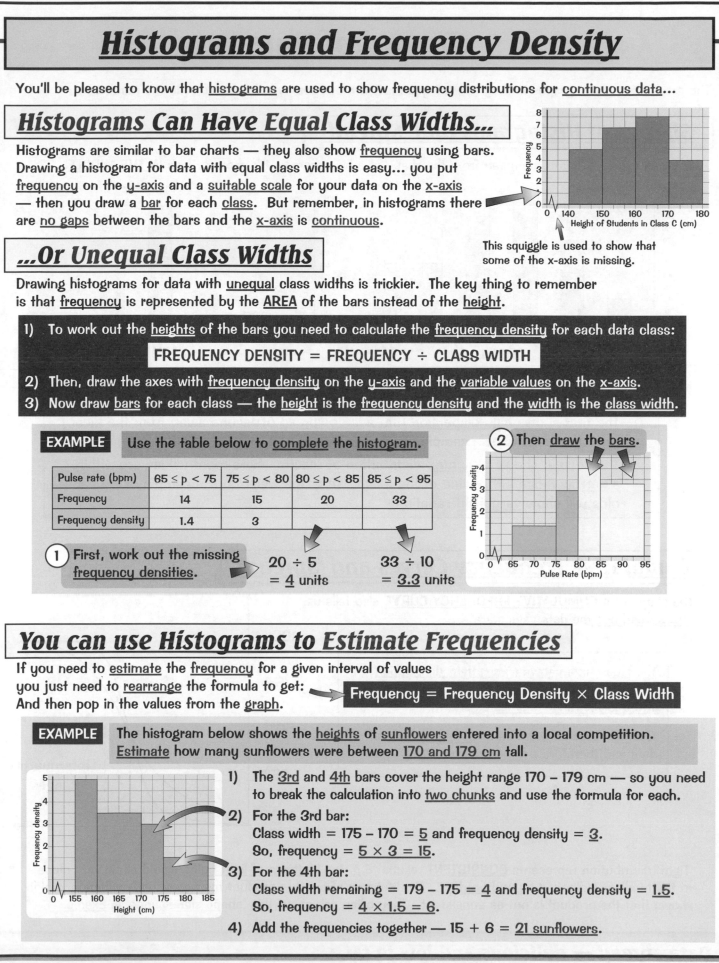

EXAMPLE   Use the table below to <u>complete</u> the histogram.

Pulse rate (bpm)	$65 \le p < 75$	$75 \le p < 80$	$80 \le p < 85$	$85 \le p < 95$
Frequency	14	15	20	33
Frequency density	1.4	3		

② Then <u>draw</u> the <u>bars</u>.

① First, work out the missing <u>frequency densities</u>.

$20 \div 5$ = **4** units

$33 \div 10$ = **3.3** units

You can use Histograms to Estimate Frequencies

If you need to <u>estimate</u> the <u>frequency</u> for a given interval of values you just need to <u>rearrange</u> the formula to get: And then pop in the values from the <u>graph</u>.

Frequency = Frequency Density × Class Width

EXAMPLE   The histogram below shows the <u>heights</u> of <u>sunflowers</u> entered into a local competition. <u>Estimate</u> how many sunflowers were between <u>170 and 179 cm</u> tall.

1) The <u>3rd</u> and <u>4th</u> bars cover the height range 170 – 179 cm — so you need to break the calculation into <u>two chunks</u> and use the formula for each.

2) For the 3rd bar:
   Class width = 175 – 170 = **5** and frequency density = **3**.
   So, frequency = **5 × 3 = 15**.

3) For the 4th bar:
   Class width remaining = 179 – 175 = **4** and frequency density = **1.5**.
   So, frequency = **4 × 1.5 = 6**.

4) Add the frequencies together — 15 + 6 = **21 sunflowers**.

My brain frequently feels very dense...

Make sure you know that formula for frequency density off by heart. Then, you know the drill...
1) Using the histogram above, estimate the number of sunflowers between 155 and 162 cm tall.

Spread of Data

The great thing about graphs is they can tell you stuff without you even having to read the numbers...

Shapes of Histograms and 'Spread'

You can easily estimate the mean from the shape of a histogram — it's more or less <u>IN THE MIDDLE</u>.

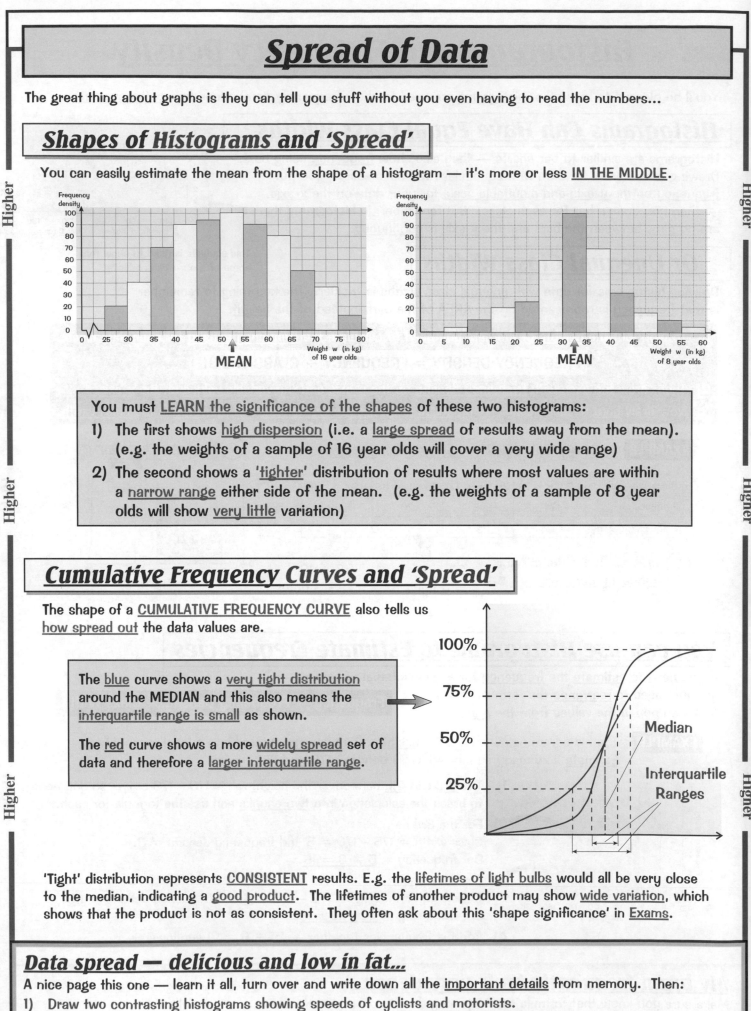

You must <u>LEARN the significance of the shapes</u> of these two histograms:

1) The first shows <u>high dispersion</u> (i.e. a <u>large spread</u> of results away from the mean). (e.g. the weights of a sample of 16 year olds will cover a very wide range)

2) The second shows a '<u>tighter</u>' distribution of results where most values are within a <u>narrow range</u> either side of the mean. (e.g. the weights of a sample of 8 year olds will show <u>very little</u> variation)

Cumulative Frequency Curves and 'Spread'

The shape of a <u>CUMULATIVE FREQUENCY CURVE</u> also tells us <u>how spread out</u> the data values are.

The <u>blue</u> curve shows a <u>very tight distribution</u> around the MEDIAN and this also means the <u>interquartile range is small</u> as shown.

The <u>red</u> curve shows a more <u>widely spread</u> set of data and therefore a <u>larger interquartile range</u>.

Median

Interquartile Ranges

'Tight' distribution represents <u>CONSISTENT</u> results. E.g. the <u>lifetimes of light bulbs</u> would all be very close to the median, indicating a <u>good product</u>. The lifetimes of another product may show <u>wide variation</u>, which shows that the product is not as consistent. They often ask about this 'shape significance' in <u>Exams</u>.

Data spread — delicious and low in fat...

A nice page this one — learn it all, turn over and write down all the <u>important details</u> from memory. Then:

1) Draw two contrasting histograms showing speeds of cyclists and motorists.

2) Sketch two cumulative frequency curves for heights of 5 yr olds and 13 yr olds.

Probability

This is nobody's favourite subject for sure, I've never really spoken to anyone who's said they do like it (not for long anyway). Although it does seem a bit of a 'Black Art' to most people, it's not as bad as you might think, but YOU MUST LEARN THE BASIC FACTS.

All Probabilities are between 0 and 1

A probability of ZERO means it will NEVER HAPPEN — P(impossibility) = 0.
A probability of ONE means it DEFINITELY WILL — P(certainty) = 1.

You can't have a probability bigger than 1.

You should be able to put the probability of any event happening on this scale from 0 to 1.

Three Important Details

1) Probabilities should be given as either a FRACTION (¼), or a DECIMAL (0.25) or a PERCENTAGE (25%)
2) The notation 'P(X) = ½' should be read as: 'THE PROBABILITY OF EVENT X HAPPENING IS ½'
3) Probabilities ALWAYS ADD UP TO 1. This is essential for finding the probability of the other outcome. E.g. If P(pass) = ¼, then P(fail) = ¾

The Probability of Something Not Happening

The probability of something not happening is just the rest of the probability that's left over. This is simple enough AS LONG AS YOU REMEMBER IT.

So, if the probability of Outcome A happening is P(A), then the chance of it NOT HAPPENING is P(not A) = 1 – P(A), i.e. it's what's left when you subtract it from 1.

P(not A) is also known as the probability of the complement of event A happening.

EXAMPLE: A spinner has a 0.25 chance of coming up TWO. What is the chance of it NOT coming up TWO?

Answer: P(not 2) = 1 – P(2) = 1 – 0.25 = 0.75.
So, the chance of the spinner not coming up TWO is 0.75.

Steve's chance of winning is 50% — they call him Evens Steven...

Nothing too scary here. When you've got your head round it all, have a go at these questions:
1) Put the probability of the following events on a scale of 0 to 1:
a) If you roll a dice it will land on an even number.
b) Pigs will fly in the sky tonight.   c) The tide will go out today.

Probability

You need to know some probability jargon, such as <u>outcome</u>, <u>event</u> and <u>sample space</u>.

An Outcome is What Might Happen

1) An <u>OUTCOME</u> is something that can happen <u>as a result of a TRIAL</u>.
(A trial can be anything from spinning a spinner to a horse race.)

2) For example, when you <u>toss a coin</u>, the only possible <u>outcomes</u> are <u>heads</u> and <u>tails</u>.

3) An <u>EVENT</u> is a specific thing that has a probability of happening, e.g. picking a king from a pack of cards.
More than one <u>outcome</u> can lead to the same <u>event</u>, e.g. 4 outcomes match this event: K♣, K♦, K♥, K♠.

EXAMPLE   If you roll a fair 6-sided dice, <u>how many outcomes</u> match each of these <u>events</u>?
Event A: Rolling a 1   Event B: Rolling an even number
Event C: Rolling a number less than or equal to 5 ◄—— *This can be written as ≤ 5.*

The <u>outcomes</u> of rolling a normal dice are the numbers <u>1</u>, <u>2</u>, <u>3</u>, <u>4</u>, <u>5</u> and <u>6</u>.
There is only <u>one outcome</u> that matches <u>Event A</u> — the number <u>1</u>.
There are <u>three outcomes</u> that match <u>Event B</u> — the numbers <u>2</u>, <u>4</u> and <u>6</u>.
There are <u>five outcomes</u> that match <u>Event C</u> — any of the numbers <u>1</u>, <u>2</u>, <u>3</u>, <u>4</u> or <u>5</u>.

You might also see, e.g. 'rolling a dice' or 'tossing a coin' described as 'events'.

A Sample Space is a List of ALL Possible Outcomes

If you roll a normal dice, there are <u>6</u> possible outcomes — 1, 2, 3, 4, 5, 6. All of these possible outcomes make up the <u>sample space</u>.

If you spin this spinner with 3 sections, there are <u>3 possible</u> outcomes — red, green, blue. These make up the <u>sample space</u>.

Rolling the dice <u>AND</u> spinning the spinner give <u>6 × 3 = 18 different combinations altogether</u> (since any number on the dice could come up with any colour on the spinner). Here, the sample space is a <u>list</u> of these <u>18 outcomes</u>. Luckily, there are some easy ways to work out what these outcomes can be.

Use a Sample Space Diagram to Record all the Outcomes

1) A <u>sample space diagram</u> is basically a posh name for a <u>table</u>. If you use one, you're less likely to <u>miss out</u> any outcomes.

2) This table uses <u>columns</u> for the spinner outcomes and <u>rows</u> for the dice. It doesn't matter which way round you do it though.

3) Sample space diagrams are useful for working out the <u>probability of an event happening</u>:

	Red	Blue	Green
1	1R	1B	1G
2	2R	2B	2G
3	3R	3B	3G
4	4R	4B	4G
5	5R	5B	5G
6	6R	6B	6G

EXAMPLE   *"Use the sample space diagram above to find the probability of the spinner landing on blue or green, and the dice landing on a number higher than three."*

1) There are 18 possible outcomes, and 6 of them match the event you're interested in.

2) So the probability if the event happening is $\frac{6}{18} = \frac{1}{3}$.

	Red	Blue	Green
1	1R	1B	1G
2	2R	2B	2G
3	3R	3B	3G
4	4R	(4B)	(4G)
5	5R	(5B)	(5G)
6	6R	(6B)	(6G)

I had a go at being an astronaut — I wanted to sample space...

Most probability questions assume things are <u>RANDOM</u> — each thing has an equally likely chance of being picked. So if you're picking socks out of a drawer, but you fancy wearing pink ones today, it's not random. Now try this:

1) List the possible outcomes of tossing a coin three times.

Probability

This is where most people start getting into trouble, and d'you know why?
I'll tell you — it's because they don't know the three simple steps and the two rules to apply:

Three Simple Steps

1) Always break down a complicated-looking probability question into A SEQUENCE of SEPARATE SINGLE EVENTS.
2) Find the probability of EACH of these SEPARATE SINGLE EVENTS.
3) Apply the AND/OR rule:

1) The OR Rule:

$$P(A \text{ or } B) = P(A) + P(B)$$

Which means:

The probability of EITHER Event A OR Event B happening is equal to the two separate probabilities ADDED together.

The two events have to be MUTUALLY EXCLUSIVE. This means that if one event happens, the other one can't happen.

EXAMPLE: " You roll a fair dice once. What's the probability of rolling a 2 OR a multiple of 3?"

The probability of rolling a 2 is 1/6.

The probability of rolling a multiple of 3 is 2/6 (because you can roll a 3 or a 6).

You can't roll a 2 and a multiple of 3 at the same time — the events are mutually exclusive.

So P(getting a 2 or a multiple of 3) = $\frac{1}{6} + \frac{2}{6} = \frac{3}{6} = \frac{1}{2}$

2) The AND Rule:

$$P(A \text{ and } B) = P(A) \times P(B)$$

Which means:

The probability of Event A AND Event B BOTH happening is equal to the two separate probabilities MULTIPLIED together.

This time the two events have to be INDEPENDENT. All that means is that one event happening doesn't affect whether the other one happens.

EXAMPLE: "Find the probability of picking a king from a pack of cards and rolling a 6 on a dice."

1) SPLIT this into TWO SEPARATE EVENTS — i.e. picking the king and then rolling a 6.

2) Find the SEPARATE probabilities of these two separate events:
$P(\text{king}) = \frac{4}{52}$ $P(6) = \frac{1}{6}$

3) Apply the AND/OR rule: BOTH events must happen, so it's the AND rule:
so multiply the two separate probabilities: $\frac{4}{52} \times \frac{1}{6} = \frac{4}{312} = \frac{1}{78}$

Revise — and/or eat cake...

Wowsers, lots of important stuff on this page. Learn the three simple steps for multiple events, and the AND/OR rule and you'll be fine and/or dandy in the exam. Ahem. Now have a go at these little jokers below...

1) Find the probability of: a) picking a jack, queen or king from a pack of cards,
   b) picking a queen from a pack of cards and getting heads when tossing a coin

Expected and Relative Frequency

This is where the terminology gets confusing. Expected frequency is a <u>result</u> predicted using a probability, but relative frequency is a <u>probability</u> calculated from a set of results.

The Expected Frequency is What's Likely to Happen

Once you know the <u>probability</u> of something happening, you can predict <u>how many times</u> it will happen in a certain number of trials, e.g. the <u>number of sixes</u> you could expect if you rolled a fair dice <u>20 times</u>. This prediction is called the EXPECTED FREQUENCY.

EXPECTED FREQUENCY	=	NUMBER OF TIMES you are going to do something (the number of trials)	×	The PROBABILITY of the outcome happening

> **EXAMPLE**   What is the <u>expected frequency</u> of <u>heads</u> when you toss a fair coin <u>200</u> times?
>
> 1) <u>First work out the probability of the outcome happening</u>.
>   Heads and tails are equally likely. So the probability of getting heads is <u>0.5</u>.
>
> 2) <u>Now use the formula for expected frequency</u>.   Expected Frequency = 200 × 0.5 = 100
>   tosses   probability of heads
>
>   So, the <u>EXPECTED FREQUENCY</u> would be <u>100 heads</u> (out of 200 tosses).

Relative Frequency is an Estimated Probability

1) Sometimes outcomes <u>aren't equally likely</u>, so you have to base the probabilities on <u>what's happened before</u>.

2) The probability of rolling a three on a <u>fair dice</u> is 1/6. BUT if the dice is a bit <u>wonky</u> (the technical term is 'biased') then each number <u>won't</u> have an equal chance of being rolled. That's where <u>relative frequency</u> comes in — you can use it to work out probabilities when things might be wonky.

3) There's a formula for <u>relative frequency</u>: $$\text{Probability of something happening (relative frequency)} = \frac{\text{Number of times it happened}}{\text{Number of trials}}$$

4) The important thing to remember is: The <u>more trials</u> there are, the <u>more accurate</u> the probability will be.

> **EXAMPLE**   A dice was suspected of being <u>biased</u> towards the number <u>3</u>. It was rolled 100 times, and the <u>relative frequency</u> of rolling a 3 for the first 10, 20, 50 and 100 rolls was recorded.
>
> a) From this data, what is the best <u>estimate</u> of the <u>probability</u> of rolling a <u>3</u>?
>
> b) Explain whether this probability suggests the dice is <u>biased</u>.
>
> | Number of rolls | 10 | 20 | 50 | 100 |
> |---|---|---|---|---|
> | Number of 3s rolled | 3 | 7 | 19 | 37 |
> | Relative frequency | $\frac{3}{10}=0.3$ | $\frac{7}{20}=0.35$ | $\frac{19}{50}=0.38$ | $\frac{37}{100}=0.37$ |
>
> *Relative frequencies are usually easier to compare as decimals.*
>
> a) There are <u>four possible probabilities</u>, but the <u>most reliable</u> one is the one worked out using the <u>greatest number of dice rolls</u>. This makes the best estimate of the probability <u>0.37</u>.
>
> b) For an unbiased dice, the probability of rolling a three is <u>1/6</u> (about 0.17). The probability of rolling a three for this dice seems to be much <u>higher</u>, so the dice is probably <u>biased</u>.

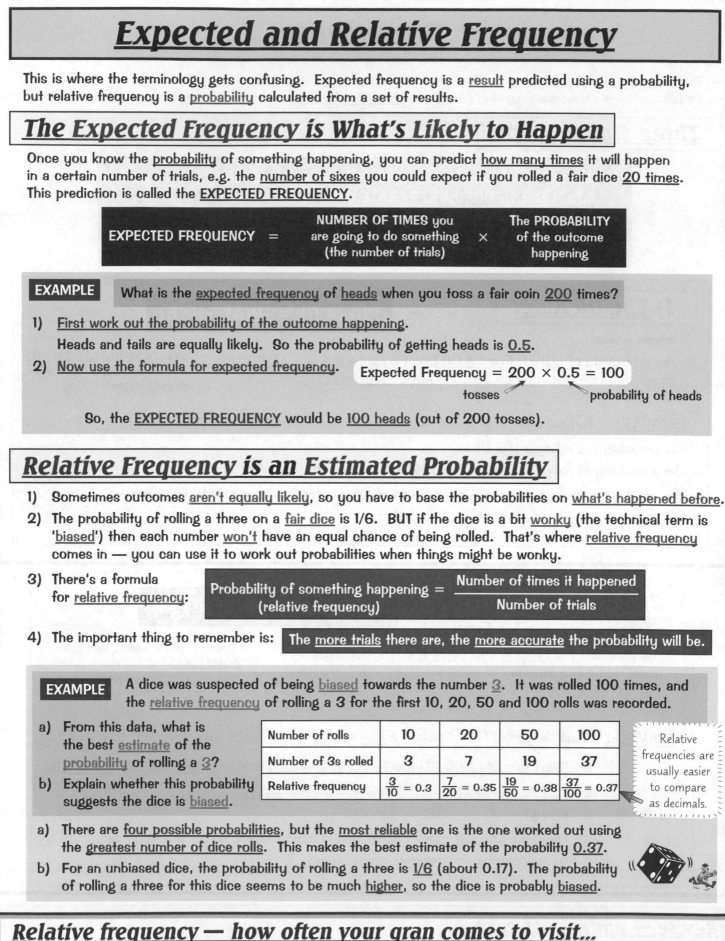

Relative frequency — how often your gran comes to visit...

Make sure you learn those lovely formulas for expected and relative frequency. Then try these questions:
1) If you roll a standard dice 24 times, how many 4s would you expect to get?
2) A three-colour spinner was spun a number of times. It landed on magenta 69 times, silver 98 times and turquoise 83 times. Estimate the probability of spinning each colour on this spinner.

Probability — Tree Diagrams

Tree diagrams are all pretty much the same, so it's a pretty darned good idea to learn these basic details (which apply to <u>ALL</u> tree diagrams) — ready for the one that's bound to be in the Exam.

General Tree Diagram

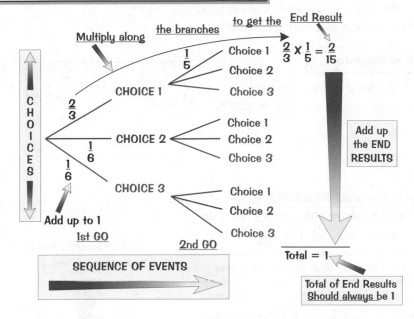

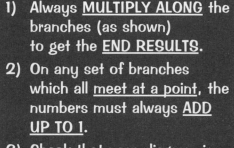

1) Always <u>MULTIPLY ALONG</u> the branches (as shown) to get the <u>END RESULTS</u>.

2) On any set of branches which all <u>meet at a point</u>, the numbers must always <u>ADD UP TO 1</u>.

3) <u>Check</u> that your diagram is correct by making sure the end results <u>ADD UP TO ONE</u>.

4) To answer any question, simply <u>ADD UP</u> the relevant <u>END RESULTS</u> (see below).

A Likely Tree Diagram Question

EXAMPLE: "A box contains 5 red disks and 3 green disks. Two disks are taken at random <u>without replacement</u>. Draw a tree diagram and hence find the probability that both disks are the same colour."

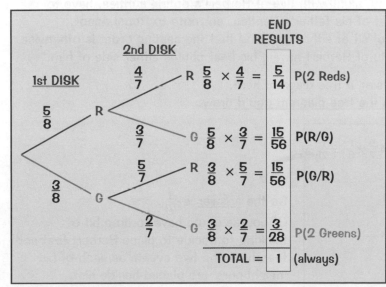

Once the tree diagram is drawn all you then need to do to answer the question is simply select the relevant <u>END RESULTS</u> and then <u>ADD THEM TOGETHER</u>:

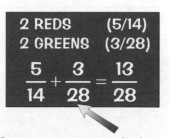

If you can, use a calculator for this.

General Tree Diagram reporting for duty sir...

How convenient — answers growing on trees. You still need to learn the <u>general tree diagram</u> and the <u>4 points</u> that go with it though — just in case there's a disappointing harvest. I'll leave you to have a go at these...

1) OK, let's see what you've learnt shall we: turn over and write down everything you know about tree diagrams.

2) A bag contains 6 red tarantulas and 4 black tarantulas. If two girls each pluck out a tarantula at random, draw a tree diagram to find the probability that they get different coloured ones.

Probability — Tree Diagrams

Four Extra Details for the Tree Diagram method:

1) Always break up the question into a SEQUENCE of Separate events.

E.g. '3 coins are tossed together' — just split it into 3 separate coin tosses.
You need this sequence of events to be able to draw any sort of tree diagram.

2) Don't feel you have to draw complete tree diagrams.

Learn to adapt them to what is required. E.g. 'What is the chance of
throwing a dice 3 times and getting 2 sixes followed by an even number?'

This diagram is all you need to get the answer: $\frac{1}{6} \times \frac{1}{6} \times \frac{1}{2} = \frac{1}{72}$

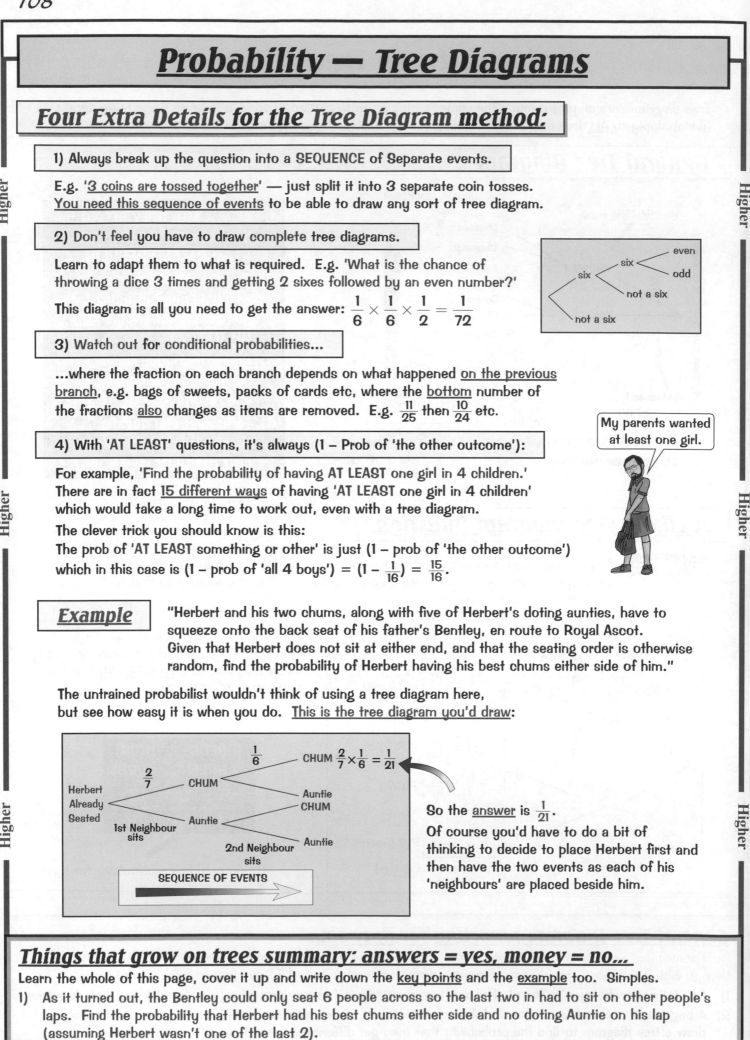

3) Watch out for conditional probabilities...

...where the fraction on each branch depends on what happened on the previous
branch, e.g. bags of sweets, packs of cards etc, where the bottom number of
the fractions also changes as items are removed. E.g. $\frac{11}{25}$ then $\frac{10}{24}$ etc.

4) With 'AT LEAST' questions, it's always (1 – Prob of 'the other outcome'):

For example, 'Find the probability of having AT LEAST one girl in 4 children.'
There are in fact 15 different ways of having 'AT LEAST one girl in 4 children'
which would take a long time to work out, even with a tree diagram.

The clever trick you should know is this:
The prob of 'AT LEAST something or other' is just (1 – prob of 'the other outcome')
which in this case is (1 – prob of 'all 4 boys') = $(1 - \frac{1}{16}) = \frac{15}{16}$.

My parents wanted at least one girl.

Example

"Herbert and his two chums, along with five of Herbert's doting aunties, have to
squeeze onto the back seat of his father's Bentley, en route to Royal Ascot.
Given that Herbert does not sit at either end, and that the seating order is otherwise
random, find the probability of Herbert having his best chums either side of him."

The untrained probabilist wouldn't think of using a tree diagram here,
but see how easy it is when you do. This is the tree diagram you'd draw:

So the answer is $\frac{1}{21}$.
Of course you'd have to do a bit of
thinking to decide to place Herbert first and
then have the two events as each of his
'neighbours' are placed beside him.

Things that grow on trees summary: answers = yes, money = no...

Learn the whole of this page, cover it up and write down the key points and the example too. Simples.
1) As it turned out, the Bentley could only seat 6 people across so the last two in had to sit on other people's
laps. Find the probability that Herbert had his best chums either side and no doting Auntie on his lap
(assuming Herbert wasn't one of the last 2).

Revision Summary

Here's the really fun page. The inevitable list of straight-down-the-middle questions to test what you know. Remember, these questions will sort out (quicker than anything else can) exactly what you <u>know</u> and what you <u>don't</u>. And that's exactly what revision is all about: <u>finding out what you DON'T know</u> and then learning it <u>until you do</u>. Enjoy.

KEEP LEARNING THESE BASIC FACTS UNTIL YOU KNOW THEM

1) Steven works in a shoe shop. His boss wants to know which is the most common size of shoe they've sold this month.
a) Which value does Steven need to work out: Mean, Median, Mode or Range?
Work this value out using the information in the table.
b) What is the mean number of that size they've sold per week?

Week / Size of shoe	1	2	3	4
5	29	11	17	12
6	21	35	7	16
7	2	17	10	2
8	15	6	2	2

2) Write down seven important details about frequency tables.

3) Jessica's science class are collecting their results in a grouped frequency table. Jessica's result is 5 g. Into which group in the table should her data go?

Mass (g)	$1 < m \leq 5$	$5 < m \leq 10$	$10 < m \leq 15$
Frequency	6	23	5

4) Calum is writing an article on the Skelly Crag half-marathon for the local paper. He wants to include the mean time taken to run the race. Estimate the mean time from the table below.

Time (min)	$60 < t \leq 90$	$90 < t \leq 120$	$120 < t \leq 150$	$150 < t \leq 180$	$180 < t \leq 210$	$210 < t \leq 240$
Frequency	15	60	351	285	206	83

5) Why is it not possible to find the exact value of the mean from a grouped frequency table?
6) Write down four key points about cumulative frequency.
7) What is a histogram?
8) Write down the formula for frequency density.
9) Explain how to estimate the frequency for a given interval of values on a histogram.
10) What is the meaning of dispersion?
11) How do you estimate the mean from looking at a histogram?
12) Sean goes for a checkup at the doctors. The doctor measures his height and checks it on a cumulative frequency curve to see how he compares with other 15 year old males.
a) What's the median height for a 15 year old male?
b) Sean is 180 cm tall. What percentage of 15 year old boys are taller than Sean?

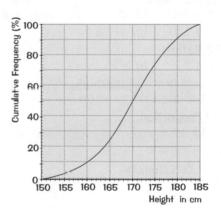

13) What is the numerical probability of an event which:
a) is certain?
b) is impossible?
c) has an even chance?
14) If two mutually exclusive events include between them every possible outcome of a trial, what does that tell you about their probabilities?
15) What is a sample space?
16) What is the OR rule of probability? What's the AND rule?
17) Jackie is preparing a game for the school fair. She wants the players to have a less than 10% chance of winning to make sure the school doesn't lose much money. In Jackie's game you roll two dice. If you roll two sixes you win £20. Is the chance of winning less than 10%?
18) How do you work out an expected frequency?
19) Describe what a relative frequency is, and give the formula for it.
20) Write down four important facts about tree diagrams.
21) Draw a general tree diagram and put all the features on it.

Answers

Section 1

P.1 Prime Numbers:
2) a) 101, 103, 107, 109   b) none   c) 503, 509

P.2 Multiples, Factors and Prime Factors:
1) 7, 14, 21, 28, 35, 42, 49, 56, 63, 70
2) Factors of 36: 1, 2, 3, 4, 6, 9, 12, 18, 36
   Factors of 84: 1, 2, 3, 4, 6, 7, 12, 14, 21, 28, 42, 84
3) a) $990 = 2 \times 3^2 \times 5 \times 11$
   b) $160 = 2^5 \times 5$

P.3 Common Factors and Common Multiples:
1) Factors of 56: 1, 2, 4, 7, 8, 14, 28, 56
   Factors of 104: 1, 2, 4, 8, 13, 26, 52, 104
   Common factors: 1, 2, 4, 8   HCF = 8
2) 12
3) Multiples of 4: 4, 8, 12, 16, 20, 24, 28, 32, 36, 40
   Multiples of 5: 5, 10, 15, 20, 25, 30, 35, 40, 45, 50
   Common multiples = 20, 40
4) LCM = 63   Other common multiples, e.g. 126 and 189

P.4 Fractions, Decimals and Percentages:
1) a) 6/10 (= 3/5)   b) 2/100 (= 1/50)   c) 77/100
   d) 555/1000 (= 111/200)   e) 56/10 (= 28/5)

P.5 Turning Decimals into Fractions
1) 1/7
2) a) terminating b) recurring c) terminating

P.6 Fractions:
1) a) 5/32   b) 32/35   c) 23/20   d) 1/40   e) 167/27
2) a) 220   b) £1.75

P.8 Ratios:
1) a) 5:7   b) 2:3   c) 3:5
2) 17½ bowls of porridge
3) £3500 : £2100 : £2800

P.9 Proportion:
1) £4.40
2) 14 minutes

P.10 Percentages:
1) 40%
2) £20 500
3) 1.39%

P.11 Compound Growth and Decay:
1) £4803.10
2) £15.30 and Forever

Revision Summary for Section 1
3) a) $270 = 2 \times 3^3 \times 5$ b) $1050 = 2 \times 3 \times 5^2 \times 7$
4) E.g. 24 and 48   5) 1, 2, 4, 8, 16
6) HCF = 14, LCM = 40   7) 0.375, 37.5 %
8) 0.24, 6/25
13) a) 3/20   b) 12/5 = 2 2/5
    c) 117/20 = 5 17/20   d) 37/24 = 1 13/24
14) 30
15) 30/42 and 7/42
16) 240
18) Jill gets £18, Heather gets £15 and Susie gets £9
22) £3710
23) Decrease of 4.96 %
24) £140.26

Section 2

P.13 Square Roots and Cube Roots:
1) a) 14.14 (other value = −14.14)   b) 20.00
2) a) $g = \pm 6$ b) $b = 4$ c) $r^3 = 27$

P.14 Manipulating Surds:
1) $4\sqrt{2}$
2) $1 + 2\sqrt{2}$

P.15 Powers and Roots:
1) a) 3^8 b) 4   c) 8^{12} d) 1   e) 7^6
2) a) 64   b) 1/625   c) 1/5   d) 2   e) 125   f) 1/25
3) a) 1.53×10^{17} b) 15.9   c) 2.89

P.17 Standard Form:
1) 8.54×10^5 ; 1.8×10^{-4}
2) 0.00456 ; 270,000
3) a) 2×10^{11} b) 1×10^8
4) 6.5×10^{102}

P.18 Rounding Numbers:
1) 3.57
2) 0.05
3) 12.910
4) 3546.1

P.19 Rounding Numbers:
1) a) 568   b) 23 400   c) 0.0456   d) 0.909
2) a) 350 g   b) 134 km/h   c) 850 g

P.20 Bounds and Estimating:
1 a) x — lower bound 2.315 m, upper bound 2.325 m
      y — lower bound 0.445 m, upper bound 0.455 m
   b) maximum value of z = 4.57 m (to 2 d.p.),
      minimum value of z = 4.51 m (to 2 d.p.)
2) Longest — 17.5 m, shortest — 16.5 m

P.21 Conversion Factors:
1) 198 mins
2) 6.5 hrs
3) £34
4) 3.2 cm

P.22 Length, Area and Volume:
1) 3.5 l
2) 2 km
3) a) 230 000 cm²   b) 3.45 m²
4) a) 5 200 000 cm³   b) 0.1 m³

P.23 Clock Time Questions:
1) 5.15 p.m.
2) 4.05 p.m.
3) 1440 mins, 86400 s
4) 3 hrs 30 mins, 5 hrs 45 mins

P.24 Speed, Distance and Time:
1) 1 hr 37 mins 30 secs
2) 1.89 km = 1890 m (to 3 sig. fig.)

P.25 Order of Operations:
1) a) 12.00   b) 39.96

P.26 Using Calculators:
1) a) 11/4   b) 33/2   c) 33/4

P27 Sets:
2) Elements in set B are 1, 4, 9, 16, 25, 36, 49, 64, 81, 100.
   22 ∉ B.

Answers

P28 Sets:
1) a) P = {2, 4, 6, 8, 10, 12}
 b) n(Q) = 4
 c) P ∪ Q = {2, 3, 4, 6, 8, 9, 10, 12}
 d) P ∩ Q = {6, 12}
 e) n(P ∩ Q) = 2

P29 Sets:
1) a) S′ = {2, 3, 5, 6, 7, 8, 10, 11, 12, 13, 14, 15, 17, 18, 19}
 b) e.g. if A = {1, 4}, A ⊂ S

Revision Summary for Section 2

2) 3, -3
5) a) $p^2 + 2p\sqrt{q} + q$ **b)** won't simplify **c)** $\sqrt{pq}$
6) a) 5^8 **b)** 3^3 **c)** 5^{12} **d)** 1/9 **e)** 2 **f)** 1/2
7) a) 9.7×10^5 **b)** 6.83×10^6 **c)** 3.56×10^9
8) 0.00000275
10) £17.33
13) £20.63
15) 1200 g
16) a) 3 m² **b)** 35600 cm² **c)** 0.03 m³ **d)** 3 560 000 cm³
17) 12.50 pm
18) 21.25
22) 3, 4, 5, 6, 7, 8, 9, 10, 11
23) a) n(W) = 50 **b)** H = ∅ **c)** Cheddar ∈ Z **d)** F ⊄ G
24)

A ∪ B = {1, 3, 5, 6, 7, 8, 9},
A ∩ B = {5, 7, 9},
n(A ∪ B) = 7, e.g. C = {1, 3}

25) a) Everyone at her school. 222 elements
 b) 126
 c) 141, the number of people who don't like limeade
 d) 111

Section 3

P.31 Basic Algebra:
1) a) +12 **b)** -6 **c)** x **d)** -3
2) a) +18 **b)** -216 **c)** +2 **d)** -27 **e)** -336

P.32 Making Formulas from Words:
1) y = 5x − 3
2) $A = \dfrac{6h + t}{2} - 5$

P.34 More Basic Algebra:
1) 4x + y − 4
2) $6p^2q - 8pq^3$
3) $8g^2 + 16g - 10$
4) $7xy^2(2xy + 3 - 5x^2y^2)$
5) $c^4/6d^3$
6) $\dfrac{2(17g - 6)}{5(3g - 4)}$

P.35 Solving Equations:
1) a) x = 2 **b)** x = - 0.2 or -1/5 **c)** x = ±3

P.36 Rearranging Formulas:
1) C = 5(F − 32)/9
2) a) $p = \dfrac{-4y}{3}$ **b)** $p = \dfrac{rq}{r + q}$ **c)** $p = \pm\sqrt{\dfrac{rq}{r + q}}$

P.37 Inequalities:
1) x ≥ −2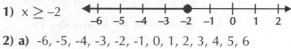
2) a) -6, -5, -4, -3, -2, -1, 0, 1, 2, 3, 4, 5, 6
 b) -4, -3, -2, -1, 0, 1, 2, 3, 4

P.38 Graphical Inequalities:
1)

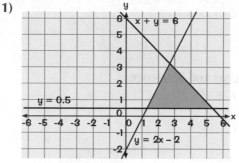

P.40 Factorising Quadratics:
1) a) x = 3 or -8 **b)** x = 7 or -1
 c) x = 1 or -7 **d)** x = 4 or -3/5

P.41 The Quadratic Formula:
1) a) x = 0.39 or -10.39 **b)** x = 1.46 or -0.46
 c) x = 0.44 or -3.44

P.42 Simultaneous Equations and Graphs:
1) a) x = 2, y = 4 **b)** x = 1½, y = 3
2)

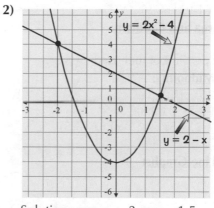

Solutions are: x = -2 or x = 1.5

P.43 Simultaneous Equations:
1) F = 3, G = -1

P.44 Simultaneous Equations:
a) f = 4 & g = 0 OR f = 40 & g = 6
b) f = -5/3 & g = -2/3 OR f = 72 & g = 5
c) f = 9 & g = -3/2 OR f = 1 & g = 1/2
d) f = -3 & g = 33 OR f = 1/4 & g = -11/4

P.45 Direct and Inverse Proportion:
1) a) E.g. total cost vs number of tins of soup bought
 b) E.g. number of people working on a job vs time taken to complete it.

P.46 Variation:
1) 0.632 Hz, 40.8 cm

Revision Summary for Section 3

1) a) 6a **b)** $-8a^2$ **c)** 2a **d)** 2
3) $p = \left(\dfrac{q}{6}\right)^3 + 4$

Answers

12) a) y > 3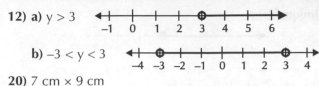

b) –3 < y < 3

20) 7 cm × 9 cm

21) a) 'm' is milk and 'c' is chocolate:
m = 1.4 – 2c, m = 2.66 – 5c

b) c = £0.42, so £6.72 owed

Section 4

P.49 Number Patterns and Sequences:

1) a) 20, 27   **b)** 2000, 20 000   **c)** 4, 2

2) 1000

3) a) 3n + 1   **b)** 5n – 2

P.50 Functions:

1) a) 19   **b)** 7   **c)** 10 – 10x

d) $5x^2 + 14$ **e)** –16   **f)** 84

g) (x + 1) / 5   **h)** (9 – 5x) / 2

P.51 Travel Graphs:

1) 0.533 km/h

2) Accelerations: $6m/s^2$, $2m/s^2$, $-8m/s^2$ (deceleration)
Speeds: 30m/s, 50m/s

P.52 Conversion Graphs:

1) a) 135 roubles (allow 131 to 139)

b) £6.67 (allow £6.61 to £6.79)

P.53 The Meaning of Area and Gradient:

1) Total babies born

2) Kilometres travelled per litre of fuel used

P.54 Coordinates and Midpoints:

1) A(4,5)   B(6,0)   C(5,-5)   D(0,-3)
E(-5,-2)   F(-4,0)   G(-3,3)   H(0,5)

2) a) (5, 2.5)   **b)** (-2, 2.5)   **c)** (0, -3.5)

3) (1, 3)

P.56 Plotting Straight Line Graphs:

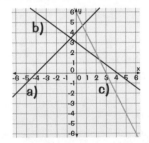

P.57 Finding the Gradient:

1) -1.5

P.58 "y = mx + c":

1)

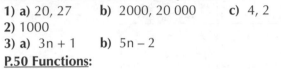

P.59 Quadratic Graphs:

1)

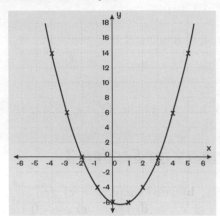

Using graph, solutions are x = -2 and x = 3.

P.60 Some Harder Graphs to Learn:

1) a) x^2 bucket shape

b) $–x^3$ wiggle (top left to bottom right)

c) +ve inverse proportion graph

d) –ve inverse proportion graph

e) $+x^3$ wiggle (bottom left to top right)

f) $–x^2$ upside down bucket shape

P.61 Differentiation:

1) a) 2x   **b)** $12x^2$ **c)** 0

d) 6x   **e)** $4 – 3x^2$

P.62 Differentiation:

1) 216

2) $v = 9t^2 + 6t$, $a = 18t + 6$

P.63 Differentiation:

1) a) (0, 0) minimum

b) (1.12, 28.4) maximum, (–1.79, –57.5) minimum

Revision Summary for Section 4

1) a) 19, 23 (Add 4 to the previous term)

b) 150, 75 (Divide the previous term by 2)

c) 31, 50 (Add the previous two terms)

2) 197 ((4 × term no.) – 3)

3) a) 6n – 7   **b)** 53

10) a) 1   **b)** 2.75

16) a) A straight line

b) Graph:

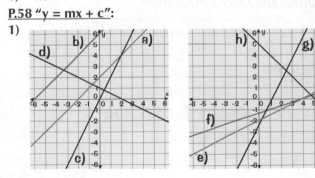

17) $2 cm^3$

22) 1217

23) $v = 6 ms^{-1}$, $a = 2 ms^{-2}$

24) a) (1, –1) minimum   **b)** (–1, 1) maximum

Answers

Section 5

P.66 Symmetry:
1) **H:** 2 lines of symmetry, rotational symmetry Order 2
   N: 0 lines of symmetry, rotational symmetry Order 2
   E: 1 line of symmetry, no rotational symmetry
   Y: 1 line of symmetry, no rotational symmetry
   M: 1 line of symmetry, no rotational symmetry
   S: 0 lines of symmetry, rotational symmetry Order 2
   T: 1 line of symmetry, no rotational symmetry

P.68 Regular Polygons:
1) Regular pentagon: exterior = 72°, interior = 108°
   12-sided regular polygon: exterior = 30°, interior = 150°
2) 15 sides
3) Pentagon, all the angles are either 36°, 72° or 108°
   Octagon as shown →

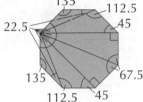

135   112.5
22.5   45
135   67.5
112.5   45

P.69 Areas:
1) Perimeter 21.4 cm, area 23.4 cm²
2) Perimeter 27.5 cm, area 35 cm²

P.70 Surface Area:
1) Square-based pyramid, 96 cm² ; Cuboid, 174 cm²
2) 364.2 cm²
3) 113.1 cm²

P.72 Volume:
1) **a)** (Trapezoidal) Prism, volume = 148.5 cm³
   b) Cylinder, volume = 0.70 m³
2) Ping pong ball: volume = 33.5 cm³
   Tennis ball: volume = 179.6 cm³

P.73 Vectors:
1) **a)** 5.39   **b)** 4.24   **c)** 8.06

P.74 Vectors:
1) **a)** $-\mathbf{m} - \mathbf{b}$
   b) $\frac{1}{2}\mathbf{b} - \frac{1}{2}\mathbf{a} + \mathbf{m}$ (because it's $\frac{1}{2}\overrightarrow{AC}$)
   c) $\frac{1}{2}(\mathbf{a} - \mathbf{b}) + \mathbf{m}$
   d) $\frac{1}{2}(\mathbf{b} - \mathbf{a})$

P.75 The Four Transformations:
1) **A→B** Rotation of 90° clockwise about the origin,
   B→C Reflection in the line y = x,
   C→A Reflection in the y-axis,
   A→D Translation 9 units left and 7 units down, or $\begin{pmatrix} -9 \\ -7 \end{pmatrix}$

P.76 Combinations of Transformations:
1) **C→D**, Reflection in the y-axis, and an enlargement SF 2, centre the origin.
   D→C, Reflection in the y-axis, and an enlargement SF ½, centre the origin.
2) **A'→B**, Rotation of 180° clockwise or anti-clockwise about the point (0,3).

P.78 Similarity and Enlargements:
1) A'(3, 3),   B'(9, 3), C'(6, 6)
2) 64 m²

Revision Summary for Section 5
1) 1.5 km
7) £1008
8) 60.5 cm²
12) 213.6 cm²
13) 78.5 cm²
16) 125
24) **a)** 150 cm wide, 300 cm long, 250 cm high.
    b) 1800 cm² or 0.18 m², 45,000 cm² or 4.5 m².
    The dimensions of the actual shed are 5 times bigger than the model, so the area is 5² = 25 times bigger.
    c) 90,000 cm³ or 0.09 m³, 11,250,000 cm³ or 11.25 m³.
    The dimensions of the actual shed are 5 times bigger than the model, so the area is 5³ = 125 times bigger.

Section 6

P.83 Angle Geometry:
1) 68° and 44°, or both 56°
2) x = 66°
3) 40

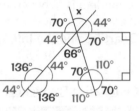

x
70°   44°
44°   70°
66°
136°   44°   70°   110°
44°   136°   110°   70°

P.85 Circle Geometry:
1) FEO = 90°, OBE = 48°
   (Rest of angles: BEO = 48°, BCD = 90°, CBO = 42°, BOE = 84°, AEB = 42°, DOE = 96°, CBE = 90°, BEF = 138°, AEO = 90°.)

P.86 Pythagoras' Theorem and Bearings:
1) BC = 8 m
2) 298°
3) 118°

P.88 Trigonometry — Sin, Cos, Tan:
1) x = 26.5 m
2) 23.6°
3) 32.6° (both)

P.89 3D Pythagoras and Trigonometry:
1) 25.1°
2) 7.07 cm

P.91 The Sine and Cosine Rules:
2) 17.13 m, 68.8°, 41.2°

P.92 Sine and Cosine for Larger Angles:
1) 64.14° or 115.9°

Revision Summary for Section 6
5) 13.5 cm
9) 4.72 m
13) 41.2°
18) 42°, 88°, 11.5 m
21) **a)** 150°   **b)** 172.8°   **c)** 101.5
22) **a)** 120°   **b)** 91°   **c)** 165.4°

Section 7

P.94 Mean, Median, Mode and Range:
Put the data in order:
   -14, -12, -5, -5, 0, 1, 3, 6, 7, 8, 10, 14, 18, 23, 25
Mean = 5.27, Median = 6, Mode = -5, Range = 39

Answers

P.96 Frequency Tables:

No. of phones	0	1	2	3	4	5	6	TOTALS
Frequency	1	25	53	34	22	5	1	141
No. × Frequency	0	25	106	102	88	25	6	352

Mean = 2.5, Median = 2, Mode = 2, Range = 6

P.97 Grouped Frequency Tables:

Length L (cm)	15.5 ≤L<16.5	16.5 ≤L<17.5	17.5 ≤L<18.5	18.5 ≤L<19.5	TOTALS
Frequency	12	18	23	8	61
Mid-Interval Value	16	17	18	19	-
Freq × M-I V	192	306	414	152	1064

1) Mean = 17.4
2) Modal Group = $17.5 \leq L < 18.5$,
The median is between the 15th and 16th pieces of data, so it is in the $16.5 \leq L < 17.5$ group.

P.98 Quartiles and the Interquartile Range:

1) a) 250   b) 750
2) 11 – 3 = 8

P.99 Cumulative Frequency:

No of fish	41 – 45	46 – 50	51 – 55	56 – 60	61 – 65	66 – 70	71 – 75
Frequency	2	7	17	25	19	8	2
Cum. Freq.	2	9	26	51	70	78	80

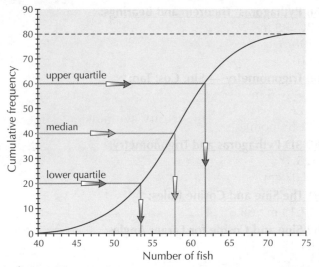

Median = 58,
Lower Quartile = 53.5
Upper Quartile = 62
Interquartile Range = 62 – 53.5 = 8.5

(Your answers don't have to be exactly the same as these, as long as they're close to these values — the main thing is to plot the curve and read the values from it correctly.)

P.100 More Graphs and Charts:

2) Guinea Pigs 68°
Rabbits 60°
Ducks 104°
Stick insects 48°

P.101 Histograms and Frequency Density:

1) 32

P.102 Spread of Data:

1) E.g.

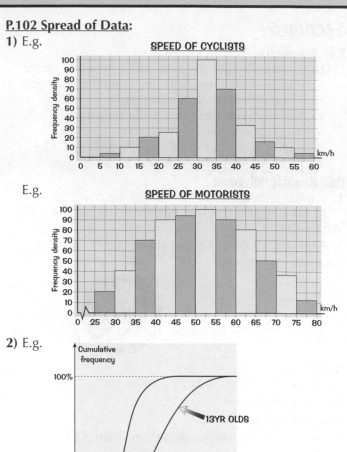

2) E.g.

P.103 Probability:

1) a) 1/2   b) 0   c) 1

P.104 Probability:

1) Possible outcomes for 3 coin tosses (H = heads, T = tails):
HHH, HHT, HTH, HTT, THH, THT, TTH, TTT

P.105 Probability:

1) a) Probability = (4/52) + (4/52) + (4/52) = 12/52 = 3/13
b) Probability = (4/52) × (1/2) = 4/104 = 1/26

P.106 Expected and Relative Frequency:

1) 4
2) Magenta: 0.276, silver: 0.392, turquoise: 0.332

P.107 Probability — Tree Diagrams:

2) 8/15

P.108 Probability — Tree Diagrams:

1) (2/7) × (1/6) × (5/6) × (4/5) = 40/1260 = 2/63

Revision Summary for Section 7

1) a) Mode = size 6   b) Mean = 19.75 pairs
3) $1 < m \leq 5$
4) 161 min
12) a) 170 cm   b) 10%
13) a) 1   b) 0   c) 1/2
14) That their probabilities add up to 1 (the probability of one of them happening in a trial is 1).
17) Yes (it's about 3%).

Index

Index